Herbert R. Axelrod

DR. AXELROD'S
ATLAS
OF
FRESHWATER
AQUARIUM FISHES

BY
DR. HERBERT R. AXELROD
DR. WARREN E. BURGESS, NEAL PRONEK AND JERRY G. WALLS

Title page photo: *Carnegiella marthae,* one of the fascinating freshwater hatchetfishes of South America.

ISBN 0-86622-052-6

Distributed in the UNITED STATES by T.F.H. Publications, Inc., 211 West Sylvania Avenue, Neptune City, NJ 07753; in CANADA by H & L Pet Supplies Inc., 27 Kingston Crescent, Kitchener, Ontario N2B 2T6; Rolf C. Hagen Ltd., 3225 Sartelon Street, Montreal 382 Quebec; in ENGLAND by T.F.H. Publications Limited, 4 Kier Park, Ascot, Berkshire SL5 7DS; in AUSTRALIA AND THE SOUTH PACIFIC by T.F.H. (Australia) Pty. Ltd., Box 149, Brookvale 2100 N.S.W., Australia; in NEW ZEALAND by Ross Haines & Son, Ltd., 18 Monmouth Street, Grey Lynn, Auckland 2 New Zealand; in SINGAPORE AND MALAYSIA by MPH Distributors (S) Pte., Ltd., 601 Sims Drive, # 03/07/21, Singapore 1438; in the PHILIPPINES by Bio-Research, 5 Lippay Street, San Lorenzo Village, Makati Rizal; in SOUTH AFRICA by Multipet Pty. Ltd., 30 Turners Avenue, Durban 4001. Published by T.F.H. Publications Inc., Ltd. the British Crown Colony of Hong Kong.

Contents

THE PURPOSE OF THIS BOOK

This book was created with the express purpose of making the identification of fishes easier for the scientist, pet dealer and hobbyist. It attempts to standardize, as much as possible, the common names applied to fishes in the English-speaking world, especially as this applies to those fishes that are so similar in size, shape and form that they cannot even be distinguished readily by an ichthyologist. These difficult fishes include the popular tank-raised varieties of swordtails, platies, mollies, guppies, angelfish and discus. As aquarists develop more skills in fish breeding, especially with the ever-increasing use of hormone injections to stimulate ripe fishes to spawn, more and more color varieties will be developed . . . and more and more books of fish standards will be needed, books that will clearly identify a fish by its color photograph.

For many years the science of ichthyology has recognized the value of a color illustration of a fish, and often a scientific name is accepted if its description is enhanced with a suitable color illustration even though there may be fatal flaws in the technical description of the fish.

But there is a great distinction between color illustrations of a fish whose body was preserved for further study after the photograph or drawing was made and one that merely happened to be photographed in someone's aquarium . . . and that's where this book fits in so well.

Throughout more than 35 years of intensive fish collecting in all the major aquarium fish areas of the world, Dr. Axelrod has specialized in collecting aquarium fishes and photographing them on the spot just where they were found. He then preserved their bodies and had them scientifically verified as to nomenclature. Thus, while many of his photographs lack the artistic beauty of an aquarium scene, they are authentic color photos of a fish whose identity is as certain as can be determined by a trained fish scientist or ichthyologist. This is especially helpful, for example, with discus for without his photographs we wouldn't know what the original species and subspecies looked like. He is the only one who has collected and photographed every species and subspecies of that popular group of fishes, the discus, known scientificially as the genus *Symphysodon*. Hundreds of his photographs have been used to describe the types of new species and many are the first and only color photographs of those fishes . . . even today!

Thus this book is unique and authentic . . . and there can never be another book like it because there can never be another color photograph made of a type in living colors since, by definition, a type is THE SINGLE FISH selected to represent the species. Of course you may photograph a fish and then identify it as being the same species as the type, but many times the characters upon which the identification is made change and that second picture loses its value while the original photograph of the type stands forever!

HOW FISHES ARE IDENTIFIED

Fishes are not identified by photographs alone, nor can anyone make an absolutely positive identification of a fish photograph without the fish's body at hand.

There are about 25,000-40,000 different kinds of fishes in the world. This includes species and subspecies, but not color varieties developed by man. There are as many species of fishes as there are combined species of the other vertebrates (amphibians, reptiles, birds and mammals) in the world. That's a lot of fishes, and unless a strict system of identification had been set up there would be lots of confusion. Even with the system there is lots of confusion, and as you go through this book you will often find remarks to the effect that much more study is needed in a certain group to make identifications certain. This can be clearly understood when you consider, for example, the author's (W.E.B.) famous work on angelfishes of the genus *Pterophyllum*. Over the years there were many species of angelfish scientifically described, such as *Zeus scalaris, Pterophyllum eimekei, P. altum, Plataxoides dumerilii,* and *Plataxoides leopoldi*. These fishes were found widely scattered from Guyana to the Rio Negro and the Rio Madeira, distances of thousands of kilometers. As additional collections of angelfishes were made between the points of original discovery, the differences between "species" became smaller and smaller as these newly discovered angelfishes had to be accommodated among the previously discovered forms. This led to the grouping of all these names into just two species. This is only one tiny example of Dr. Burgess's experiences in naming fishes, but it serves to show the complexities of fish identification.

In 1758 the famous botanist Linnaeus of Sweden proposed the binomial system for naming living things. The process of "How Fishes Get Their Scientific Names" was best described by the world's greatest living ichthyologist, Dr. Leonard P. Schultz, in *The Handbook of Tropical Aquarium Fishes* (Axelrod and Schultz). With their permission, the following section is reprinted from that book.

"This binomial system provides a generic and a specific name, usually based on Latin or Greek words, such as *Gambusia affinis* (Baird and Girard). The scientific names are followed by the name of the author who first described the species and named it according to the International Rules of Zoological Nomenclature. When the author's name is enclosed in parentheses, that means that the species was described in another genus and that recent authors have transferred it to the present genus, in this case *Gambusia,* since Baird and Girard in their original description named this species *Heterandria affinis.* It is not necessary for scientific names of animals to have a specific or significant meaning, although many do.

"Both generic and specific names may be chosen in honor of the collector, a friend, or a colleague, as well as for a geographical locality, a ship, or almost anything. Species names must be latinized, however; and when named after a man they must end in *i,* for example, *hollandi,* or after a woman, in *ae,* for example, *aliceae.* Although the International Commission of Zoological Nomenclature has established many pages of rules governing the naming of animals, the basic theory of the system is that of priority—the oldest name established for genus, species, or subspecies is the valid one, going back to the year 1758, the tenth edition of *Systema naturae* by Linnaeus.

"Whenever an ichthyologist thinks he has a new species, he must search the ichthyological literature all the way back to 1758 to be certain that it is not already named. This is a difficult and time-consuming process, requiring the facilities of extensive libraries such as the Library of Congress at Washington and those in the largest universities which have specialized in ichthyological literature. Bibliographical indices are used, such as the three-volume work by Bashford Dean, *Bibliography of Fishes* (1916-1923), along with the Pisces section of the *Zoological Record,* to find papers on the group being studied. The *Zoological Record,* published in London since 1864, classifies natural history literature on an annual basis. Although these tools are useful, the experience of the ichthyologist is important, too. The more expert ichthyologists do not name new species of fish on hunches; instead they review all other species in the genus to which they assign their new one, and if they are able to construct a key that separates the new one from all other species in that genus, they then feel that much reliance may be placed on their claim that the species is actually new.

"The expert ichthyologists of today are continually confronted with the inadequate descriptions and figures of fishes printed during the past 200 years. So many authors have named fishes that were already named that on the average each species has one or two synonyms, and some may have as many as a dozen or more. This troublesome affliction of systematic ichthyology could be greatly improved if novices in the field submitted their new species to ichthyologists in the larger museums of the world for expert opinion. These museums, with a million or more specimens distributed among 10,000 to 20,000 species, are in a fine position to make careful comparisons.

"The International Rules of Zoological Nomenclature require that whenever a new species is described and named a specimen must be designated as the *holotype*, the specimen on which the species is based. Other specimens used in describing the new species become *paratypes*, and data from them are included in the description. It is the custom for ichthyologists to give the type specimens to museums for permanent preservation, such as the United States National Museum in Washington, which makes its research collections available for study to all qualified students and professional ichthyologists.

"To illustrate how complicated the process of naming a species may become before the matter is finally settled, let us refer to one of our commonest aquarium fishes, the molly or sailfin.

"The first author to publish a description and give a scientific name for the molly was the early American ichthyologist, LeSueur. In the year 1821, in volume 2, page 3, of the *Journal of the Academy of Natural Sciences of Philadelphia*, there appeared as a boldface center head the name *Mollinesia latipinna*. This generic and specific name as first published would be the valid scientific name under ordinary circumstances, but further study of the original article indicates that the generic name was intended to honor Monsieur Mollien. However, there was a great amount of carelessness in those days, and on the plate in this first printing the name is spelled *Molienisia Latipinua*, whereas in the reference to the plate on page 409 it is spelled *Molinesia Latipinna*. Thus the molly had its generic name spelled three ways and the specific name two ways when first published. For more than 100 years the generic name of the molly has been spelled in at least three ways. To settle this and similar controversies in nomenclature, rules were established more than half a century ago to pass on such matters. The commission that considers nomenclatorial problems acts as a sort of international "supreme court" and the rule of priority, or the rule of long established use, is followed.

"Two recent papers have given the history of the name. Fowler in 1945 and Bailey and Miller in 1950 chose to emend the name to *Mollienesia*, which follows closely the name of the man LeSueur intended to honor, and they use the ending *-esia*, which appears twice in the article. Thus the best conclusion that can be reached, according to usage and rules, is that the common molly should carry the name *Mollienesia latipinna* LeSueur.

"This is only one of many complicated cases that occur in the naming of fishes; in general, about 95 per cent are named with sufficient care and accuracy so that no controversies are involved.

"By 1900 the number of fish species became so numerous that the trend was to revise or review fishes on the basis of genera or of families. During the past 25 years statistical methods of analysis have been applied to what were previously considered species. Carefully made counts and measurements now reveal that many of these early species can actually be differentiated into subspecies or into two or more species.

"To make these statistical studies large series of specimens are needed from numerous localities. This trend has caused a change in the policies of research museums. Whereas in the early days a species was represented by a single specimen, now that species should be represented by 25 or more specimens per lot, and each lot from as many localities within the range of the species as is practical. Such large collections in museums open the way for the solution of innumerable problems in ichthyology and in racial investigations in the field of fisheries biology. These methods apply to fresh-water fishes as well as marine. Many fresh-water species differ from stream system to stream system, whereas in marine fishes the differences appear from island group to island group, or according to latitude.

"At times the layman naturalist will argue about 'lumpers' and 'splitters'. Lumpers have a tendency to throw doubtful species together as a single form, whereas splitters differentiate a species into its component populations and give these populations a subspecific scientific name.

"Isaac Ginsburg has proposed a principle to guide him as to when it is mathematically sound to give a population a scientific name and when it is not. This 'law' or yardstick proposes that two subspecies are distinct biological units in nature when the character showing the greatest divergence overlaps approximately 10 to 20 percent. A full species may overlap in one character by not more than 10 per cent. The percentage is calculated on the total number of observations for both supposed species or subspecies combined.

"In the recognition of species and subspecies there remain certain characters that cannot be measured or counted, for example, the basic color pattern. This may be defined as those colors which occur regularly on specific areas of the fish. The basic color pattern may not include quality, tone, or shade of colors.

"Experience has demonstrated that in both fresh-water and marine fishes the importance of basic color patterns cannot be overemphasized. Once the variability has been determined for a series of specimens, it is of the utmost importance as a factor in the recognition of species and subspecies. This has been demonstrated in studies of the reef-inhabiting species of the Phoenix, Marshall, and Philippine Islands by the constancy with which basic color patterns of browns, blackish shades, and light areas, in the form of spots, bars, and streaks, occur in preserved specimens of certain species and subspecies. These patterns were observed first in live specimens and were recorded by means of color photographs and colored drawings. Their persistence after a few years of alcoholic preservation was later confirmed by comparison of the photographs and drawings with the preserved specimens. Thus as a result of careful observation the older idea of lumping species or combining species into one catch-all species was not the true picture in nature. Authors who disregard such details as the basic color pattern are guilty of lumping species and subspecies incorrectly.

"The recognition of genera has never been placed on so definite a mathematical basis. Therefore, the splitters and lumpers have had a freer hand and sometimes the splitters actually have set up new generic and subgeneric units for nearly every species in a particular group. This has been especially noticeable in the poeciliid fishes.

"The concept of a genus should be to group closely related species together so that these species represent a small natural phyletic line. These phyletic lines are not all of the same value or definiteness in any family of fishes; they represent to a considerable extent the personal opinion of the ichthyological researcher.

"The characters by which genera are recognized are variable. In general, dentition and small constant differences in the bones, their shape and relationship to each other, are excellent guides. Fleshy characters such as barbels or their absence, development of glandular scales, specializations of the digestive tract, presence or absence of luminous glands or scales, specialized development of lips, fins, arrangement and size of scales are most useful in recognition of fish genera.

"No particular character or set of characters can be named in advance to cover the recognition of genera because fishes are so variable in structure from one order to another and from one family to another that the ichthyologist must test the characters he uses for each family. Those that reveal constancy for large series of specimens among few to several species may be used as generic characters."

CONTINENTAL DRIFT AND FISH DISTRIBUTION

The last few decades have seen a gradual accumulation of data to prove the once-maligned theory of continental drift. The basic idea of this theory is that the existing continents have not always been where they are now but have gradually drifted to their present positions over millions of years, the cooler and more solid rocks of the Earth's crust floating on the semi-liquid magma under the crust.

During the period when life was becoming well established on earth and even as late as the first terrestrial experiments by invertebrates and vertebrates, all the major land masses were connected to form a single ancient continent, Pangaea. Sometime about 170 to 200 million years ago, during the Jurassic period, Pangaea began to break up because of internal stresses and the fragments slowly drifted apart.

For convenience of terminology and also because of the way certain groups of plants and animals are distributed in the fossil record, two "supercontinents" are said to have come into being, the northern Laurasia (comprising the present North America, Europe, Asia, and Greenland) and the southern Gondwana (made up of Africa, South America, Antarctica, Australia, Madagascar, and India). Antarctica until recently was tropical and had a large fauna and flora. Over the last 100 million years or so the continents have continued to separate and collide seemingly at random until they reached their present positions. India broke totally away from Gondwana and drifted north to collide with Asia, forming the Himalayas.

With them the continents carried their floras and faunas, allowing the evolution of some groups of plants and animals to be traced along with the movements of the continents. For instance, certain early terrestrial amphibians are known only as fossils from Antarctica, Australia, South Africa, and India, a distribution well in keeping with the former close connection of these now widely separated areas. Similarly, a small freshwater fossil reptile is known from the same sediments of eastern South America and western Africa. These animals were not capable of crossing the oceans from one present continent to the other, but were carried as the continents separated.

There is increasing evidence that the history of many groups of living fishes is a long one, as most of the living major families of freshwater fishes were recognizable by at least the Cretaceous period, about 140 to 65 million years ago. Thus at least some freshwater fishes have had their current distributions influenced or controlled by the drifting continents. The varous tetras, for instance, are almost strictly African and South American in distribution, the expansion into Central America being of geologically recent origin. A look at a map will show that Africa and South America were once connected and would have certainly shared the same fauna to some extent. In fact, it is not impossible that the predecessors of some of the existing rivers of Brazil once flowed together with the ancestral Congo of Africa. The osteoglossid fishes are also found in South America and Africa (plus a genus in southern Asia and Australia), and of course the cichlids are typically South American—African fishes. It would seem likely that these groups of fishes originated at least in part in Pangaea in the area that was to later become Gondwana and then even later South America and Africa.

Other fish families that may trace their distribution to continental drift are the Cyprinidae and Galaxiidae. The typical cyprinids are northern in distribution, with fossils in North America and Eurasia. The great abundance of cyprinids in tropical Asia is perhaps a recent event, with cold-oriented fishes moving into an area with little competition and speciating rapidly and abundantly. The odd little galaxiids of Australia are not alone in the world—they also occur in New Zealand (readily explainable) and southwestern South America (not so readily understandable).

By the way, the continents are still moving. Recent satellite measurements plus other data indicate that North America and Europe are moving 2 cm farther apart each year, a seemingly insignificant figure that mounts up over millions of years.

THE ANCIENT CONTINENTS

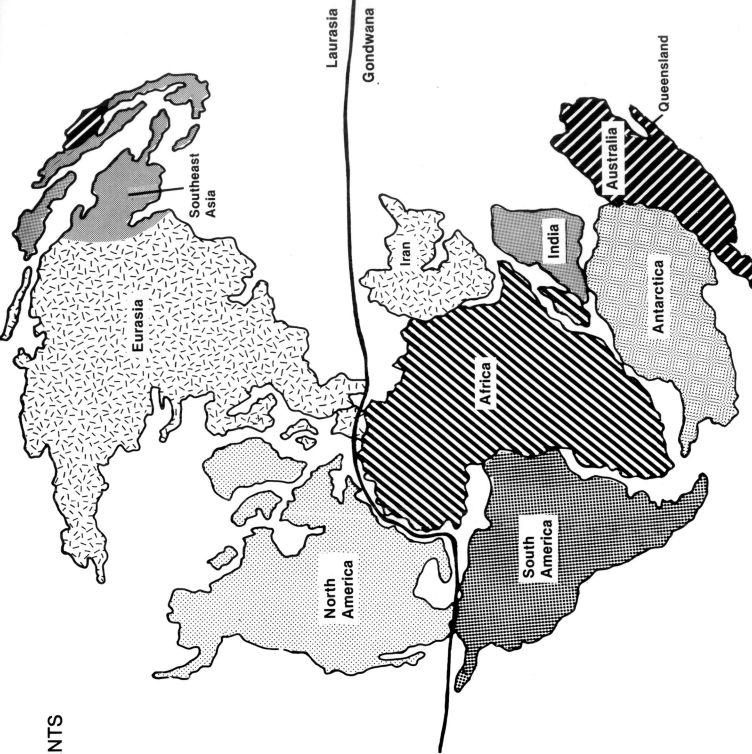

Movement of the continents. Shown at right is Pangaea after its breakup into the predecessors of the modern continents. The area above the line constitutes Laurasia, that below the line Gondwana. The shading corresponds to the current continental limits as used in this book. Notice especially that India, originally part of the southern continent, is now part of a northern continents, Southeast Asia of Eurasia. This helps explain the unusual fauna of modern India, which retains many relicts of the old southern fauna. North and South America have undergone a complicated history of connection and disconnection across the Central American area, resulting in faunas that are remarkably different for such closely linked areas. When using these maps, remember that the map of the modern continents is on a flat plane projection to allow all the areas to be seen in one surface, while the map of the ancient continents is on more of a polar projection, so distances are distorted. Smaller islands are shown on neither map unless important zoogeographically.

THE MODERN CONTINENTS

North America

South America

Eurasia

India

Southeast
Asia

Australia

Africa

Antarctica

ABOUT THE AUTHORS

Dr. Herbert R. Axelrod (HRA), Dr. Warren E. Burgess (WEB), Neal Pronek and Jerry G. Walls are all full-time employees of T.F.H. Publications in Neptune, New Jersey. ("T.F.H.," by the way, refers to the initials of *Tropical Fish Hobbyist* magazine, a monthly publication.) They are in daily contact with the aquarium world, the ichthyological world, and the world of publishing. This unique combination has used its talents to produce this book.

T.F.H. owns and operates its own engraving, typesetting, art, printing, and binding facilities in what is considered to be the most modern publishing plant in the book-publishing world. Very few book publishers do their own manufacturing. T.F.H. found it necessary to produce its own books so the ichthyologists working on the premises could "OK" proofs on press, etc. T.F.H. is also the world's largest publisher of fish books, and its magazine (*Tropical Fish Hobbyist*) has the widest paid circulation of any aquarium magazine in any language. Thus this book is one produced by people who are specialists in producing books like this. . .and we are very proud of this book, which took more effort than any book we've published in our 35 years of existence under the continuous management of our founders.

HOW TO USE THIS BOOK

There are many ways to lay out a book of fishes: alphabetically; anatomically (systematically by families, genera and species); haphazardly (say, for example, classifying fishes by their color or color pattern); or zoogeographically. Some books are even organized according to a fish's spawning habits such as egglayers, livebearers, etc. But each of these methods has its shortcoming.

The problem with an ALPHABETICAL listing of fishes is that name changes are difficult to accommodate in future editions, and every book on fishes is obsolete by the time the printing, editing and binding processes are completed.

The problem with a rigid evolutionary ANATOMICAL listing is that most people in the fish hobby and business don't know to which group most of the fishes belong and thus would be unable to easily locate a fish they have before them without thumbing through the whole book.

The problem with a HAPHAZARD color cataloging of fishes is that colors change and color varieties (just think about guppies, platies and swordtails!) would of necessity be listed in different sections of the book. Sexual dimorphism also would split species into different sections. Turmoil!

The problem with a ZOOGEOGRAPHICAL listing is that you would have to know the continent on which a certain fish is found. For some reason, aquarium fishes from within a certain zoogeographical area have a "familiar" look, and many hobbyists and dealers can fairly accurately identify the continent from which a fish comes just by looking at it, even if they have never seen it before. The main advantage of this system is that dealers who export fishes can use this as the basis of a price list and dealers who import fishes can more easily identify the fishes they got from a certain area even if the exporter doesn't clearly identify them. Many rarities slip in unidentified and mixed in with more usual, familiar species. These often grow up in a dealer's tank and must be identified. The final value of this kind of book design is that new species or new identifications can readily be dealt with without the very expensive alternative of moving color plates from one part of the book to the other.

This book is laid out zoogeographically. It took many, many years to produce this book since the accumulation of identified and verified photographs took so long. Simply buying photographs without having the fish's body available for verification was the worst case; having photographs of the holotype was the best case. This book is rich in that regard, bringing together many of the original illustrations used in the descriptions of many of these new species.

Photography

In addition to the photos taken by Dr. Axelrod, this book also contains many photographs by other photographers of fishes and aquarium subjects. The book is indebted to all of the people listed here. . .and to anyone else whose name might have been inadvertently omitted from the list.

Hiromitsu Akiyama
Dr. Gerald R. Allen
K. Attwood
Glen Axelrod
Dr. Hiroshi Azuma
Heiko Bleher
Pierre Brichard
Dr. Martin Brittan
Dr. Warren E. Burgess
Dr. Brooks Burr
Vojtech Elek
Dr. Augustin Fernandez-Yepez
Walter Foersch
Dr. Stanislav Frank
H. J. Franke
Dan Fromm
Dr. Jacques Gery
Dr. Robert J. Goldstein
Dr. Myron Gordon
Dr. Harry Grier
K. Jeno
Rodney Jonklaas
Burkhard Kahl
S. Kochetov
R. Lawrence
Ken Lucas, Steinhart Aquarium
Gerhard Marcuse
Dr. Richard L. Mayden

Midori Shobo (Fish Magazine, Japan)
New York Zoological Society
Aaron Norman
Dr. Joanne Norton
Y. W. Ong
Dr. Lawrence M. Page
Klaus Paysan
Kurt Quitschau
Hans-Joachim Richter
Mervin F. Roberts
Erhard Roloff
Andre Roth
Jorgen Scheel
Gunter Schmida
Harald Schultz
Rainier Stawikowski
Glenn Y. Takeshita
Edward C. Taylor
Dr. D. Terver, Nancy Aquarium
Gerard J. M. Timmerman
Dr. Bruce J. Turner
Arend van den Nieuwenhuizen
Braz Walker
Wardley Products Co.
Franz Werner
Uwe Werner
Gene Wolfsheimer
Ruda Zukal

North American Region

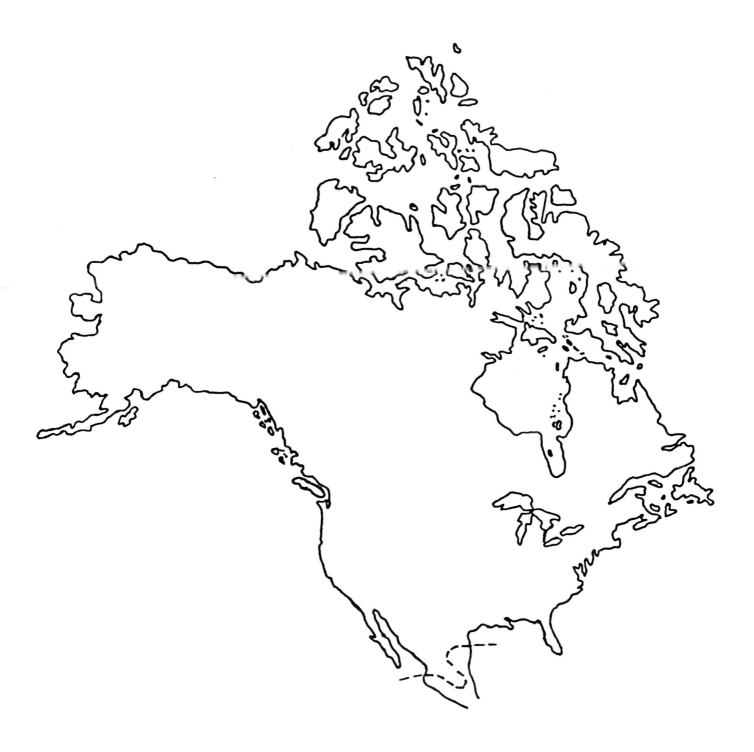

Ichthyomyzon bdellium (Jordan) • Ohio Lamprey

RANGE: The U.S.A. in lakes, rivers, and streams of the Ohio River Valley.

HABITS: A parasitic fish that occurs in rivers and lakes. May be kept in an aquarium and fed normal fish foods, but should be isolated from other fishes.

WATER CONDITIONS: Lives in unheated aquarium waters that are from fresh to very slightly brackish.

SIZE: Small lampreys are interesting aquarium inhabitants, but this species grows to 37.5 cm.

FOOD REQUIREMENTS: Depending upon the size and age, this fish will usually take chunks of spinach and chopped beef heart. Smaller specimens eat algae.

Aphredoderus sayanus (Gilliams) • Pirate Perch

RANGE: Atlantic coast of the U.S. from New York to Texas; Mississippi Basin to Michigan.

HABITS: Nocturnal predator. Will hunt for food at night and will eat any smaller fishes in the aquarium.

WATER CONDITIONS: Not critical.

SIZE: Attains a length of about 12.5 cm.

FOOD REQUIREMENTS: Usually spurns anything but live foods, with minnows its favorites.

Polyodon spathula (Walbaum) • Paddlefish

RANGE: The Mississippi River drainage and its larger tributaries in the U.S.A.

HABITS: An interesting inhabitant of the large aquarium. It must have lots of room as it grows quickly, reaching about 100 kg. (The Chinese paddlefish, *Psephurus gladius*, is reputed to reach 20 feet (610 cm) in length!)

WATER CONDITIONS: Fresh, clean, filtered water. pH as close to 7.0 as possible. Not fussy once it acclimates.

SIZE: A large fish perhaps reaching 225 pounds (100 kg).

FOOD REQUIREMENTS: It swims constantly with its mouth open, eating tiny cladoceran and copepod crustaceans. Swarms of daphnia living in its tank would probably suffice.

Lepisosteus oculatus (Winchell) • Spotted Gar

RANGE: From the Great Lakes of North America south to the Gulf of Mexico.

HABITS: A slow-moving fish often staying stationary in the water until a meal swims by, at which time it moves with great speed. Not meant for the home aquarium, though successful in large tanks. Beware: The eggs of this fish may be poisonous. The same is true of all gars.

WATER CONDITIONS: A freshwater fish that tolerates most aquarium conditions.

SIZE: Grows to about 2½ meters and more than 140 kg.

FOOD REQUIREMENTS: Thrives on small living fishes that it preys upon, but it can be acclimated to dead fish.

Scaphirhynchus platorynchus (Rafinesque) • Shovelnose Sturgeon

RANGE: Mississippi Valley south to Texas in the U.S.A.

HABITS: These make very interesting aquarium inhabitants when they are small. They swim in top-to-bottom upside-down circles at times and are very active when live foods are placed into their tanks. Their eggs make caviar, and their flesh is a smoked delicacy.

WATER CONDITIONS: Unheated freshwater aquaria with heavy filtration and aeration.

SIZE: They get very large in nature, but the record for an aquarium specimen is growing a 20 cm fish to 50 cm.

FOOD REQUIREMENTS: Will take small worms and insect larvae from the bottom.

Acipenser transmontanus Richardson • White Sturgeon

RANGE: Pacific shores of North America from the Aleutian Islands to Monterey, California.

HABITS: In nature this anadromous fish spends most of its time in the Pacific Ocean, returning to freshwater to spawn several times during its long life. Aquarium specimens thrive on chironomids.

WATER CONDITIONS: Large unheated aquarium with filtration. Not fussy about pH, salinity, hardness, or clarity.

SIZE: Probably the largest freshwater fish now available. Grows to 20 feet (610 cm) and well over 1,000 pounds.

FOOD REQUIREMENTS: Heavy, constant feeding of chironomids or any similar small insect larvae and worms. They gradually accept everything including dried food.

Lepisosteus spatula Lacepede • Alligator Gar

RANGE: Southeastern United States in both freshwater and saline waters of varying densities, including the Gulf of Mexico.

HABITS: This is a predatory fish that rarely accepts anything but live foods in the form of smaller fishes. It is only suitable for very large public aquaria.

WATER CONDITIONS: Tolerates almost any kind of water from fresh to salt with temperatures between 10° and 23°C.

SIZE: A very large fish reaching 3 meters in length and 150 kg.

FOOD REQUIREMENTS: A heavy eater of smaller living fishes. It grows fast if properly fed, otherwise it quickly perishes.

Lepisosteus osseus (Linnaeus) • Longnose Gar

RANGE: North America; Gulf states, Mississippi Basin northward to Great Lakes, eastern seaboard.

HABITS: Highly predatory and not to be trusted with fishes small enough to swallow; rather slow-moving most times, but capable of great bursts of speed.

WATER CONDITIONS: Not at all critical; often found surviving where other fishes have succumbed. Tolerates a wide temperature range.

SIZE: To 2 meter in nature, much less in aquaria; size can be reasonably controlled.

FOOD REQUIREMENTS: Live fishes preferred; acclimated fish can often be converted to strips of beef heart or other substitutes.

Ichthyomyzon bdellium

Scaphirhynchus platorynchus

Aphredoderus sayanus

Acipenser transmontanus

Polyodon spathula

Lepisosteus spatula

Lepisosteus oculatus

Lepisosteus osseus

17

Amia calva Linnaeus • Bowfin, Mudfish, Dogfish

RANGE: Found in the United States from Vermont to the Dakotas, from Florida to Texas.

HABITS: A vicious, voracious fish, not to be kept with any fish smaller than itself.

WATER CONDITIONS: Capable of living in any water which is not poisoned, though it prefers warm water from 21 to 30°C.

SIZE: Males grow to 50 cm; females to 75 cm.

FOOD REQUIREMENTS: This is a fish which will only eat live foods. Small earthworms are acceptable. Larger specimens can be taught to accept beef heart and other meat products.

Oncorhynchus kisutch (Walbaum) • Coho Salmon

RANGE: The Pacific Ocean and its drainage from the Anadyr River in the USSR to Hokkaido, Japan, and Alaska south to California. It has been transplanted into many freshwater lakes.

HABITS: One of the world's economic wonders, eaten as a delicacy all over the world. It thrives in rivers, lakes, and oceans. Easy to keep in large refrigerated aquaria.

WATER CONDITIONS: Almost any clean, well-aerated water in which it has lots of swimming space. Water temperatures should be under 18°C as much as possible.

SIZE: The usual maximum size is about 2 feet (about 60 cm).

FOOD REQUIREMENTS: These are fast-growing fish and must have small live fishes to satisfy their huge appetites.

Salmo trutta Linnaeus • Brown Trout

RANGE: Though native to Europe and western Asia, it is now found in the British Isles, Iceland, Afghanistan, Canada, and the U.S.A. A major game and food fish of the world.

HABITS: Brown trout spawn in shallow gravelly headwaters in late fall or early winter when the water is about 7-8°C. They spawn in pits dug by the female and covered over after spawning. They average only 2000 eggs per spawning.

WATER CONDITIONS: May be kept in refrigerated aquaria only as they readily fall prey to bacterial infections if kept in warmer waters.

SIZE: May reach 50 cm, but average 40 cm.

FOOD REQUIREMENTS: Carnivorous fish that eat insects, crustaceans, small fishes, frogs, and just about anything else that moves in the water.

Megalops atlanticus Valenciennes • Tarpon

RANGE: Tropical and temperate Atlantic Ocean, ranging into brackish water when young.

HABITS: Keep well in large heated public aquaria, but they require lots of space. In the wild they are topnotch game-fishes, putting on a jumping display when hooked.

WATER CONDITIONS: Basically marine fish, though they often move into freshwater and brackish water in the Florida Keys. Water temperatures should be above 18°C.

SIZE: To 8 feet (about 2½ m).

FOOD REQUIREMENTS: A very fast-growing fish that requires large quantities of smaller fishes as daily food. They can be acclimated to dead fresh fishes in the aquarium. Not a home aquarium fish.

Salvelinus fontinalis (Mitchill) • Brook Trout

RANGE: Endemic North American species that originally occurred only in the northeastern U.S.A. and Canada. Now more widespread throughout the world.

HABITS: Spawns in late summer or fall. Usually travels many miles upstream to spawn in shallow water. Requires refrigerated aquaria for successful maintenance.

WATER CONDITIONS: Cold, clear, fast-running or heavily aerated water that is clean and non-polluted.

SIZE: World's record is 6.6 kg.

FOOD REQUIREMENTS: Eats many things, from crustaceans to smaller fishes, which it can ingest whole. Aquatic insects are a favorite food, as are flying insects that fall onto the water's surface.

Salvelinus namaycush (Walbaum) • Lake Trout

RANGE: Originally from northern North America, it has been introduced all over the world.

HABITS: Spawns in the fall, usually in lakes over large stones. Spawning usually takes place between 5 PM and 10 PM. The eggs are non-adhesive and fall into the crevices. A typical female lays 18,000 eggs.

WATER CONDITIONS: Clear, cool water. Must be refrigerated if kept in an aquarium. Small specimens keep well.

SIZE: There are reports of fish up to 43 kg, but usually half that weight is considered large.

FOOD REQUIREMENTS: Eats live foods small enough to ingest whole, including fishes, molluscs, insects, etc.

Amia calva (adult)

Amia calva (juvenile)

Oncorhynchus kisutch

Megalops atlanticus

Salmo trutta

Salvelinus fontinalis

Salvelinus fontinalis

Salvelinus namaycush

Esox americanus (Gmelin) • Redfin Pickerel

RANGE: Throughout eastern North America.
HABITS: Though a very streamlined fish, this predator prefers still waters in lakes or ponds, especially those heavily vegetated.
WATER CONDITIONS: Large aquarium necessary. Unheated, clean water. Thrives in unheated tanks but can tolerate temperatures in the 15-22°C. range.
SIZE: A small pickerel that hardly ever gets larger than 375 mm.
FOOD REQUIREMENTS: They prefer live fishes smaller than themselves, but they can be acclimated to chunks of fish, shrimp or beef.

Esox lucius Linnaeus • Northern Pike

RANGE: Circumpolar distribution in the Northern Hemisphere. In the U.S.A., from Alaska to Missouri; also in the British Isles and most of Europe, through the USSR to Lake Baikal. Very widely distributed.
HABITS: Its wide distribution attests to its ability to acclimate to all types and temperatures of water including brackish (it is found in brackish waters in the Baltic Sea). Spawns in the spring.
WATER CONDITIONS: Cold, clear waters. Must be kept in refrigerated aquarium waters.
SIZE: Up to about 75 cm; exceptional specimens are larger.
FOOD REQUIREMENTS: It eats living fishes but is easily tempted by both dried and fresh dead fishes.

Gila robusta Baird & Girard • Roundtail Chub

RANGE: Colorado River drainage, western U.S.A.
HABITS: Spawning individuals with breeding tubercles were taken in shallow pools and eddies over rubble or boulder substrates covered with silt. Spawning generally occurred in June or July when temperatures rose to about 18°C.
WATER CONDITIONS: Clear, well-oxygenated water required. This is a coldwater species, so refrigerated tanks may be necessary.
SIZE: Attains a length of about 14 to 15 inches (35-40 cm).
FOOD REQUIREMENTS: Adults will eat small fishes and insects as well as plant debris and algae in nature. Juveniles ate only insects.

Notemigonus crysoleucas (Mitchill) • Golden Shiner

RANGE: Over most of the eastern half of North America from the Maritime Provinces south to Florida and west to the Dakotas and Texas.
HABITS: It spawns in the spring and early summer, attaching sticky eggs onto bushy plants or protruding fine root systems.
WATER CONDITIONS: Clear, heavily vegetated non-flowing waters are preferred. Can easily be kept in unheated (or heated) aquaria.
SIZE: Records of over 26 cm are known, but the usual size is 6 cm.
FOOD REQUIREMENTS: Eats anything in the way of aquarium foods, both flake and freeze-dried.

Umbra pygmaea (DeKay) • The Eastern Mudminnow

RANGE: Eastern United States from New York to Florida.
HABITS: A small mudminnow that is found in swamps and very slow moving streams.
WATER CONDITIONS: They do well in unheated aquariums where their tankmates are not too active. The water must be well aged or they develop skin problems manifested by fungus growth.
SIZE: About 150 mm is the maximum size but most aquarium specimens are much smaller.
FOOD REQUIREMENTS: They prefer live foods (as do most fishes) but they quickly adapt to a typical aquarium diet.

Esox niger Lesueur • Chain Pickerel

RANGE: Eastern and south-central North America.
HABITS: A spring spawner that makes an interesting aquarium pet when small. The smaller fish (shown here) does not have the chain pattern of coloration that only develops in specimens over 150-200 mm.
WATER CONDITIONS: Freshwater with a high pH, though it tolerates most waters which are fresh, clear, and cool. A solitary fish that hides motionless in vegetation awaiting its next meal.
SIZE: As large as 80 cm.
FOOD REQUIREMENTS: Live fishes are preferred, though pickerel are usually easily acclimated to other foods when young.

Exoglossum maxillingua (Lesueur) • Cutlips Minnow

RANGE: Northeastern North America.
HABITS: A rather sluggish, slow-moving fish. It stays on the bottom picking on the gravel and hiding under larger stones, plants, etc. It eagerly takes tubifex worms and daphnia that are near the bottom of the tank. Available from bait dealers. A good substitute for catfish as scavengers.
WATER CONDITIONS: Not fussy, but the water should be cool. Does well in the unheated aquarium.
SIZE: Males: 140 mm. Females: smaller, about 130 mm maximum.
FOOD REQUIREMENTS: They eat most of the ordinary fish foods, both living and prepared.

Esox americanus

Umbra pygmaea

Esox lucius

Esox lucius

Gila robusta

Esox niger

Notemigonus crysoleucas

Exoglossum maxillingua

Notropis welaka Evermann & Kendall • Bluenose Shiner

RANGE: Restricted to the area from eastern Florida (St. Johns River) to the Pearl River which forms part of the boundary between Louisiana and Mississippi.
HABITS: Peaceful. Can be kept with other fishes of similar size and temperament.
WATER CONDITIONS: Not critical. Tolerates a wide range of pH and hardness, but for best results should be kept in soft, slightly acid water. Temperature range from about 6° to 26°C, but prefers it cool.
SIZE: Reaches a maximum length of about 65 mm (average 50 mm).
FOOD REQUIREMENTS: Will accept a wide range of aquarium foods.

Notropis cornutus (Mitchill) • Common Shiner

RANGE: Central North America from the Mississippi valley to Nova Scotia and south to Virginia's James River system.
HABITS: Spawns in the spring when water temperatures reach 16°C. Spawns over gravel beds excavated in a half-hearted manner.
WATER CONDITIONS: They prefer clear, cool water, but they can take heated or unheated aquaria.
SIZE: Males grow large, to 200 mm, while females rarely exceed 160 mm.
FOOD REQUIREMENTS: These are basically bottom feeders, searching for small worms and crustaceans in nature. They also take dried foods in aquaria.

Notropis hypselopterus (Guenther) • Sailfin Shiner

RANGE: South Carolina, Georgia, Florida and Alabama.
HABITS: A peaceful, active fish which will not molest its tankmates.
WATER CONDITIONS: Clean, soft, slightly acid water and a good-sized, well-planted tank are preferred.
SIZE: 8 cm.
FOOD REQUIREMENTS: Will take dried as well as live or frozen foods.

Notropis atherinoides Rafinesque •Emerald Shiner

RANGE: Large lakes and rivers in Canada and throughout the north central states along the Mississippi River valley.
HABITS: The emerald shiner is an open water, pelagic species. It requires larger tanks to really thrive and it schools when enough fish are in one tank. Not really a home aquarium fish. Lives about three years.
WATER CONDITIONS: Cool, still water. Very easy to acclimate to life in a very large aquarium (over 500 liters). Best kept in an unheated aquarium.
SIZE: Males reach 85 mm.
FOOD REQUIREMENTS: Prefers live foods like daphnia, but quickly learns to accept typical dried aquarium fare.

Notropsis lutrensis (Baird and Girard) • Red Shiner

RANGE: Wyoming to Minnesota, Iowa, Illinois, south to Mexico, and west to Colorado and California.
HABITS: The breeding males have bright orange ventral fins and very dark vertical bars on the sides. The males are covered almost completely with fine tubercles, giving them the nickname "Sandpaper Shiners."
WATER CONDITIONS: Prefers unheated tanks that are very cool in the winter and not more than 23°C in the summer.
SIZE: This very popular bait minnow reaches a maximum of 76 mm with the male usually larger than the female.
FOOD REQUIREMENTS: Prefers live foods as do most fishes, but gets along quite well on dried and frozen aquarium diets.

Ptychocheilus lucius Girard • Colorado Squawfish

RANGE: Colorado basin.
HABITS: Voracious pike-like predators that put up a respectable fight when caught on hook and line and are good to eat.
WATER CONDITIONS: Need cold, clear water. A large refrigerated tank in public aquariums would be the most likely place to see one in captivity.
SIZE: Said to attain a length of over 1½ meters and a weight of 35 kilos in past years but now even 1 to 1⅓ meters long specimens are generally rare.
FOOD REQUIREMENTS: Voracious feeders on other fishes, commonly young trout and salmon in the wild. Will accept other available fishes, such as feeder goldfish.

Phoxinus erythrogaster Rafinesque • Southern Redbelly Dace

RANGE: Restricted to the tributaries of the Mississippi, from the Cannon River to the Missouri drainage
HABITS: This is one of the most colorful of all American fishes. Unfortunately the photo is of a female. In breeding males the ventral fins, flanks, and belly are blood red, bright and obvious.
WATER CONDITIONS: Unheated or heated aquariums suit them equally well.
SIZE: About 80 mm. Males are larger and have longer fins.
FOOD REQUIREMENTS: Dried aquarium foods are accepted but they need daphnia or live brine shrimp to achieve spawning condition.

Notropis welaka (male)

Notropis welaka (female)

Notropis cornutus (male)

Notropis hypselopterus

Notropis atherinoides

Notropis lutrensis

Ptychocheilus lucius

Phoxinus erythrogaster

23

Rhinichthys atratulus (Hermann) • Blacknose Dace

RANGE: Manitoba and Nova Scotia in Canada to North Dakota, North Carolina, and Nebraska.

HABITS: Spawns in riffles over gravel and debris in very shallow water (sometimes only two inches deep). Eggs are laid in a nest of stones, but the eggs are not cared for.

WATER CONDITIONS: Clear, aerated water. Unheated tanks are necessary and if the water gets over 23°C it should be cooled down.

SIZE: Rarely exceed 100 mm. Breeding males have a dark red lateral band; males have longer fins.

FOOD REQUIREMENTS: In nature it feeds on small algae, small insects, and small worms. In the aquarium it readily accepts live brine shrimp, tubifex, and daphnia plus the usual dry food fare.

Catostomus catostomus (Forster) • Longnose Sucker

RANGE: North America, from Maryland to Minnesota, to the Arctic and northern Asia.

HABITS: Spawns in the spring in streams or any other place when the water thaws to 5°C. They prefer to spawn in moving water during daylight hours. White, sticky eggs fall to the bottom as several fish spawn together.

WATER CONDITIONS: Prefers colder water. Cannot live for long under heated aquarium conditions.

SIZE: Various populations grow to different lengths. Individuals from the Great Slave Lake, Canada, population reach 642 mm, while the Saskatchewan fish rarely get over 439 mm.

Xyrauchen texanus (Abbott) • Razorback Sucker

RANGE: Lower parts of the Colorado River. Rare and on the endangered species list.

HABITS: Lives in swift-flowing waters where the unusual shape of its back is said to act like an inverted keel causing the flowing water to push them down against the bottom

WATER CONDITIONS: Lives in cold, highly oxygenated water that at the same time may also be silt-laden.

SIZE: Attains a length of up to 60 cm.

FOOD REQUIREMENTS: Apparently feeds primarily by taste like many other suckers. This is a bottom-grubbing species feeding on material living on or attached to the substrate.

Noturus miurus Jordan • Brindled Madtom

RANGE: From Iowa and Minnesota to Lake Erie and its tributaries to New York and south to Mississippi, Louisiana, Arkansas, and northeastern Oklahoma.

HABITS: Lives in riffles to quiet areas on sand/clay bottoms; does not like mud bottoms. May bury themselves in the bottom during the day and forage at night. Their dorsal and pectoral fin spines are mildly poisonous.

WATER CONDITIONS: They do best in clear, clean, well-oxygenated water. A gravel bottom and hiding places are recommended. Breed at 25-30°C.

SIZE: Less than 12 cm.

FOOD REQUIREMENTS: Brine shrimp, raw liver, flake food, and tubifex worms are favorites.

Semotilus atromaculatus (Mitchill) • Creek Chub

RANGE: From Montana to the Gaspe Peninsula in Canada, south to the Gulf states. Several subspecies are recognized.

HABITS: In nature the fish is a creek fish rather than a lake fish. It spawns in fast-moving water riffles over gravel about 1 cm in diameter. The breeding males are beautiful, with large tubercles on their heads and sides which are orange, blue and purple.

WATER CONDITIONS: Depends upon the source of the fish. Southern fishes do well under normal aquarium conditions. Northern fishes require unheated tanks.

SIZE: May reach 30 cm in 7 years.

FOOD REQUIREMENTS: They eat everything and are often caught on a hook by fly fishermen or trout fishermen.

Erimyzon sucetta (Lacepede) • Lake Chubsucker

RANGE: Eastern North America to midwest, from southern New York to Florida, west to Texas, and north to Minnesota, Michigan and Wisconsin.

HABITS: A specialty fish that should be kept in cool water aquaria.

WATER CONDITIONS: Variable except that temperatures higher than 21°C usually cause problems.

SIZE: Reaches a length of about 25 cm.

FOOD REQUIREMENTS: Will usually take daphnia, brine shrimp, chironomids, copepods.

Ictalurus catus (Linnaeus) • White Catfish

RANGE: Eastern United States from New England to Florida. Widely introduced elsewhere in the U.S.

HABITS: Typical catfish, grubbing on the bottom with their barbels for food. Spawned eggs of some bullheads (Ictalurus) have been known to stick to wading birds' legs and thereby become distributed into other areas.

WATER CONDITIONS: Not critical. These catfish can survive in water with a very low oxygen content due to their accessory breathing apparatus.

SIZE: To 7 kilos, but average closer to 1½ kilos.

FOOD REQUIREMENTS: Will eat almost anything and have very good appetites. Normally take food from the bottom like other catfishes.

Ictalurus punctatus (Rafinesque) • Channel Catfish

RANGE: U.S.A., Great Lakes to Florida and Texas.

HABITS: Small ones are excellent scavengers and peaceful.

WATER CONDITIONS: Not critical as long as the water is clean and not too warm. Temperature about 18°C.

SIZE: Only babies are recommended for the aquarium; reaches 90 cm in length.

FOOD REQUIREMENTS: Tubifex worms and frozen brine shrimp are eaten with gusto by juveniles, but adults have large mouths and large appetites.

Rhinichthys atratulus

Semotilus atromaculatus

Catostomus catostomus

Erimyzon sucetta

Xyrauchen texanus

Ictalurus catus

Noturus miurus

Ictalurus punctatus (albino)

Fundulus chrysotus (Guenther) • Golden Ear, Golden Topminnow

RANGE: South Carolina, Georgia, Florida; found in standing water near the coastline.
HABITS: Peaceful when kept with fishes its own size.
WATER CONDITIONS: It is advisable to add one teaspoon of salt to every 20 liters of aquarium water. Temperature 23 to 25°C.
SIZE: To 7 cm.
FOOD REQUIREMENTS: Will eat most aquarium fish foods, including dried flake food, freeze-dried food and live food.

Cyprinodon macularius Baird & Girard • Desert Pupfish

RANGE: Salton Sea, Colorado delta, and Rio Sonoyata, southwestern United States.
HABITS: Usually peaceful, but best kept by themselves because of their water requirements and spawning type.
WATER CONDITIONS: Hard, alkaline water with temperatures from 24 to 32°C. Some salt may be added to the water.
SIZE: Up to about 6 to 8 cm.
FOOD REQUIREMENTS: Prefers live foods like tubifex and brine shrimp but can be coaxed onto frozen, flake or other types of foods.

Fundulus heteroclitus (Linnaeus) • Zebra Killie, Mummichog

RANGE: Atlantic Coast from Canada to Florida.
HABITS: Fairly peaceful, but may pick on smaller fishes.
WATER CONDITIONS: Water should be alkaline and hard (about 20 DH), with some salt added, at least a teaspoonful to every 4 liters; will take full salt water. Should be kept at room temperature.
SIZE: To 20 cm.
FOOD REQUIREMENTS: All kinds of live foods, also dried foods which have a vegetable content, such as the so-called "Molly food."

Fundulus cingulatus Cuvier & Valenciennes • Banded Topminnow

RANGE: South Carolina, Georgia, Florida; found in standing water near the coastline.
HABITS: Peaceful when kept with fishes its own size.
WATER CONDITIONS: It is advisable to add one teaspoon of salt to every 20 liters of aquarium water. Temperature 23 to 25°C.
SIZE: To 7 cm.
FOOD REQUIREMENTS: Will eat most aquarium fish foods, including dried flake food, freeze-dried food and live food.

Lucania goodei Jordan • Bluefin Killifish

RANGE: Southern Florida.
HABITS: An active species which will sometimes pursue other fishes, but seldom attacks.
WATER CONDITIONS: Should be kept in roomy aquaria, well planted and cool (15°C).
SIZE: 5 cm.
FOOD REQUIREMENTS: Small live foods only; dried foods are accepted only if the fish are starving.

Jordanella floridae Goode & Bean • American Flagfish

RANGE: Florida, especially in the southern portion.
HABITS: Males are apt to be very quarrelsome, especially at spawning time; it is best to give pairs their own aquarium.
WATER CONDITIONS: Prefers a sunny aquarium with slightly alkaline water. Temperature should be around 21°C, slightly higher for spawning.
SIZE: About 5 cm.
FOOD REQUIREMENTS: Will eat dried as well as live foods, but should get a good deal of vegetable matter in its diet.

Heterandria formosa Agassiz • Least Killifish

RANGE: U.S., North Carolina to eastern Texas, coastal.
HABITS: Peaceful; males are small enough to be eaten by bigger fish, and this species is best kept by itself.
WATER CONDITIONS: Not critical, as long as the water is not too far from neutral. Temperature about 24°C.
SIZE: Males about 2 cm; females almost 3.5 cm.
FOOD REQUIREMENTS: All small live foods, also frozen. Prepared foods also taken.

Leptolucania ommata (Jordan) • Swamp Killie, Pygmy Killifish

RANGE: Southern Georgia to Florida, in swamps.
HABITS: Peaceful, but should not be kept with larger fishes.
WATER CONDITIONS: Neutral to slightly acid water; tank should be well planted. Temperature 21 to 24°C.
SIZE: To about 4 cm.
FOOD REQUIREMENTS: Small living foods are preferred, but dried foods are accepted.

Fundulus chrysotus

Cyprinodon macularius

Fundulus heteroclitus

Fundulus cingulatus

Lucania goodei

Jordanella floridae

Heterandria formosa

Leptolucania ommata

Spawning the American Flagfish, *Jordanella floridae*
Goode & Bean

There are two patterns of spawning in this fish. In habitats with a muddy, mulm bottom, the fish hang their eggs among floating plants. When the bottom is clean and gravelly, they spawn like many cichlids. The male usually searches out a site (on # 1 photo facing page). When he finds it he indicates his acceptance by taking a position over the site. The female then comes to inspect the site (# 2) and the male tries to inspire her acceptance by dancing about her with extended fins (# 3). He then sidles up to her (#4) and tries to press her into a mass of fine roots (#5). If she cooperates, he will drape his large dorsal fin over her back (# 6, 7 and 8), pressing her as he quivers. He fertilizes the eggs as they are expelled. The male then guards the eggs. The female should be left in the aquarium since she often comes back every day for a week to add more eggs to the nest. Hatching of the first eggs takes about a week. The male also cares for the young.

Spawning the American Flagfish, *Jordanella floridae*

Gasterosteus aculeatus Linnaeus • Three-spined Stickleback

RANGE: Most of Europe, both coasts of North America, nothern Africa and northern Asia.

HABITS: Inclined to be pugnacious toward other fishes, and therefore should have their own tank.

WATER CONDITIONS: Water should be slightly alkaline with a salt content of about a quarter teaspoonful of salt per liter. Temperature 16 to 18°C.

SIZE: Up to 10 cm.

FOOD REQUIREMENTS: Living foods only, such as daphnia, tubifex worms and white worms.

Centrarchus macropterus (Lacepede) • Flier

RANGE: Widespread from Virginia to Texas and Louisiana, north to Illinois and Indiana.

HABITS: This monotypic genus contains a lovely fish that is almost round in appearance. The anal fin is almost as large as the dorsal. Some South American cichlids look similar to this fish.

WATER CONDITIONS: Does well in most aquarium situations where there is plenty of room, heavy aeration and an unheated environment.

SIZE: May reach 200 mm and weigh up to a pound making it a small game fish for children.

FOOD REQUIREMENTS: Eats just about everything that is normally offered to aquarium fishes including fishes small enough for it to ingest whole.

Elassoma evergladei Jordan • Everglades Pygmy Sunfish

RANGE: Florida and Georgia.

HABITS: Very timid with other fishes; should be kept by themselves in a small aquarium.

WATER CONDITIONS: Slightly alkaline water. Room temperatures, about 18 to 20°C, are perfect.

SIZE: About 3 cm; females a little smaller.

FOOD REQUIREMENTS: Small live foods are best, like sifted Daphnia, newly hatched brine shrimp, etc.

Enneacanthus gloriosus (Holbrook) • Diamond Sunfish, Bluespotted Sunfish

RANGE: Eastern coastal United States from New York to Florida.

HABITS: Peaceful when kept with fishes of its size.

WATER CONDITIONS: Slightly alkaline water which is kept unheated at room temperature.

Size: To 8 cm.

FOOD REQUIREMENTS: Variety of live or frozen foods. Dried foods are accepted unwillingly.

Micropterus salmoides (Lacepede) • Largemouth Bass

RANGE: Native to Canada and the U.S.A. east of the Rockies, southward to Mexico.

HABITS: Spawning is controlled in nature by temperature. When the waters warm up to about 18°C. the fish spawn. A depression almost 1 m in diameter is prepared by the male. After spawning he guards the nest with great vigor. They don't eat while guarding their nests.

WATER CONDITIONS: Large unheated tanks with aeration and filtration. Water chemistry is not important as long as the water is clear and unpolluted.

SIZE: A large fish reaching up to 8 kg. in nature. They are easily stunted by being kept in an aquarium.

FOOD REQUIREMENTS: They eat everything small enough to ingest in one gulp, from frogs to insects to other smaller fishes. Pellets are satisfactory for fish 7 cm or larger.

Archoplites interruptus (Girard) • Sacramento Perch

RANGE: The Sacramento and San Joaquin basins in California.

HABITS: A large sunfish (centrarchid). These fish, and all centrarchids, spawn like cichlids. They make a depression in the sand, entice a female to join them in spawning, then chase away all fishes, including the female, while they guard the nest.

WATER CONDITIONS: They are not fussy about their water chemistry as long as it is clean, cool (unheated), and well aerated.

SIZE: They reach about 300 mm.

FOOD REQUIREMENTS: Live foods are much preferred, but they acclimate to normal aquarium fare especially frozen (thawed) beef heart.

Enneacanthus chaetodon (Baird) • Blackbanded Sunfish

RANGE: New Jersey south to northern Florida, coastal.

HABITS: Usually peaceful, but should not be trusted with smaller fishes. Also shy when with active fishes.

WATER CONDITIONS: Water should be kept alkaline and a part of it frequently changed. Temperature around 21°C.

SIZE: 8 cm.

FOOD REQUIREMENTS: Live foods only; it might be possible to induce them to eat frozen foods, but they will seldom take dried foods.

COLOR VARIATIONS: Body silvery to light yellow, with a number of dark bars running vertically. First ventral rays are orange.

Enneacanthus obesus (Girard) • Banded Sunfish

RANGE: Eastern United States from Massachusetts to northern Florida, coastal.

HABITS: Because of the cooler temperatures enjoyed by this species it should probably have a tank all to itself.

WATER CONDITIONS: Not critical. Should have partial periodic changes. Temperature for breeding a cool 20°C.

SIZE: About 8 cm.

FOOD REQUIREMENTS: Feed a wide variety of live foods such as daphnia, cyclops, chironomid larvae, brine shrimp, etc. and perhaps some frozen or freeze-dried prepared foods.

Gasterosteus aculeatus

Micropterus salmoides

Centrarchus macropterus

Archoplites interruptus

Elassoma evergladei

Enneacanthus chaetodon

Enneacanthus gloriosus

Enneacanthus obesus

31

Lepomis megalotis (Rafinesque) • Longeared Sunfish

RANGE: Eastern United States, Canada to Mexican border.
HABITS: Best kept by themselves.
WATER CONDITIONS: Not critical, but water should be clean and well aerated.
SIZE: Wild specimens 20 cm; in the aquarium seldom over 13 cm.
FOOD REQUIREMENTS: Hearty eaters whose live food diet can be supplemented with chopped beef heart, liver, etc.

Lepomis gibbosus (Linnaeus) • Sunfish, Pumpkinseed

RANGE: Maine to Florida west to the Mississippi.
HABITS: Should be kept by themselves or with others of the same genus.
WATER CONDITIONS: Tank should be roomy and the water clean. Room temperatures suffice without any additional heat.
SIZE: Seldom larger than 15 cm.
FOOD REQUIREMENTS: Hearty eaters which require frequent feeding with large live foods such as chopped earthworms or frozen foods like beef heart.

Lepomis gulosus (Cuvier) • Warmouth

RANGE: Widely distributed in the United States with the exception of the extreme northeastern section.
HABITS: Spawns in depressions constructed in the bottom like other species of Lepomis.
WATER CONDITIONS: Water chemistry not critical. An unheated tank with clean, clear, well-aerated water is recommended.
SIZE: Attains a length of up to 25 cm.
FOOD REQUIREMENTS: Feeds on small fishes and aquatic invertebrates. Food should be living when offered.

Micropterus punctulatus (Rafinesque) • Spotted Bass

RANGE: From Ohio River system in Indiana, Illinois, and Ohio to the Gulf states.
HABITS: Usually found in deep pools of moderate or large streams. Behaves much like other species of Micropterus.
WATER CONDITIONS: Requires a large tank. Water should be clean, cool, and well aerated. Likes slightly higher temperatures than other species of Micropterus.
SIZE: Attains lengths of up to 50 cm.
FOOD REQUIREMENTS: Adults thrive on live fishes; smaller individuals take smaller live fishes and live crustaceans (brine shrimp, etc.).

Pomoxis nigromaculatus (LeSueur) • Black Crappie

RANGE: Common in lakes and large streams from southern Manitoba to Quebec and south along the eastern United States to Florida and Texas.
HABITS: Very prolific, spawning up to 140,000 eggs at a time. May spawn in their first or second year in the late spring. Nests for spawning are constructed in water a meter or two deep.
WATER CONDITIONS: Not critical. A cool water species that can live in an unheated aquarium.
SIZE: Seldom more than 30 cm.
FOOD REQUIREMENTS: Feed on a wide variety of foods such as aquatic insects, small crustaceans, and small fishes.

Lepomis macrochirus Rafinesque • Bluegill

RANGE: United States from Minnesota to Texas (and south to northern Mexico) and eastward to the East Coast from New York to Florida. Introduced into areas as far west as California.
HABITS: Generally aggressive. Diggers and plant uprooters.
WATER CONDITIONS: Not critical. A cool-water species but can tolerate temperatures from 2-30°C.
SIZE: Reaches maturity at about 9 cm, but a record Bluegill of 380 cm has been recorded.
FOOD REQUIREMENTS: Easily fed on a variety of foods including earthworms, small live fishes, beef heart, etc.

Lepomis humilis (Girard) • Orangespotted Sunfish

RANGE: From the Dakotas to Ohio and south to Texas and northern Alabama.
HABITS: Spawns like other Lepomis species and in the same areas, sometimes leading to hybridization.
WATER CONDITIONS: Water chemistry not critical. Clean, clear water at room temperatures will suffice.
SIZE: A small species of usually 5 to 8 cm but occasionally to 10 cm.
FOOD REQUIREMENTS: Feeds on small crustaceans and aquatic insects.

Micropterus dolomieui Lacepede • Smallmouth Bass

RANGE: From Lake of the Woods region to Quebec and south to eastern Oklahoma and northern Alabama. Has also been introduced elsewhere.
HABITS: Prefers clear, moderately cool, swift-flowing streams or clear gravel-bottomed lakes. Spawns over clean gravel and sand bottoms in a current. Nests are hollow depressions. Normally blackish fry spread out over the spawning bed shortly after darkness and turn a light gray color; at sunrise next day they return to their natural dark color.
WATER CONDITIONS: Need a large, clean, well-aerated tank, preferably with some current. Unheated tanks are preferred (they spawn at 18°C).
SIZE: Attains a length of over 31 cm.
FOOD REQUIREMENTS: Small individuals will take live crustaceans; larger ones take larger crustaceans and small live fishes. Dead food is usually ignored.

Lepomis megalotus

Pomoxis nigromaculatus

Lepomis gibbosus

Lepomis macrochirus

Lepomis gulosus

Lepomis humilis

Micropterus punctulatus

Micropterus dolomieui

The Darters

Darters are strictly North American in distribution, with species to be found in suitable habitats in most of the drainages of the Mississippi and Ohio Rivers, the Great Lakes, the Gulf of Mexico,Hudson Bay in Canada, and on the Atlantic coastal plain. Many species are found in the eastern mountain ranges, the Appalachians, Ozarks, and their outliers. All together there are about 150 species contained in three genera that constitute the tribe Etheostomatini of the family Percidae. All darters have two dorsal fins, with spines present only in the first dorsal. The three genera are *Percina*, *Ammocrypta*, and *Etheostoma*. It is often difficult to differentiate between the genera by observing them in an aquarium since they are told apart primarily by such things as possessing translucent bodies, specialized scales in males, and form of the lateral line system on the head. There are numerous subgenera as well.

For the aquarist, the darters present a rare challenge, for here are fishes that almost always require running water habitats (like some of the rainbowfishes of Australia and New Guinea) and range in size from the tiny *E. fonticola* (to about 4 cm long) to the giant *P. lenticula*, which reaches the length of about 16 cm. They are often colorful and will eat most live foods and many dried foods. Darters are hardy, easy to sex and breed, and usually don't require heaters, pumps, or filters if you know how to properly maintain an aquarium and don't overfeed your fishes!

Almost every creek and stream within their range contains one darter species or another, and they often occur in great numbers where found. As a matter of fact, in studies made of darter population densities, a rare density would be a mere one fish per square yard; some studies collected 33 to the square yard! In drought-affected areas in New Jersey, the author (H.R.A.) found *E. olmstedi* in a small stream with a sandy bottom in numbers of 80 individuals to the square yard; this was likely an unnatural concentration due to the lack of rain in the area over an extended period of time.

To effectively collect darters, get yourself a minnow seine about 6 feet long and, with some help, wedge the seine in sand or rocks on the bottom of a stream where darters have been observed. Set the seine up in such a way that once the darters have been driven into the seine they become trapped. Then merely wade toward the seine trap from a distance of about 20 yards upstream, shuffling your feet so as to drive the fleeing darters in front of you. Take only as many fish as you need—perhaps five males and five females—and release the rest.

Be sure to check with your local conservation authorities as to the laws governing fishing with a seine in your area. Local regulations vary, and some conservation officers may look the other way where a dozen darters are concerned—but check first! Many darters are on state and/or federal endangered species lists and cannot be taken at all under normal circumstances.

Once collected, set the fish up in a small tank with a sandy bottom. Most darters can be found by determining and locating their preferred habitat. Most like open, fast-running water flowing over sand, gravel and rocks. Young fish are often found in quieter waters, however. Try to collect some smooth stones from the same area in which you found the fish.

Most darters reach maturity in a year. A few species occurring in Canada's colder northern areas may take two years to reach adulthood, but for aquarists, if you catch them in more open waters, they are probably already mature. While most darters spawn only in the spring, they often breed year-round in captivity if provided with a diet of live daphnia and tubifex worms. The spawning cycle is similar to that of the African annuals—eggs are laid continually. A six-month breeding period can normally be expected, but the heightened color of the male and the abdominal bulge of the female will be the best indications that spawning is imminent . . . don't worry about the calendar. Females usually spawn an average of once a week during their spawning cycle, but the author has kept individuals that spawned every two or three days!

Darter eggs are strongly adhesive, heavier than water, translucent, and contain a few oil droplets. Egg sizes vary from 0.7 to 2.7 mm, with the smaller species, of course, producing the smallest eggs. To induce the fish to spawn, give good feedings of live daphnia or brine shrimp for a week. Then a gradual increase in water temperature should guarantee spawning. In at least one species studied, the length of the day or intensity of the light doesn't affect their spawning cycle; rather, it is determined by temperature and the condition of the fish.

Darters have two modes of reproduction. Perhaps after aquarists have studied the species in the genus *Ammocrypta*, additional modes may be described, for up to now no *Ammocrypta* species have been spawned in an aquarium.

The basic reproductive mode is the attachment of the sticky eggs to a rock or leaf, while some species bury their eggs. All species of *Percina* so far studied bury their eggs, and a few species of *Etheostoma* do so as well. As a rule, though, *Etheostoma* species usually attach their eggs to natural objects in the habitat. The following chart, taken from Dr. Page's book, *Handbook of Darters*, identifies the spawning habits of the various species for which this information is known.

With species as similar in appearance and behavior as these, hybridization would not be an unlikely occurrence in captivity. Some hybrids have even been found in nature.

Species in Each of Three Categories of Spawning Behavior in Darters and, in Parentheses After the Name, Mean Diameters of Eggs in mm.

| | Attached to rocks, plants, *etc.* | |
Buriers (Eggs buried in substrate)	Attachers (Eggs attached and abandoned)	Clusterers (Eggs clustered on underside of stone and guarded by male)
P. (Alvordius) maculata (2.0)	E. (Etheostoma) blennioides (1.9)	E. (Boleosoma) nigrum (1.5)
P. (Alvordius) peltata	E. (Nanostoma) zonale	E. (Boleosoma) olmstedi
P. (Alvordius) notogramma (1.2)	E. (Nanostoma) atripinne	E. (Boleosoma) perlongum
P. (Hypohomus) aurantiaca (2.1)	E. (Nanostoma) sp. (Barren R.)	E. (Nothonotus) maculatum (2.0)
P. (Cottogaster) copelandi (1.4)	E. (Nanostoma) sp. (Green R.)	E. (Catonotus) olivaceum (2.0)
P. (Percina) caprodes (1.1-1.3)	E. (Ioa) vitreum	E. (Catonotus) squamiceps (1.8)
E. (Litocara) nianguae	E. (Vaillantia) chlorosomum	E. (Catonotus) neopterum
E. (Etheostoma) tetrazonum	E. (Belophlox) okaloosae	E. (Catonotus) kennicotti (2.1)
E. (Etheostoma) variatum	E. (Villora) edwini	E. (Catonotus) flabellare (2.2-2.7)
E. (Doration) stigmaeum (1.7)	E. (Ozarka) boschungi	E. (Catonotus) virgatum
E. (Nothonotus) rufilineatum	E. (Ozarka) trisella	E. (Catonotus) smithi (2.2)
E. (Nothonotus) camurum	E. (Oligocephalus) lepidum (1.3)	E. (Catonotus) striatulum (2.0)
E. (Nothonotus) tippecanoe	E. (Oligocephalus) grahami	
E. (Oligocephalus) spectabile (1.2-1.5)	E. (Oligocephalus) ditrema (1.1-1.2)	
E. (Oligocephalus) caeruleum (1.6-1.9)	E. (Boleichthys) fusiforme	
E. (Oligocephalus) radiosum (1.2-1.5)	E. (Boleichthys) exile (1.1)	
	E. (Boleichthys) gracile (1.0)	
	E. (Boleichthys) proeliare (0.7)	
	E. (Boleichthys) fonticola (1.1)	
	E. (Boleichthys) microperca (0.9-1.1)	

Percina sciera. 63 mm SL male, Embarras River, Cumberland Co., IL, 5 Nov. 1978.

Percina sciera. 73 mm SL female, Middle Fork, Vermilion Co., IL, 7 June 1977.

Percina aurolineata. 62 mm SL male, Little Cahaba River, Bibb Co., AL, 18 Feb. 1978.

Percina aurolineata. 56 mm SL female, Little Cahaba River, Bibb Co., AL, 2 July 1978.

North American Fishes • *Plate #10* • *Darters*

Percina nigrofasciata. 85 mm SL male, Murphy Creek, Blount Co., AL, 19 Apr. 1977.

Percina nigrofasciata. 62 mm SL female, Tangipahoa River, Pike Co., MS, 12 Apr. 1977.

Percina squamata. Male, Watauga River, Johnson Co., TN, 17 June 1973 (photo by D.A. Etnier).

Percina squamata. Female, Nolichucky River, Hamblen Co., TN, 13 Aug. 1978 (photo by D.A. Etnier).

Percina lenticula. 79 mm SL male, Schultz Creek, Bibb Co., AL, 18 Feb. 1978.

Percina oxyrhyncha. 78 mm SL male, Elk River, Braxton Co., WV, 28 Apr. 1979.

Percina nasuta. 66 mm SL male, Ouachita River, Polk Co., AR, 26 May 1978.

Percina nasuta. 69 mm SL female, Ouachita River, Montgomery Co., AR, 25 May 1978.

North American Fishes • Plate #11 • Darters

Percina phoxocephala. 58 mm SL male, Embarras River, Cumberland Co., IL, 22 July 1980.

Percina phoxocephala. 54 mm SL female, Embarras River, Cumberland Co., IL, 22 July 1980.

Percina macrocephala. 73 mm SL male, Elk River, Braxton Co., WV, 28 Apr. 1979.

Percina pantherina. 62 mm SL male, Cossatot River, Howard Co., AR, 17 March 1978 (alcohol-stored spec.).

Percina maculata. 52 mm SL male, Kankakee River, Kankakee Co., IL, 12 Oct. 1979.

Percina maculata. 56 mm SL female, Kankakee River, Kankakee Co., IL, 12 Oct. 1979.

Percina notogramma. 43 mm SL male, Craig Creek, Craig Co., VA, 25 May 1980.

Percina notogramma. 43 mm SL female, Craig Creek, Craig Co., VA, 25 May 1980.

North American Fishes • *Plate #12* • *Darters*

Percina gymnocephala. 50 mm SL male, Little River, Alleghany Co., NC, 5 May 1979.

Percina peltata. 56 mm SL female, Little River, Durham Co., NC, 1 May 1979.

Percina crassa. 67 mm SL male, Little Alamance Creek, Guilford Co., NC, 26 June 1977.

Percina crassa. 66 mm SL female, Little Alamance Creek, Guilford Co., NC, 26 June 1977.

Percina roanoka. 57 mm SL male, Roanoke River, Roanoke Co., VA, 30 Apr. 1979.

Percina palmaris. 81 mm SL male, Conasauga River, Bradley Co., TN, 24 Feb. 1978.

Percina roanoka. 54 mm SL female, Blackwater River, Franklin Co., VA, 26 June 1977.

Percina palmaris. 64 mm SL female, Conasauga River, Bradley Co., TN, 24 Feb. 1978.

North American Fishes • Plate #13 • Darters

Percina evides. 53 mm SL male, Cane River, Yancey Co., NC, 4 May 1979.

Percina evides. 64 mm SL male, St. Francis River, Wayne Co., MO, 18 May 1977.

Percina evides. 46 mm SL female, Cane River, Yancey Co., NC, 4 May 1979.

Percina evides. 58 mm SL female, St. Francis River, Wayne Co., MO, 18 May 1977.

Percina cymatotaenia. 64 mm SL male, Gasconade R., LaClede Co., MO, 11 Oct. 1970 (alcohol-stored spec.).

Percina cymatotaenia. 68 mm SL female, Gasconade River, Pulaski Co., MO, 21 May 1977.

Percina (Odontopholis) species. 62 mm SL male, Red Bird Creek, Clay Co., KY, 22 Mar. 1978.

Percina tanasi. 45 mm SL male, Little Tennessee River, Loudon Co., TN, 6 June 1975 (alcohol-stored spec.).

North American Fishes • Plate #14 • Darters

Percina aurantiaca. 103 mm SL male, Middle Prong Pigeon R., Sevier Co., TN, 22 June 1973 (D.A. Etnier photo).

Percina aurantiaca. 93 mm SL female, Little River, Blount Co., TN, 9 Apr. 1980.

Percina copelandi. 50 mm SL male, Blue River, Johnston Co., OK, 26 May 1978.

Percina copelandi. 43 mm SL female, Ouachita River, Polk Co., AR, 26 May 1978.

Percina shumardi. 50 mm SL male, Ditch No. 1, New Madrid Co., MO, 31 Oct. 1980.

Percina uranidea. 52 mm SL male, Current River, Randolph Co., AR, 17 Aug. 1979.

Percina shumardi. 45 mm SL female, Ditch No. 1, New Madrid Co., MO, 31 Oct. 1980.

Percina uranidea. 58 mm SL female, Current River, Randolph Co., AR, 17 Aug. 1979.

North American Fishes • Plate #15 • Darters

Percina ouachitae. 50 mm SL male, Mud River, Muhlenberg Co., KY, 30 Oct. 1980.

Percina antesella. 70 mm SL male, Conasauga River, Bradley Co., TN, 20 Sept. 1977 (photo by D.A. Etnier).

Percina ouachitae. 48 mm SL female, Mud River, Muhlenberg Co., KY, 30 Oct. 1980.

Percina antesella. 57 mm SL female, Conasauga River, Bradley Co., TN, 24 Apr. 1979.

Percina burtoni. 90 mm SL male, Copper Creek, Scott Co., VA, 21 Apr. 1979.

Percina burtoni. 74 mm SL female, Little River, Blount Co., TN, 10 Aug. 1979.

Percina carbonaria. 98 mm SL male, Guadalupe River, Kerr Co., TX, 27 May 1978.

Percina carbonaria. 85 mm SL female, Guadalupe River, Kerr Co., TX, 27 May 1978.

North American Fishes • *Plate #16* • *Darters*

Percina caprodes fulvitaenia. 132 mm SL male, Big Piney River, Texas Co., MO, 25 Apr. 1978.

Percina c. caprodes? 86 mm SL male, Ouachita River, Polk Co., AR, 26 May 1978.

Percina c. caprodes. 120 mm SL female, Embarras River, Cumberland Co., IL, 22 July 1980.

Percina c. caprodes. 79 mm SL female, Big Sycamore Creek, Claiborne Co., TN, 21 Mar. 1978.

Percina rex. 117 mm SL male, Roanoke River, Montgomery Co., VA, 30 Apr. 1979.

Percina macrolepida. 53 mm SL female, South Bosque River, McLennan Co., TX, 17 June 1980.

Ammocrypta asprella. 72 mm SL male, Tombigbee R., Greene Co., AL, 12 Sept. 1968 (alcohol-specimen).

Ammocrypta asprella. 75 mm SL female, Bayou Pierre, Claiborne Co., MS, 22 June 1980.

North American Fishes • Plate #17 • *Darters*

Ammocrypta vivax. 51 mm SL male, Sabine River, Vernon Pa., LA, 19 June 1980.

Ammocrypta vivax. 53 mm SL female, Leaf River, Jones Co., MS, 16 Apr. 1977.

Ammocrypta meridiana. 53 mm SL male, Trussels Cr., Greene Co., AL, 6 May 1978 (alcohol-specimen).

Ammocrypta meridiana. 56 mm SL female, Trussels Cr., Greene Co., AL, 6 May 1978 (alcohol-specimen).

Ammocrypta pellucida. 53 mm SL male, Middle Fork
Vermilion River, Vermilion Co., IL, 11 July 1978.

Ammocrypta clara. 43 mm SL male, Mississippi R.,
Pike Co., MO, 26 June 1963 (alcohol-specimen).

Ammocrypta beani. 46 mm SL male, Big Black River,
Marion Co., MS, 21 June 1980.

Ammocrypta beani. 43 mm SL female, Big Black
River, Marion Co., MS, 21 June 1980.

North American Fishes • Plate #18 • *Darters*

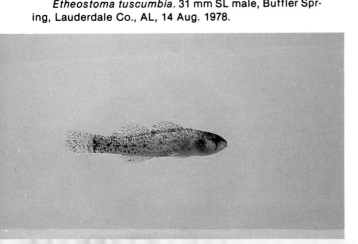

Ammocrypta bifascia. 50 mm SL male, Escambia
Creek, Escambia Co., AL, 24 June 1980.

Ammocrypta bifascia. 44 mm SL female, Escambia
Creek, Escambia Co., AL, 24 June 1980.

Etheostoma tuscumbia. 31 mm SL male, Buffler Spring, Lauderdale Co., AL, 14 Aug. 1978.

Etheostoma tuscumbia. 34 mm SL female, Buffler
Spring, Lauderdale Co., AL, 14 Aug. 1978.

Etheostoma nianguae. Male, Big Tavern Creek, Miller Co., MO, 6 Apr. 1972 (photo by W.L. Pflieger).

Etheostoma sagitta. 64 mm SL male, Youngs Creek, Whitley Co., KY, 19 Mar. 1978.

Etheostoma nianguae. 79 mm male, Brush Creek, St. Clair Co., MO, 14 Aug. 1979.

Etheostoma sagitta. 56 mm SL female, Little Clear Creek, Bell Co., KY, 14 Mar. 1977.

North American Fishes • Plate #19 • Darters

Etheostoma euzonum euzonum. 92 mm SL male, Beaver Creek, Taney Co., MO, 25 Apr. 1978.

Etheostoma euzonum. 57 mm SL male, Fourche Creek, Randolph Co., AR, 15 Aug. 1979.

Etheostoma e. euzonum. 81 mm SL female, Beaver Creek, Taney Co., MO, 25 Apr. 1978.

Etheostoma euzonum. 60 mm SL female, Fourche Creek, Randolph Co., AR, 15 Aug. 1979.

Etheostoma cinereum. Male, Little River, Blount Co., TN, 11 Feb. 1978 (photo by B.H. Bauer).

Etheostoma cinereum. 58 mm SL female, Buffalo River, Lewis Co., TN, 14 Apr. 1978.

Etheostoma tetrazonum. 55 mm SL male, Mill Creek, LaClede Co., MO, 24 Apr. 1978.

Etheostoma tetrazonum. 48 mm SL female, Mill Creek, LaClede Co., MO, 24 Apr. 1978.

North American Fishes • Plate #20 • Darters

Etheostoma variatum. 77 mm SL male, Red Bird Creek, Clay Co., KY, 22 Mar. 1978.

Etheostoma variatum. 60 mm SL female, Red Bird Creek, Clay Co., KY, 22 Mar. 1978.

Etheostoma kanawhae. 60 mm SL male, Little River, Floyd Co., VA, 27 Apr. 1979.

Etheostoma kanawhae. 58 mm SL female, Little River, Floyd Co., VA, 27 Apr. 1979.

Etheostoma osburni. 69 mm SL male, Greenbrier River, Pocahontas Co., WV, 28 Apr. 1979.

Etheostoma thalassinum. 50 mm SL male, South Saluda River, Pickens Co., SC, 25 June 1977.

Etheostoma osburni. 60 mm SL female, Greenbrier River, Pocahontas Co., WV, 28 Apr. 1979.

Etheostoma thalassinum. 52 mm SL female, Mid-Saluda River, Greenville Co., SC, 25 June 1977.

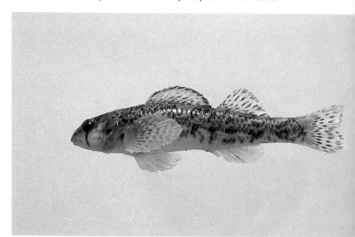

North American Fishes • Plate #21 • Darters

Etheostoma inscriptum. 51 mm SL male, Eastatoe Creek, Pickens Co., SC, 25 June 1977.

Etheostoma swannanoa. 85 mm SL male, Little Pigeon River, Sevier Co., TN, 20 Mar. 1978.

Etheostoma inscriptum. 53 mm SL female, Eastatoe Creek, Pickens Co., SC, 25 June 1977.

Etheostoma swannanoa. 69 mm SL female, Little Pigeon River, Sevier Co., TN, 20 Mar. 1978.

Etheostoma blennius blennius. 60 mm SL male, Thompson Creek, Bedford Co., TN, 20 Apr. 1977.

Etheostoma b. sequatchiense. 60 mm SL male, Sequatchie River, Bledsoe Co., TN, 10 Aug. 1977.

Etheostoma b. blennius. 60 mm SL female, Thompson Creek, Bedford Co., TN, 20 Apr. 1977.

Etheostoma b. sequatchiense. 47 mm SL female, Sequatchie River, Bledsoe Co., TN, 10 Aug. 1977.

North American Fishes • Plate #22 • Darters

Etheostoma blennioides pholidotum. 76 mm SL male, Jordan Creek, Vermilion Co., IL, 17 May 1979.

Etheostoma b. newmani. 82 mm SL male, Little Pigeon River, Sevier Co., TN, 21 Mar. 1978.

Etheostoma b. newmani. 119 mm SL male, Jacks Fork, Shannon Co., MO, 30 Mar. 1980.

Etheostoma b. gutselli. 68 mm SL female, Tuckasegee River, Swain Co., NC, 22 May 1980.

Etheostoma rupestre. 54 mm SL male, Cahaba River, Bibb Co., AL, 26 Feb. 1978.

Etheostoma histrio. 50 mm SL male, Bayou Pierre, Copiah Co., MS, 16 Feb. 1979.

Etheostoma rupestre. 48 mm SL female, Opintoloco Creek, Macon Co., AL, 26 Feb. 1978.

Etheostoma histrio. 42 mm SL female, Bayou Pierre, Copiah Co., MS, 16 Feb. 1979.

North American Fishes • Plate #23 • *Darters*

Etheostoma barrenensis. 44 mm SL male, Trammel Fork, Allen Co., KY, 13 Apr. 1978.

Etheostoma rafinesquei. 41 mm SL male, Nolin River, LaRue Co., KY, 19 May 1980.

Etheostoma barrenensis. 38 mm SL female, T mel Fork, Allen Co., KY, 13 Apr. 1978.

Etheostoma rafinesquei. 49 mm SL female, C Fork, Green Co., KY, 19 May 1980.

Lowland snubnose darter. 46 mm SL male, Pickens Creek, Tishomingo Co., MS, 20 Apr. 1977.

Lowland snubnose darter. 48 mm SL female, Pickens Creek, Tishomingo Co., MS, 20 Apr. 1977.

Red snubnose darter. 54 mm SL male, Terrapin Creek, Henry Co., TN, 29 May 1981.

Red snubnose darter, 44 mm SL female, Terrapin Creek, Henry Co., TN, 29 May 1981.

North American Fishes • Plate #24 • Darters

Etheostoma baileyi. 45 mm SL male, Sexton Creek, Clay Co., KY, 22 Mar. 1978.

Etheostoma baileyi. 44 mm SL female, Little Sexton Creek, Clay Co., KY, 20 May 1980.

Golden snubnose darter. 55 mm SL male, Jones Creek, Dickson Co., TN, 15 Apr. 1978.

Etheostoma simoterum. 46 mm SL female, Wartrace Creek, Bedford Co., TN, 2 Mar. 1977.

Etheostoma sellare. 58 mm SL male, Deer Creek, Harford Co., MD, 10 Nov. 1965 (alcohol-stored spec.).

Warrior darter. 50 mm SL male, Murphy Creek, Blount Co., AL, 19 Apr. 1977.

Etheostoma sellare. 55 mm SL female, Deer Creek, Harford Co., MD, 10 Nov. 1965 (alcohol-stored spec.).

Warrior darter. 38 mm SL female, Murphy Creek, Blount Co., AL, 19 Apr. 1977.

North American Fishes • Plate #25 • Darters

Tallapoosa darter, 58 mm SL male, Crooked Creek, Clay Co., AL, 25 Feb. 1978.

Coastal Plain darter. 52 mm SL male, trib., Minter Creek, Greene Co., AL, 17 Apr. 1977.

Tallapoosa darter. 52 mm SL female, Crooked Creek, Clay Co., AL, 25 Feb. 1978.

Coastal Plain darter. 42 mm SL female, trib., Minter Creek, Greene Co., AL, 17 Apr. 1977.

Etheostoma zonale zonale. 57 mm SL male, Trammel Fork, Allen Co., KY, 18 Oct. 1977.

Etheostoma z. lynceum. 41 mm SL male, Leaf River, Jones Co., MS, 16 Apr. 1977.

Etheostoma z. zonale. 45 mm SL female, Gasconade River, LaClede Co., MO, 21 May 1977.

Etheostoma z. lynceum. 40 mm SL female, Terrapin Creek, Graves Co., KY, 1 Oct. 1978.

North American Fishes • Plate #26 • *Darters*

Etheostoma atripinne. 52 mm SL male, Brush Creek, Smith Co., TN, 16 Apr. 1978.

Etheostoma simoterum. 53 mm SL male, Copper Creek, Scott Co., VA, 21 Apr. 1979.

Etheostoma atripinne. 51 mm SL female, Brush Creek, Smith Co., TN, 16 Apr. 1978.

Etheostoma simoterum. 54 mm SL female, Little River, Blount Co., TN, 20 Mar. 1978.

Etheostoma duryi. 53 mm SL male, Walker Creek, Madison Co., AL, 29 Apr. 1978.

Etheostoma etnieri. 64 mm SL male, Charles Creek, Warren Co., TN, 20 Apr. 1977.

Etheostoma duryi. 44 mm SL female, Walker Creek, Madison Co., AL, 29 Apr. 1978.

Etheostoma etnieri. 43 mm SL female, trib., Calf-killer River, White Co., TN, 25 July 1978.

North American Fishes • Plate #27 • Darters

Etheostoma coosae. 49 mm SL male, Salacoa Creek, Gordon Co., GA, 9 June 1976.

Etheostoma jessiae. 66 mm SL male, Little Pigeon River, Sevier Co., TN, 21 Mar. 1978.

Etheostoma coosae. 45 mm SL female, Salacoa Creek, Gordon Co., GA, 9 June 1976.

Etheostoma jessiae. 57 mm SL female, Little Pigeon River, Sevier Co., TN, 21 Mar. 1978.

Etheostoma stigmaeum. 45 mm SL male, Opin-toloco Creek, Macon Co., AL, 26 Feb. 1978.

Etheostoma stigmaeum. 43 mm SL female, West Fork Drakes Creek, Sumner Co., TN, 31 Jan. 1979.

Etheostoma nigrum. 44 mm SL male, North Branch Otter Creek, Winnebago Co., IL, 7 May 1980.

Etheostoma nigrum. 56 mm SL female, North Branch Otter Creek, Winnebago Co., IL, 7 June 1979.

North American Fishes • Plate #28 • Darters

Etheostoma olmstedi. 57 mm SL male, trib., Potomac River, Morgan Co., MD, 5 June 1975.

Etheostoma olmstedi. 38 mm SL female, trib., Potomac River, Morgan Co., MD, 5 June 1975.

Etheostoma perlongum. 70 mm SL male, Lake Waccamaw, Columbus Co., NC, 2 May 1979.

Etheostoma perlongum. 51 mm SL female, Lake Waccamaw, Columbus Co., NC, 2 May 1979.

Etheostoma longimanum. 62 mm SL male, Dunlap
Creek, Alleghany Co., VA, 29 Apr. 1979.

Etheostoma longimanum. 45 mm SL female, Dunlap
Creek, Alleghany Co., VA, 29 Apr. 1979.

Etheostoma podostemone. 59 mm SL male,
Roanoke River, Montgomery Co., VA, 30 Apr. 1979.

Etheostoma podostemone. 51 mm SL female,
Blackwater River, Franklin Co., VA, 26 June 1977.

North American Fishes • Plate #29 • Darters

Etheostoma vitreum. 59 mm SL male, Blackwater
River, Franklin Co., VA, 26 June 1977.

Etheostoma vitreum. 44 mm SL female, Blackwater
River, Franklin Co., VA, 26 June 1977.

Etheostoma chlorosomum. 45 mm SL male, Copiah
Creek, Copiah Co., MS, 12 Apr. 1977.

Etheostoma chlorosomum. 40 mm SL female, Lees
Creek, Washington Co., MS, 16 Apr. 1977.

Etheostoma davisoni. 46 mm SL male, East Pitman Creek, Holmes Co., FL, 27 Feb. 1978.

Etheostoma davisoni. 42 mm SL female, Five Runs Creek, Covington Co., AL, 27 Feb. 1978.

Etheostoma juliae. 55 mm SL male, Beaver Creek, Taney Co., MO, 25 Apr. 1978.

Etheostoma juliae. 50 mm SL female, Beaver Creek, Taney Co., MO, 25 Apr. 1978.

North American Fishes • Plate #30 • Darters

Etheostoma microlepidum. 49 mm SL male, East Fork Stones River, Rutherford Co., TN, 6 May 1981.

Etheostoma microlepidum. 40 mm SL female, East Fork Stones River, Rutherford Co., TN, 6 May 1981.

Etheostoma aquali. 57 mm SL male, Buffalo River, Lewis Co., TN, 14 Apr. 1978.

Etheostoma aquali. 52 mm SL female, Buffalo River, Lewis Co., TN, 14 Apr. 1978.

Etheostoma maculatum sanguifluum. 57 mm SL male, Big South Fork, Scott Co., TN, 23 Oct. 1976.

Etheostoma m. vulneratum. 43 mm SL male, Little River, Blount Co., TN, 10 Aug. 1979.

Etheostoma m. maculatum. 55 mm SL male, French Creek, Crawford Co., PA, 27 July 1980.

Etheostoma m. maculatum. 60 mm SL female, French Creek, Crawford Co., PA, 27 July 1980.

North American Fishes • Plate #31 • Darters

Etheostoma rufilineatum. 52 mm SL male, Copper Creek, Scott Co., VA, 6 May 1979.

Etheostoma rufilineatum. 56 mm SL female, Little River, Blount Co., TN, 20 Mar. 1978.

Etheostoma acuticeps. 60 mm SL male, Nolichucky River, Hamblen Co., TN, 17 June 1976.

Etheostoma acuticeps. 51 mm SL female, Nolichucky River, Hamblen Co., TN, 17 June 1976.

Etheostoma rubrum. 48 mm SL male, Bayou Pierre, Copiah Co., MS, 16 Feb. 1979.

Etheostoma rubrum. 46 mm SL female, Bayou Pierre, Copiah Co., MS, 21 May 1976.

Etheostoma moorei. 51 mm SL male, South Fork Red River, Van Buren Co., AR, 25 May 1978.

Etheostoma moorei. 40 mm SL female, South Fork Red River, Van Buren Co., AR, 25 May 1978.

North American Fishes • Plate #32 • Darters

Etheostoma chlorobranchium. 73 mm SL male, Little Pigeon River, Sevier Co., TN, 20 Mar. 1978.

Etheostoma chlorobranchium. 60 mm SL female, Tuckasegee River, Swain Co., NC, 22 May 1980.

Etheostoma camurum. 60 mm SL male, Middle Fork Vermilion River, Vermilion Co., IL, 13 Aug. 1970.

Etheostoma camurum. 48 mm SL female, Middle Fork Vermilion River, Vermilion Co., IL, 7 June 1977.

Etheostoma bellum. 51 mm SL male, Trammel Fork, Allen Co., KY, 18 Oct. 1977.

Etheostoma jordani. 46 mm SL male, Stamp Creek, Bartow Co., GA, 9 June 1976.

Etheostoma bellum. 54 mm SL female, Trammel Fork, Allen Co., KY, 18 Oct. 1977.

Etheostoma jordani. 50 mm SL female, Stamp Creek, Bartow Co., GA, 9 June 1976.

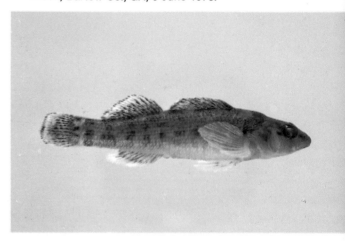

North American Fishes • Plate #33 • Darters

Etheostoma tippecanoe. 29 mm SL male, Big South Fork, Scott Co., TN, 23 Oct. 1976.

Etheostoma parvipinne. 41 mm SL male, trib., Powell Creek, Weakley Co., TN, 16 July 1980.

Etheostoma tippecanoe. 26 mm SL female, Big South Fork, Scott Co., TN, 23 Oct. 1976.

Etheostoma parvipinne. 38 mm SL female, trib., Powell Creek, Weakley Co., TN, 16 July 1980.

Etheostoma fricksium. 47 mm SL male, Little Selkehatchee River, Bamberg Co., SC, 24 June 1977.

Etheostoma fricksium. 43 mm SL female, Little Selkehatchee River, Bamberg Co., SC, 24 June 1977.

Etheostoma mariae. 54 mm SL male, trib., Lumber River, Hoke Co., NC, 13 June 1976.

Etheostoma mariae. 46 mm SL female, trib., Lumber River, Hoke Co., NC, 13 June 1976.

North American Fishes • *Plate #34* • *Darters*

Etheostoma okaloosae. 29 mm SL male, Toms Creek, Okaloosa Co., FL, 18 Aug. 1978.

Etheostoma okaloosae. 35 mm SL female, Toms Creek, Okaloosa Co., FL, 18 Aug. 1978.

Etheostoma edwini. 39 mm SL male, Rocky Creek, Walton Co., FL, Apr. 1977 (photo by M.F. Mettee).

Etheostoma edwini. 28 mm SL female, Swift Creek, Okaloosa Co., FL, 18 Aug. 1978.

Etheostoma trisella. 28 mm SL male, trib., Mill Cr., Bradley Co., TN, 10 Mar. 1979 (B.H. Bauer photo).

Etheostoma trisella. 38 mm SL female, Conasauga River, Bradley Co., TN, 24 Feb. 1978.

Etheostoma punctulatum. 68 mm SL male, Massie Creek, Warren Co., MO, 13 Apr. 1980 (T.M. Keevin photo).

Etheostoma punctulatum. 52 mm SL female, trib., Spring River, Lawrence Co., MO, 2 Sept. 1976.

North American Fishes • Plate #35 • Darters

Etheostoma boschungi. 60 mm SL male, Shoal Creek, Lawrence Co., TN, 16 May 1978.

Etheostoma boschungi. 67 mm SL female, Shoal Creek, Lawrence Co., TN, 16 May 1978.

Etheostoma cragini. 41 mm SL male, trib., Spring River, Lawrence Co., MO, 2 Sept. 1976.

Etheostoma cragini. 43 mm SL female, trib., Spring River, Lawrence Co., MO, 2 Sept. 1976.

Etheostoma pallididorsum. 43 mm SL male, Caddo River, Montgomery Co., AR, 26 May 1978.

Etheostoma whipplei. 57 mm SL male, Heard Branch, Crawford Co., AR, 31 Mar. 1980.

Etheostoma pallididorsum. 41 mm SL female, Caddo River, Montgomery Co., AR, 26 May 1978.

Etheostoma whipplei. 52 mm SL female, Heard Branch, Crawford Co., AR, 31 Mar. 1980.

Etheostoma radiosum. 44 mm SL male, Caddo River, Montgomery Co., AR, 26 May 1978.

Etheostoma ditrema. 42 mm SL male, pond (Conasauga drainage), Murray Co., GA, 24 Feb. 1978.

Etheostoma radiosum. 43 mm SL female, Caddo River, Montgomery Co., AR, 26 May 1978.

Etheostoma ditrema. 33 mm SL female, pond (Conasauga drainage), Murray Co., GA, 24 Feb. 1978.

Etheostoma nuchale. 34 mm SL male, Roebuck Spring, Jefferson Co., AL, 17 Aug. 1978.

Etheostoma swaini. 46 mm SL male, Sandy Hook Creek, Marion Co., MS, 3 Mar. 1978.

Etheostoma nuchale. 32 mm SL female, Roebuck Spring, Jefferson Co., AL, 17 Aug. 1978.

Etheostoma swaini. 48 mm SL female, Sandy Hook Creek, Marion Co., MS, 3 Mar. 1978.

North American Fishes • Plate #37 • Darters

Etheostoma collettei. 57 mm SL male, Little Corney Bayou, Union Pa., LA, 18 Feb. 1977.

Etheostoma asprigene. 54 mm SL male, trib., Cache River, 1 mi. S Unity, Alexander Co., IL, 27 Oct. 1979.

Etheostoma collettei. 50 mm SL female, Little Corney Bayou, Union Pa., LA, 18 Feb. 1977.

Etheostoma asprigene. 45 mm SL female, trib., Cache R., 1 mi. S Unity, Alexander Co., IL, 27 Oct. 1979.

Etheostoma caeruleum caeruleum. 46 mm SL male, South Fork Little Red R., Van Buren Co., AR, 25 May 1978.

Etheostoma c. caeruleum. 47 mm SL female, Bled-soe Creek, Sumn er Co., TN, 18 Oct. 1977.

Etheostoma c. caeruleum. 50 mm SL male, Jordan Creek, Vermilion Co., IL, 2 May 1980.

Etheostoma c. subspecies. 51 mm SL male, Beaver Creek, Taney Co., MO, 25 Apr. 1978.

North American Fishes • Plate #38 • Darters

Etheostoma luteovinctum. 50 mm SL male, War-trace Creek, Bedford Co., TN, 2 Mar. 1977.

Etheostoma luteovinctum. 36 mm SL female, War-trace Creek, Bedford Co., TN, 2 Mar. 1977.

Etheostoma lepidum. 45 mm SL male, Comal Creek, Comal Co., TX, 16 Feb. 1977.

Etheostoma lepidum. 35 mm SL female, Comal Creek, Comal Co., TX, 16 Feb. 1977.

Etheostoma spectabile uniporum. 40 mm SL male, Myatt Creek, Fulton Co., AR, 30 Mar. 1980.

Etheostoma s. pulchellum. 45 mm SL male, Little Frog Bayou, Crawford Co., AR, 31 Mar. 1980.

Etheostoma s. fragi. 48 mm SL male, Piney Fork, Izard Co., AR, 30 Mar. 1980.

Etheostoma s. squamosum. 45 mm SL male, Spring River, Lawrence Co., MO, 25 Apr. 1978.

North American Fishes • Plate #39 • Darters

Etheostoma s. spectabile. 42 mm SL male, Osage Fork, Webster Co., MO, 18 March 1977.

Etheostoma s. spectabile. 56 mm SL male, Buffalo River, Lawrence Co., TN, 14 Apr. 1978.

Etheostoma s. spectabile. 47 mm SL male, trib., Goose Creek, Russell Co., KY, 18 Mar. 1978.

Etheostoma s. spectabile. 46 mm SL female, Jordan Creek, Vermilion Co., IL, 2 May 1980.

Etheostoma hopkinsi. 45 mm SL male, Log Creek, Edgefield Co., SC, 24 June 1977.

Etheostoma hopkinsi. 40 mm SL female, Log Creek, Edgefield Co., SC, 24 June 1977.

Etheostoma australe. 47 mm SL male, Rio Santa Isabel, Chihuahua, 24 Feb. 1979.

Etheostoma australe. 41 mm SL female, Rio Santa Isabel, Chihuahua, 24 Feb. 1979.

North American Fishes • Plate #40 • Darters

Etheostoma grahami. 35 mm SL male, Devils River, Val Verde Co., TX, 29 May 1978.

Etheostoma grahami. 32 mm SL female, Devils River, Val Verde Co., TX, 29 May 1978.

Etheostoma pottsi. 41 mm SL male, Rio Atotonilco, Zacatecas, 14 July 1975.

Etheostoma pottsi. 36 mm SL female, Rio Atotonilco, Zacatecas, 14 July 1975.

Etheostoma olivaceum. 56 mm SL male, Brush Creek, Smith Co., TN, 16 Apr. 1978.

Etheostoma squamiceps. 63 mm SL male, Ferguson Cr., Livingston Co., KY, 26 Apr. 1975 (alcohol-spec.).

Etheostoma olivaceum. 47 mm SL female, Brush Creek, Smith Co., TN, 16 Apr. 1978.

Etheostoma squamiceps. 58 mm SL male, Wartrace Creek, Bedford Co., TN, 20 Apr. 1977.

North American Fishes • *Plate #41* • *Darters*

Etheostoma squamiceps. 61 mm SL male, Buffler Spring, Lauderdale Co., AL, 14 Aug. 1978.

Etheostoma neopterum. 48 mm SL male, Beaverdam Cr., Benton Co., TN, 12 May 1973 (alcohol-spec.).

Etheostoma squamiceps. 42 mm SL female, Richland Creek, Davidson Co., TN, 1 Mar. 1977.

Etheostoma neopterum. 47 mm SL female, Jonathan Creek, Calloway Co., KY, 15 July 1980.

Etheostoma flabellare. 51 mm SL male, North Branch Kishwaukee River, McHenry Co., IL, 7 May 1980.

Etheostoma flabellare. 53 mm SL male, Catawba River, McDowell Co., NC, 12 June 1976.

Etheostoma flabellare. 46 mm SL male, Little Alamance Creek, Guilford Co., NC, 26 June 1977.

Etheostoma flabellare. 53 mm SL female, Roanoke River, Roanoke Co., VA, 30 Apr. 1979.

North American Fishes • Plate #42 • Darters

Etheostoma kennicotti. 36 mm SL female, Big Creek, Hardin Co., IL, 10 Apr. 1979.

Etheostoma kennicotti. 49 mm SL male, Big Creek, Hardin Co., IL, 10 Apr. 1979.

Etheostoma virgatum. 56 mm SL male, trib., Indian Creek, Jackson Co., KY, 20 May 1980.

Etheostoma virgatum. 47 mm SL female, trib., Indian Creek, Jackson Co., KY, 20 May 1980.

Etheostoma obeyense. 64 mm SL male, Smith Creek, Clinton Co., KY, 21 May 1980.

Etheostoma obeyense. 47 mm SL female, Smith Creek, Clinton Co., KY, 21 May 1980.

Etheostoma smithi. 40 mm SL male, Bradley Creek, Rutherford Co., TN, 14 Apr. 1978.

Etheostoma smithi. 31 mm SL female, Ferguson Creek, Livingston Co., KY, 10 Apr. 1979.

North American Fishes • *Plate #43* • *Darters*

Etheostoma striatulum. 38 mm SL male, Wartrace Creek, Bedford Co., TN, 20 Apr. 1977.

Etheostoma striatulum. 36 mm SL female, Wartrace Creek, Bedford Co., TN, 2 Mar. 1977.

Etheostoma barbouri. 46 mm SL male, trib., Trace Creek, Casey Co., KY, 20 May 1980.

Etheostoma barbouri. 40 mm SL female, trib., Trace Creek, Casey Co., KY, 20 May 1980.

Etheostoma exile. 51 mm SL male, Wolf Lake, Cook Co., IL, 8 May 1980.

Etheostoma serriferum. 38 mm SL male, South River, Bladen Co., NC, 1 May 1979.

Etheostoma exile. 43 mm SL female, Wolf Lake, Cook Co., IL, 8 May 1980.

Etheostoma serriferum. 34 mm SL female, South River, Bladen Co., NC, 1 May 1979.

North American Fishes • Plate #44 • Darters

Etheostoma gracile. 44 mm SL male, Wades Creek, Calloway Co., KY, 11 Apr. 1979.

Etheostoma zoniferum. 36 mm SL male, Chilatchee Creek, Dallas Co., AL, 23 July 1980.

Etheostoma gracile. 39 mm SL female, Max Creek, Johnson Co., IL, 10 Apr. 1979.

Etheostoma zoniferum. 24 mm SL female, Chilatchee Creek, Dallas Co., AL, 23 July 1980.

Etheostoma fusiforme. 39 mm SL male, Chenerie Lake, Ouachita Pa., LA, 21 June 1980.

Etheostoma fusiforme. 43 mm SL female, Chenerie Lake, Ouachita Pa., LA, 21 June 1980.

Etheostoma saludae. 40 mm SL male, trib., Little Saluda River, Saluda Co., SC, 3 May 1979.

Etheostoma saludae. 40 mm SL female, trib., Little Saluda River, Saluda Co., SC, 3 May 1979.

North American Fishes • Plate #45 • Darters

Etheostoma collis. 50 mm SL male, North Fork Crooked Creek, Union Co., NC, 2 May 1979.

Etheostoma collis. 42 mm SL female, North Fork Crooked Creek, Union Co., NC, 2 May 1979.

Etheostoma proeliare. 28 mm SL male, Max Creek, Johnson Co., IL, 10 Apr. 1979.

Etheostoma proeliare. 30 mm SL female, Max Creek, Johnson Co., IL, 26 Feb. 1976.

Etheostoma microperca. 31 mm SL male, trib., Iroquois River, Iroquois Co., IL, 8 May 1980.

Etheostoma microperca. 29 mm SL female, trib., Iroquois River, Iroquois Co., IL, 8 May 1980.

Etheostoma fonticola. 32 mm SL male, San Marcos River, Hays Co., TX, 16 Feb. 1977.

Etheostoma proeliare spawning in an aquarium. Eggs are being attached to the leaf.

Etheostoma atripinne spawning in an aquarium. Eggs are being deposited on the rock.

Etheostoma squamiceps spawning in an aquarium. Eggs are being attached to the underside of the stone.

Big South Fork Cumberland River, Scott Co., TN, 30 Sept. 1978. Swift rocky riffles contain *Percina squamata, P. caprodes, Etheostoma camurum, E. caeruleum, E. maculatum, E. tippecanoe, E. blennioides,* and *E. zonale*; adjacent pools contain *P. copelandi, E. cinereum,* and *E. stigmaeum.*

Gasconade River, LaClede Co., MO, 21 May 1977. Swift rocky riffle is habitat of *Percina evides* and *Etheostoma tetrazonum.*

Gasconade River, LaClede Co., MO, 21 May 1977. Vegetated backwater pool is habitat of *Percina cymatotaenia.*

Tributary of Calfkiller River, Putnam Co., TN, 19 Oct. 1977. Pool is habitat of *Etheostoma etnieri.*

Max Creek, Johnson Co., IL, 4 May 1977. Sluggish mud-bottomed pool is habitat of *Etheostoma chlorosomum, E. proeliare,* and *E. gracile.*

Toms Creek, Okaloosa Co., FL, 18 Aug. 1978. Habitat of *Etheostoma okaloosae.*

Buffler Spring, Lauderdale Co., AL, 14 Aug. 1978. Habitat of *Etheostoma tuscumbia*.

Etheostoma neopterum male and his nest of eggs on the underside of a stone removed from a stream on 15 April 1978. The male was guarding the eggs prior to their removal from the stream (Page & Mayden, 1979).

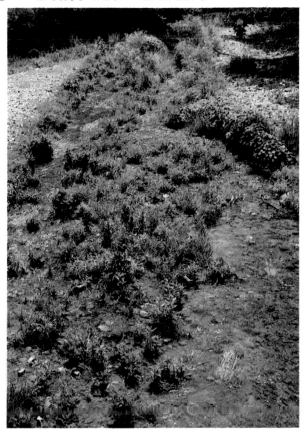

Caddo River headwaters, Montgomery Co., AR, 26 May 1978 (photo by R.L. Mayden). Habitat for *Etheostoma pallididorsum*.

Ammocrypta pellucida buried in sand in an aquarium. The habit of burying in sand with only the eyes and top of the head exposed is probably typical behavior of all sand darters.

Stizostedion vitreum (Mitchill) • Walleye

RANGE: Northwest Territories in Canada into northern Labrador, then south along the Atlantic Coast to North Carolina, west to Arkansas.

HABITS: A very voracious fish whose greed makes it a year-round game fish within its range. It is a favorite ice-fishing target and has been transplanted into hundreds of lakes throughout its range, with stocking by the millions being the norm.

WATER CONDITIONS: The fish likes still water lakes that run deep and don't freeze solid. Suitable for unheated tanks. Feeds both day and night.

SIZE: A prized food fish and game fish. Reaches 15 pounds but most are caught at less than half that weight.

FOOD REQUIREMENTS: Eats everything small enough to swallow in terms of live foods; easy to acclimate to chunky pieces of beef, fish, shrimp, and large pellets.

Agonostomus monticola (Bancroft) • Mountain Mullet

RANGE: Fresh waters surrounding the Caribbean Sea and Gulf of Mexico.

HABITS: A freshwater and brackish water fish that apparently spawns in the sea since fry were found in the sea but not in fresh water.

WATER CONDITIONS: Not fussy about water chemistry, but does best in clean, clear water between 15 and 25°C. Water should be aerated and filtered.

SIZE: Attains a length of 25 to 30 cm.

FOOD REQUIREMENTS: Basically a plankton feeder. Thrives on brine shrimp, clouds of daphnia, and other small crustaceans. Can be trained to a prepared aquarium diet.

Dormitator maculatus (Bloch) • Spotted Sleeper

RANGE: Atlantic coastal waters from the Carolinas to Brazil.

HABITS: Inactive and predatory; should not be kept with small fishes.

WATER CONDITIONS: Water should have a salt content, about a quarter teaspoonful per liter. Temperatuare 21 to 24°C

SIZE: To 25 cm.

FOOD REQUIREMENTS: Eats anything and everything; bits of raw fish are especially relished.

Cottus bairdi Girard • Mottled Sculpin

RANGE: Widely dispersed from Georgia and Alabama north through Labrador and west to the entire Great Lakes system. . .skipping over to the Pacific northwest.

HABITS: There are dozens of color varieties and this fish is known by many names in various parts of North America. Spawns in early summer, May, and early June. Likes sandy bottom lakes and streams.

WATER CONDITIONS: Prefers cool, clean water at 16°C. Best kept in unheated aquaria. Water chemistry not important as long as the water is clean.

SIZE: Averages about 76 mm.

FOOD REQUIREMENTS: Eats everything small enough to ingest. Especially fond of other fishes' eggs. Thrives on brine shrimp, both live and frozen.

Perca flavescens (Mitchill) • Yellow Perch

RANGE: Ranges around the world in the northern hemisphere since the Yellow Perch of North America is considered by many to be identical to the Eurasian perch P. fluviatilis.

HABITS: This is a major commercial and sport fish. It spawns in the spring from mid-April to mid-May, except far north where it spawns later. Spawning habits are not precisely known but it has never spawned in captivity.

WATER CONDITIONS: Unheated, very large aquaria with clean, clear water. Does best with water temperatures between 8-15°C.

SIZE: A large size yellow perch is 260 mm.

FOOD REQUIREMENTS: Eats everything living and small enough to ingest from fishes to insects. Can be trained to the more usual aquarium diet.

Cichlasoma cyanoguttatum (Baird & Girard) • Texas Cichlid

RANGE: Southern Texas and northern Mexico.

HABITS: All the bad cichlid habits: digs a great deal and uproots plants; usually quarrelsome if kept with other fishes.

WATER CONDITIONS: Not critical; not sensitive to temperature drops. Best breeding temperature about 24°C.

SIZE: In native waters up to 30 cm. In captivity seldom exceeds 15 cm.

FOOD REQUIREMENTS: Larger specimens require chunks of food, such as cut-up earthworms or pieces of beef heart or other lean meat.

Mugil cephalus Linnaeus • Striped Mullet

RANGE: Throughout the southern United States in fresh water, brackish water, and pure ocean water.

HABITS: This fish is found in a very wide range of habitats from the Gulf of Mexico in very deep waters, to shallow ponds, streams, and bayous.

WATER CONDITIONS: Warmer waters and lots of room. Does well in large tropical aquariums with either fresh, brackish or salt water. Thrives at temperatures over 20°C.

SIZE: May reach 60 cm, but usually found at half that size.

FOOD REQUIREMENTS: A plankton feeder. Eats brine shrimp when small.

Gobioides broussonetti Lacepede • Violet Goby

RANGE: Most common in brackish water marshes of the Gulf of Mexico; rarely found in deep waters.

HABITS: A shallow water species that attacks any size fish to defend its eggs. A very beautiful fish.

WATER CONDITIONS: Brackish water is preferred; but adapts to fresh and marine environments; temperatures above 18°C.

SIZE: Maximum about 50 cm; small aquarium sizes (under 10 cm) are difficult to find.

FOOD REQUIREMENTS: Eats small crustaceans. Thrives on live brine shrimp and tubifex worms.

Stizostedion vitreum

Perca flavescens

Agonostomus monticola

Cichlasoma cyanoguttatum

Dormitator maculatus

Mugil cephalus

Cottus bairdi

Gobioides broussonetti

Eurasian Region

Huso huso (Linnaeus) • Beluga Sturgeon

RANGE: Caspian and Black Seas, Volga River.
HABITS: The largest sturgeon and a major source of caviar since a female could have as many as 5 million eggs. Small fish are released into the aquarium trade (from Hungary where they are cultivated). They are interesting aquarium fish, constantly swimming about the tank.
WATER CONDITIONS: A coldwater fish that requires lots of room and copious amounts of food because of its rapid growth rate. May be stunted in a small aquarium. Requires aerated, clean water.
SIZE: Probably lives as long as the average man and grows to 9 m (almost 30 feet) and may weigh almost 1½ tons.
FOOD REQUIREMENTS: In the aquarium they do well on a diet of chopped fish. They take a long time to find the food so keep them in a dedicated aquarium without competitive fishes.

Umbra krameri Walbaum • European Mudminnow

RANGE: Danube and Baltic River systems.
HABITS: Stays around the muddy bottoms of lakes and streams.
WATER CONDITIONS: Colder waters. Does best in unheated aquaria. Not sensitive to most unpolluted water chemistries.
SIZE: Females may reach 115 mm; males smaller.
FOOD REQUIREMENTS: Thrive on small crustaceans but may be acclimated to other foods.

Alburnoides bipunctatus (Bloch) • Tailorfish

RANGE: Central, temperate Europe to the U.S.S.R.
HABITS: Resembles the bleak but prefers fast-moving waters. In an aquarium it must have cold, highly aerated water.
WATER CONDITIONS: Cold water fish that can take temperatures as low as freezing but not higher than 22°C for very long. Water should be clean.
SIZE: 15 cm is the maximum size.
FOOD REQUIREMENTS: Eats live brine shrimp and daphnia; can be acclimated to the usual aquarium fare.

Cyprinus carpio Linnaeus • Carp

RANGE: Throughout Europe; introduced to every temperate area of the world, more or less.
HABITS: Cultivated in China, Japan, Israel, and eastern Europe. A staple food fish in eastern Europe. Fished for in Pennsylvania and New Jersey. This is the parent stock from which Japanese koi was derived.
WATER CONDITIONS: Thrives in almost any freshwater environment where the water doesn't move too fast. Lakes are its usual habitat. Insensitive to most water chemistry as long as the water is moderately clean. Lives where most other fishes perish.
SIZE: Averages about 3 kg at 50 cm but may grow to 20 kg.
FOOD REQUIREMENTS: Eats everything from plant matter to small living fishes and crustaceans.

Acipenser ruthenus Linnaeus • Sterlet Sturgeon

RANGE: The rivers that drain into the Black, Azov, and Caspian Seas.
HABITS: There are about 15 species of sturgeons in central Europe and about 9 species in North America. They all have the same habits of poking over the bottom with their whiskers. Their eyes are small and they have poor vision.
WATER CONDITIONS: Clean, clear fresh water; unheated aquaria.
SIZE: This is a small species, growing to a maximum length of 125 cm and a weight of 16 kilograms.
FOOD REQUIREMENTS: Chopped fishes is an adequate aquarium diet.

Pseudoscaphirhynchus kaufmani (Bogdanov) • Whiptail Sturgeonfish

RANGE: Amudarja River.
HABITS: Occurs in channels or river beds with sand bottom. Reaches sexual maturity at 25 cm and between 6 and 7 years (females) or 7 or 8 years (males). Spawns in April, releasing 1,000-2,000 eggs (a larger female may release as many as 3,700 eggs). Juveniles descend to the lower parts of the river.
WATER CONDITIONS: Requires clean, clear, unheated water.
SIZE: Attains a length of 60 cm standard length and a weight of about a kilogram.
FOOD REQUIREMENTS: Feeds on aquatic insects as well as the eggs and fry of other fishes.

Abramis brama (Linnaeus) • Bronze Bream

RANGE: British Isles through central Europe to the Caspian Sea basin.
HABITS: Likes warmer waters and is a highly prized game fish in its range. Its usual habitat of lowland waters makes it available inside city limits of many European cities built along rivers.
WATER CONDITIONS: Not sensitive to any particular water conditions providing the water is fresh, unpolluted, and aerated.
SIZE: Reaches to 30 cm.
FOOD REQUIREMENTS: Small fish eat small crustaceans such as brine shrimp, daphnia, and cyclops; larger fish eat larger crustaceans as well as algae, weeds, and organic debris.

Alburnus alburnus (Linnaeus) • Bleak

RANGE: Northern Europe, parts of Scandinavia.
HABITS: A gregarious species that prefers settled waters in lakes and very slow moving streams. Spawns from April to June depending upon the water temperature.
WATER CONDITIONS: Prefers cold water from 5 to 15°C. Does well in large, unheated aquaria.
SIZE: Reaches about 20 cm.
FOOD REQUIREMENTS: This pelagic fish thrives on live brine shrimp and most other living things that are very small, even small schooling fishes. Easily acclimated to aquarium foods.

Huso huso

Acipenser ruthenus

Umbra krameri

Pseudoscaphrhynchus kaufmani

Alburnoides bipunctatus

Abramis brama

Cyprinus carpio

Alburnus alburnus

Koi, Japanese Colored Carp

Koi are highly developed forms of the common Carp in a similar way that fancy-tail Guppies are highly developed forms of the common Guppy. The Koi is particularly well suited to keep in a garden pool, where its touch of brilliant colors would add a great deal of decorative effect. The Koi was produced by Japanese breeders. The results came in a great variety of color variations, and selective breeding did the rest. At the present time there are many recognized basic varieties, with the possibility of many more to come.

Koi Varieties

Because of their size, Koi are basically pool fish and do best in an outdoor environment. They are able to withstand a wide temperature range and are undemanding as to water composition, provided that their water is richly supplied with oxygen. In an outdoor pool, suitable filtration and aeration can easily be provided through the use of the pool filters designed specifically for use with garden ponds. Feeding Koi presents no great problems, as they are heavy eaters and accept a wide variety of foods. Worms, shrimp, insects and insect larvae form the major portion of the Koi diet, but vegetable materials in the form of chopped terrestrial and aquatic plants must be included as regular portions. Although Koi are heavy eaters, they will not eat food that is left to stagnate in their pool, so all uneaten food should be removed immediately. After they become accustomed to their surroundings Koi are quite willing to accept food right from their owner's fingers.

Koi breed substantially the same as goldfish, scattering their eggs into the fine leaves or root systems of plants (water lettuce and water hyacinths are ideal) after a vigorous chase by the males of the females. Normally, more than one male per female is used. Sex differences among mature Koi are easily distinguishable; viewed from directly above, females will be seen to be much stockier from behind the head to just behind the dorsal fin.

Maruten-Kohaku (Gin-Goke)

Sandan-Kohaku (Gin-Goke)

Hana-Shusui

Taisho-Sanke

Taisho-Sanke

Tancho-Sanke

Doitsu Taisho-Sanke

Aka-Muji

81

Doitsu Kuyaku

Hikari-Moyo-Mono

Showa Sanke

Kawari-Mono

Shiro-Utsuri

Hikari Shiro-Utsuri

Shiro-Bekko Ginlin

Doitsu Ogon

Plate #52 • Koi

Asagi

Asagi

Yamabuki Ogon or Ogon (Gold)

Harewake-Ogon or Ogon (Platinum)

Matsuba-Ogon or Ogon (Orange)

Kin Ki-Utsuri

Sakura Kanoko Ogon

Kohaku-Ginrin

Plate #53 • Koi

Goldfish (*Carassius auratus*)

The hobby of fish-keeping owes its popularity more than anything else to the Goldfish. Goldfish are mentioned as early as 970 A.D. by the Chinese, and in the sixteenth century their care and breeding, which were at first playthings of the nobility, became commonplace and a number of fancy breeds were developed. Because of their innate love for beauty and living things, the Chinese and Japanese have remained the world leaders in the development and production of the many fancy breeds of Goldfish available today. We see such freakish fish as the Lionhead, Pompon, Telescope, Celestial, Eggfish and many others too numerous for this small space. There are fish with short single fins and others with long flowing fins. Some breeds have double fins; some have large, sail-like dorsal fins; and others have no dorsal fin at all. Some are pure white; others are midnight black. Still others vary from light yellow to deep red, and some are peppered with red, white, black, yellow and even blue. Goldfish have a wide temperature tolerance, and fish which have been kept outdoors can live under a layer of ice for quite a time. They are also kept successfully in the tropics.

Fancy Goldfish Varieties

It seems that the lessened popularity of the common Goldfish has come about as result of the recognition on the part of hobby newcomers of the advantages the true tropical fishes have over Goldfish. However, warm-water fish tanks within the home have not greatly affected the interest in fancy Goldfish varieties. Really good Goldfish of the hard-to-get varieties are eagerly sought after and command high prices. Unfortunately, not enough hobbyists ever get a chance to see some of the fancier varieties; the excellent Goldfish photos shown here will help to make these products of patient and skillful breeding programs more familiar to everyone.

Common

Comet

Pearl Scale

Pearl Scale

Calico Fantail

Red Curly-Tail Fantail

Japanese Fantail (Ryukin)

Veiltail

Lionhead

Lionhead

Oranda (Immature)

Redcap, Tancho or Hon Tou

Young Bubble-Eye

Bubble-Eye

Bubble-Eye

Bubble-Eye

Plate #55 • Goldfishes

Chinese Oranda (Hi-Cap)

Chinese Oranda (Hi-Cap)

Oranda

Chinese Oranda (Hi-Cap)

Telescope Calico

Albino Oranda

Telescope Black Moor

Telescope Black Moor

Plate #56 • Goldfishes

Leuciscus idus (Linnaeus) • Ide or Orfe

RANGE: Central and western Europe, Scandinavia.
HABITS: A peaceful fish for the coldwater pond or aquarium. The golden orfe is a common fish in European outdoor ponds along with koi or goldfish. They spawn like goldfish in the spring, laying adhesive eggs on bushy plants in the shallows.
WATER CONDITIONS: Cool, clean water. Adapts well to life in cultivated ponds.
SIZE: Grows up to 1 m in length but averages 35 cm.
FOOD REQUIREMENTS: Eats everythng, thus making it easy for the pondkeeper and easy for the angler.

Gnathopogon chankaensis (Dybowski) • Amur Minnow

RANGE: Middle and lower Amur River basin.
HABITS: Inhabits the lower (bottom) levels of the water. Mature in their second year (at 4.5 cm) and spawn in June, laying up to 3000 eggs on willow roots and other such objects along the sandy shores. At least two forms exist, one with short barbels and one with long barbels.
WATER CONDITIONS: Prefers unheated tanks with lots of space but also well planted and perhaps with some driftwood.
SIZE: Attains a length of 9 cm.
FOOD REQUIREMENTS: Feeds on plankton in the wild. Will accept newly hatched brine shrimp and other small live foods.

Ctenopharyngodon idella (Valenciennes) • Grass Carp, White Amur

RANGE: Native to Asia, but introduced all over central Europe and the Mississippi basin in the U.S.A.
HABITS: Spawns over a specialized bottom that might only be 3-cm stones or pebbles being flushed with fast-moving, highly oxygenated water. Used for weed control in ponds where it cannot or does not spawn. Freed during floods to spawn in more suitable habitats. Good eating fish.
WATER CONDITIONS: Lives in almost any freshwater situation that is not polluted though it thrives best in moving water.
SIZE: The maximum size is unknown, but it reaches 1 m when enough food and space are available.
FOOD REQUIREMENTS: Basically a grass eater, but it must eat the grass by the blade with the point entering the mouth. It cannot bite through the side of a blade of grass.

Carassius carassius (Linnaeus) • Crucian Carp

RANGE: Widely distributed in Europe and the British Isles. Probably in the USSR as well.
HABITS: Same as for the goldfish, *Carassius auratus*. This species grows large enough to eat. It is released in still waters unsuited for any other food fishes and harvested mainly in eastern Europe.
WATER CONDITIONS: Tolerates almost any water conditions, but thrives in still ponds. Suitable for the garden pool.
SIZE: A maximum of about 30 cm.
FOOD REQUIREMENTS: Eats anything small enough to ingest, but also thrives on algae and other vegetable material.

Leuciscus cephalus (Linnaeus) • Chub

RANGE: Throughout central and eastern Europe, Scandinavia, Britain, and western Asia.
HABITS: An aggressive fish. Spawns in May and June when the male becomes covered with white nuptial tubercles. Spawns in shoals over gravel and plants.
WATER CONDITIONS: Not fussy about water quality as long as it's cool.
SIZE: May reach 8½ kg; English record is 60 cm at 4.76 kg.
FOOD REQUIREMENTS: Adults eat any living fishes small enough to ingest. When smaller they thrive on live crustaceans and the usual aquarium diet. When hungry they even eat algae and plants. Not recommended for the garden pool.

Gobio gobio (Linnaeus) • Gudgeon

RANGE: Throughout temperate Europe and the British Isles into the U.S.S.R.
HABITS: Widely distributed all over Europe in every kind of habitat from still ponds to moving streams. Suitable for garden pools and large unheated tanks. Spawns in the spring by scattering adhesive eggs at night over sticks and stones.
WATER CONDITIONS: Almost any water that is fairly clean. Unheated aquaria.
SIZE: Maximum of 15 cm.
FOOD REQUIREMENTS: Same as goldfish. Eats almost all small crustaceans, but also thrives on stale bread and the usual aquarium food fare.

Chondrostoma nasus (Linnaeus) • Nase, Nosefish

RANGE: Temperate Europe to the Caspian Sea.
HABITS: A good scavenger for the garden pond, this fish stays on the bottom most of the time. In nature it stays in deep water in fast moving rivers and deep streams. Spawns from February to April. Rarely caught and considered a very rare aquarium fish.
WATER CONDITIONS: Clean, clear, cold water that is aerated and filtered.
SIZE: May reach 50 cm.
FOOD REQUIREMENTS: A good scavenger as it eats mainly algae growing on the rocks and sticks on the bottom. Suitable for a garden pond if you can find specimens.

Leuciscus idus (var.)

Leuciscus idus

Gnathopogon chankaensis

Leuciscus cephalus

Ctenopharyngodon idella

Gobio gobio

Carassius carassius

Chondrostomas nasu

1

2

3

4

5

6

7

8

Phoxinus phoxinus (Linnaeus) • Eurasian Dace

RANGE: Throughout Europe and the U.S.S.R.
HABITS: Inhabits every type of clean, clear water, even high up in the Alps (to 2000 m). Must be kept in a large, unheated aquarium with lots of room. This is the bait fish and food fodder fish for most of central Europe. It occurs in large schools in some lakes.
WATER CONDITIONS: Cold, clean, clear water that is aerated and filtered.
SIZE: Rare specimens get to 12 cm; most are found at 8 cm.
FOOD REQUIREMENTS: Eats small crustaceans, diatoms, algae, and higher plants.

Scardineus erythrophthalmus (Linnaeus) • Rudd

RANGE: Throughout central Europe, Scandinavia, and England.
HABITS: Widespread in still and slowly moving waters but not necessarily present in contiguous bodies of water where predators eat them as soon as they appear. A food fish in eastern Europe but not eaten by people of higher economic means.
WATER CONDITIONS: Thrives in many lakes, rivers, and streams. Not fussy about water conditions as long as their aquarium is clean, well filtered, and aerated. This is a coldwater species.
SIZE: Exceptional specimens reach 30 cm. Usually found at 20 cm.
FOOD REQUIREMENTS: Prefers live or frozen foods, but accepts prepared foods when hungry.

Vimba vimba (Linnaeus) • Vimba

RANGE: Isolated areas in Sweden and Germany and along the brackish marshes of the Baltic Sea.
HABITS: Found in the lower reaches of lakes and rivers. Netted in Sweden, where large quantities used to be consumed. The fish usually stays on the bottom of rivers and lakes, but it migrates during the breeding season (as do many fishes), and that's when it is trapped.
WATER CONDITIONS: Clean, clear, aerated water. Does better in slightly brackish water with a specific gravity of about 1.005.
SIZE: Rarely reaches its maximum growth of about 50 cm.
FOOD REQUIREMENTS: Mostly a mollusc and worm eater, but it feeds on several other categories of living foods when its special foods are not available. Can be weaned to chopped fish in the aquarium.

Acanthorhodeus asmussi (Dybowski) • Russian Bitterling, Gorchak

RANGE: Occurs in the middle and lower Amur River basin.
HABITS: Reaches sexual maturity in its third year (at 7+ cm). Spawns from the end of May to July, releasing an average of 300 to 600 eggs (up to 1100). A black spot on the juvenile disappears with growth.
WATER CONDITIONS: Acclimates to aquarium life relatively easily. An unheated tank with scattered rocks and cleaned mussel shells is recommended.
SIZE: Attains a length of 16 cm on the average.
FOOD REQUIREMENTS: Feeds on aquatic plants.

Rhodeus sericeus (Pallas) • Bitterling

RANGE: Throughout central Europe.
HABITS: A unique fish whose relatives join it in laying their eggs inside mussels belonging to the genera Anodonta, Pseudanodonta, and Unio. In return the Bitterling is the host of the parasitic early stages of the mussels.
WATER CONDITIONS: A very popular aquarium fish that is very difficult to spawn. Aquarists introduced it into English waters (Lancashire and Cheshire) in the 1920's but it has since become expensive and probably has been seined out of existence in England.
SIZE: A small fish that rarely reaches its maximum size of 10 cm.
FOOD REQUIREMENTS: Eats most aquarium diets but prefers mosquito larvae and small crustaceans.

Tinca tinca (Linnaeus) • Tench

RANGE: Throughout central Europe including the British Isles.
HABITS: A stillwater fish occurring mostly in lakes. They have a great ability to survive in marginal water situations and can be raised side-by-side with carp in many fish farms.
WATER CONDITIONS: They thrive in unaerated, unfiltered water where most other fishes perish, but they do best in clean, cool, aerated water providing they do not have aggressive tankmates.
SIZE: Reaches a maximum of about 63 cm but usually are caught at half that size.
FOOD REQUIREMENTS: Young fish eat algae; older fish eat everything found on the bottom of a lake including snails and water fleas of all types. In the aquarium it eats the usual aquarium diet for coldwater fishes.

Chilogobio czerskii Berg • Rainbow gudgeon, Peskar

RANGE: Amur River basin.
HABITS: Reaches sexual maturity in third year (about 6 cm). It has a short spawning season (June-July) when it deposits its large yellowish eggs. Juveniles have a dark longitudinal stripe and will school with fishes similarly patterned.
WATER CONDITIONS: Requires an unheated aquarium with relatively clean water.
SIZE: Attains a length of 11 cm.
FOOD REQUIREMENTS: Will accept many of the live foods available to aquarists.

Phoxinus phoxinus

Acanthorhodeus asmussi

Scardineus erythrophthalmus

Rhodeus sericeus

Vimba vimba

Tinca tinca

Chilogobio czerskii

Chilogobius czerskii

91

Weatherfishes

The loaches in the genera *Misgurnus* and *Cobitis* (plus several other very similar genera) are members of the family Cobitidae and thus are very closely related. These "weatherfishes" get their common name because they actually respond to differences in atmospheric (barometric) pressure. This has to do with the complicated structure of their Weberian apparatus and swim (air) bladders. For the aquarist this is of little interest except when the fish "dance" wildly before a storm. They have protruding mouthparts and barbels that assist them in scrounging through the mulm at the bottom of the aquarium searching for small offerings of uneaten food particles, worms, fish eggs, or whatever.

The genus *Cobitis*

Fishes of this genus are found very widely spread through Europe to Japan and everywhere in between, including North Africa. Linnaeus first described the genus in 1758, using *Cobitis taenia* as the type. *Cobitis taenia* is very widespread, but some ichthyologists have found small, localized populations that they have described as separate species. One such species is *Cobitis biwae,* which was described by Temminck & Schlegel from a specimen found in Totori, Japan. *Cobitis taenia palludicola* was found in Spain and described by DeBuen in 1959, while *C. t. dolichorhynchus* was described by Nicholas in 1936 from fish found in Chekiang, China. Klausewitz found a doubtful species in Valencia, Spain that he called *Cobitis haasi,* but this is quite similar to DeBuen's fish. In any case, all of the known *Cobitis* (there are literally dozens of these fishes named) have similar patterns of a series of line, spots, dots, or whatever that makes them all look alike. Their color patterns change considerably in the aquarium depending upon their size, age, and the background in which they reside. They are never colorful and have never been very popular with aquarium hobbyists since thermostatic heaters allowed tropicals to be maintained. *Cobitis* are great for the unheated tank, and they are excellent scavengers, too.

Cobitis taenia

Leptobotia mantchurica

Lefua costata (female)

Lefua costata

Nemacheilus kessleri

Nemacheilus barbatulus

Misgurnus fossilis (var.)

Misgurnus fossilis

A loach of the genus *Niwaela*

Misgurnus anguillicaudatus

Golden form of *Misgurnus anguillicaudatus*

Above and below: *Leptobotia curta*

Nemacheilus barbatulus toni

Cobitis taenia

Cobitis biwae

Cobitis taenia taenia

Cobitis taenia taenia

Left and right above: The same loach shown over different substrates

Cobitis taenia striata

Cobitis taenia striata (spotted form)

Cobitis takatsuensis

Cobitis takatsuensis

Pseudobagrus fulvidraco (Richardson) • Tawny Dragon Catfish

RANGE: Middle and lower Amur River basin.
HABITS: Semi-retiring and generally peaceful with larger fishes. Matures in third or fourth year. Male digs pitcher-shaped burrow where 15,000 to 100,000 eggs may be deposited and then guards them. Nests may be close together in a generalized spawning area.
WATER CONDITIONS: Wide tolerance of pH and hardness, but extremes are best avoided. Tank should be unheated.
SIZE: Attains a length of up to 35 cm.
FOOD REQUIREMENTS: Feeds on various bottom dwelling insects and small fishes. In aquaria takes live foods and eventually prepared aquarium foods.

Siniperca chuatsi (Basilewski) • Chinese Perch

RANGE: Central and northern China at least as far as the Amur River.
HABITS: Predatory on small fishes. Tankmates must be large and able to take care of themselves.
WATER CONDITIONS: Not critical, but this is a cool-water fish so temperatures should be no higher than 23 to 24°C.
SIZE: Reaches a length of up to 50 cm in standard length.
FOOD REQUIREMENTS: Easily fed with small fishes, crustaceans and many of the frozen foods.

Perca fluviatilis Linnaeus • Eurasian Yellow Perch

RANGE: Throughout most of Europe, Scandinavia, the British Isles, and the U.S.S.R.
HABITS: Found in lakes, ponds, rivers, and streams, usually near water obstacles like large rocks and bridge pilings. Spawns in May. Large specimens eat small fishes.
WATER CONDITIONS: Thrives under most unheated aquarium conditions if given enough space.
SIZE: May reach 50 cm.
FOOD REQUIREMENTS: Small fish eat leeches and sticklebacks, their favorite foods. Larger fish eat any fishes small enough to swallow.

Perccottus glehni Dybowski • Russian Sleeper, Goloveshka

RANGE: Lakes, swamps, and ponds of the middle and lower parts of the Amur River basin.
HABITS: Prefers standing waters. Spawns in June and July, when it places about 1000 eggs on the lower surface of leaves, etc., floating in the water. Mature in their second year (at 5.5+ cm).
WATER CONDITIONS: Lives in unheated tanks without much water movement. Should be given adequate space.
SIZE: Attains a length of up to 25 cm.
FOOD REQUIREMENTS: Feeds on aquatic invertebrates, especially insects, and small fishes.

Pelteobagrus brashnikowi (Berg) • Brashnikov's Catfish

RANGE: Occurs in lakes and slow-flowing waters of the middle and lower Amur River basin.
HABITS: Males attain sexual maturity in third year (12 cm). They spawn in late June and July. About 1000 to 2700 eggs are deposited in places where the water moves slowly and there is a steep bank.
WATER CONDITIONS: Water chemistry is not critical as long as extremes are avoided. Does well in an unheated aquarium.
SIZE: Attains a length of up to 20 cm.
FOOD REQUIREMENTS: Feeds on various invertebrates.

Silurus glanis Linnaeus • Eurasian Giant Catfish, Wels

RANGE: Freshwater lakes and streams from central Europe through western Asia.
HABITS: After a prespawning courtship, lays its large (2-3 mm) eggs in primitive nests among the plants. The male, larger than the female, guards the nest. Nocturnal, solitary fish.
WATER CONDITIONS: Rather tolerant of different water chemistries. Needs unheated large aquarium, preferably with some aquatic plants.
SIZE: Attains a length of up to 5 meters and a weight of 300 kilograms.
FOOD REQUIREMENTS: A predator from the first year. Accepts live foods, especially fishes.

Stizostedion lucioperca (Linnaeus) • European Pikeperch

RANGE: Central Europe to the Caspian basin. Scandinavia and a few isolated spots in England.
HABITS: Occurs in large lakes and large rivers where it prefers a habitat with a hard, clean, sandy bottom. It has been introduced into many areas where a sport fish is required. It is a good food fish, is widely cultivated, and is even raised with carp.
WATER CONDITIONS: Unheated, clean surroundings with lots of room and heavily filtered and aerated water.
SIZE: Reaches 50 cm.
FOOD REQUIREMENTS: A carnivorous fish that requires live brine shrimp, daphnia, and small fishes throughout its life cycle. Starving fish can be acclimated to normal aquarium fare, but they never do well until they are offered small live fishes.

Proterorhinus marmoratus (Pallas) • Tube-nosed Goby, Bychock

RANGE: Black, Azov, and Caspian Sea basins.
HABITS: Inhabits near-shore areas around plants or stones. Spawns from April to August after reaching one year of age. It lays its eggs between stones and in the shells of molluscs.
WATER CONDITIONS: Should be kept in clean water in an unheated tank with stones and plants that create hiding places.
SIZE: Attains a length of up to 12 cm.
FOOD REQUIREMENTS: Generally feeds on bottom invertebrates such as small worms. Aquarium fare should be similar, such as tubificid worms.

Pseudobagrus fulvidraco

Pelteobagrus brashnikowi

Siniperca chuatsi

Silurus glanis

Perca fluviatilis

Stizostedion lucioperca

Perccottus glehni

Proterorhinus marmoratus

97

Spawning Bitterlings

Bitterlings are small freshwater fishes that are found throughout the entire temperate zone of Europe, eastward through Russia and China, and into Korea and Japan. As far as is known, they spawn by laying their eggs in living mussels. They may be the only group of fishes that do this, though many small cichlids in Africa and South America lay their eggs inside dead, vacated snail shells.

Depending upon the species, the bitterling searches for a suitable mussel in early spring, summer, or fall. The male is the one that does the hunting. When he finds a suitable mussel he has a way of teasing the mussel to make it open its shell. Once it has been able to do this, the male then searches for a suitable female with a clearly projecting ovipositor (egg tube). During this time the male protects the mussel from other fishes, especially other male bitterlings.

When a female is encountered, she is wooed onto the spawning mussel and deposits her eggs in the inlet siphon of the mussel. She may lay from one to six eggs at a time. Then the male takes a position over the inlet siphon and releases sperm. This continues for an hour or two until the female is depleted. Both fish then leave the scene and the eggs become attached to the areas between the mussel's gills. They remain there for up to a month before they hatch.

The fry of most species are between 6 and 8 mm in length when they have absorbed their yolk sacs. They do not parasitize the mussel but rely upon the food stored in their egg sacs. The mussel seems to be annoyed by these wriggling fry and "exhales" them with its waste breathing water. During their stay within the mussel, many of the fry become parasitized by mussel larvae, and when the fry are liberated they have a cargo of mussel larvae attached to them. The mussel larvae feed on the juices of the developing fish, but there are never enough larvae to seriously hurt the developing bitterling. This then ensures the distribution of the mussel, as the mussel larvae fall off after a few weeks.

The aquarist would find it almost impossible to obtain the exact kind of freshwater mussel to which a particular species of bitterling is attracted in nature, but many bitterlings will accept almost any healthy mussel as a host for their eggs. Some species will spawn readily in a well-aerated clean tank kept at room temperature and stocked with several types of local mussels.

After spawning, the breeders should be placed in a separate tank and the mussel be allowed to roam about the sandy bottom of the tank. No filtration should be used, as the mussel gets its food by filtering microorganisms from the water. Use only enough aeration to keep the surface of the water broken. The bitterling fry require freshly hatched brine shrimp when they appear and soon graduate to powdery fine foods.

Tanakia tanago

Acheilognathus cyanostigma

Acheilognathus lanceolata

Acheilognathus tabira tabira

Acheilognathus tabira

Acheilognathus moriokae

Acheilognathus limbata

Acheilognathus rhombea

Rhodeus ocellatus ocellatus

Rhodeus ocellatus

Above and below: *Rhodeus ocellatus* spawning

Rhodeus suigensis

Plate #64 • Bitterlings

Rhodeus ocellatus

100

Acheilognathus longipinnis

Barbodes sinensis

Rhodeus sericeus

Above and below: Eggs and fry of *Rhodeus ocellatus* in the gills of mussels.

Plate #65 • Bitterlings

Neotropical Region

Freshwater Stingrays

The stingrays shown on the facing page were all collected by the author (HRA) in Brazil. These are small rays that are typical of those exported in the aquarium trade. Most are juveniles and have lots of growing to do. Most South American freshwater stingrays grow to a diameter of about one meter, but some are a bit larger. Stingrays are not recommended for the home aquarium because the stings are venomous and dangerous. The fish also spend most of their time half buried in the sand and are difficult to feed unless some shellfish are available for them.

In Brazil, these rays are found lying semi-hidden in the sand close to shore. They burrow through the top layer of the sand in search of small clams, mussels, and invertebrates living in the sand. The natives who live where stingrays are found are very wary of stepping on them and usually patrol the beach areas with a raised harpoon ready to lance the familiar sandy outline of the hidden stingray.

The Brazilian stingrays have very powerful teeth that easily crush the shells of the most dense-shelled animals. Clams are their preferred diet, though freshwater mussels are equally acceptable. In the aquarium they may be trained to take a clam or mussel from your hand . . . but be careful, for many of these stingrays can swing their tails forward as well as sideward. I once saw a Brazilian Indian so crazy with the pain of a sting that he tried to commit suicide by running headfirst into a tree! Children in the jungle have sometimes been painfully killed by diving into shallow water, landing on a buried stingray, and getting lanced in the abdomen. Death may occur within a day of the infliction of an abdominal wound.

Wounds in the hands or feet are never fatal of themselves, but infections following the wound may be fatal if not treated immediately. The wound should be flushed with water either from a hose or from a bucket. Then the wound should be searched for remnants of the spine. All areas should be carefully cut open to probe for tiny hidden pieces of broken spine teeth. This is done carefully with a fine probe to feel for something hard buried in the flesh. The injured part should then be soaked for an hour in the hottest water possible. If it is high on the arm or leg, the wound should be wrapped in heavy towelling and hot water poured on it as often as necessary. The hotter the water the better, but don't scald the patient. After an hour of hot soaks the search for spine fragments should continue. When cleaned, the wound may be sutured and bandaged, and a regimen of antibiotic and anti-tetanus agents should be administered. Professional medical care should be sought as quickly as possible. Of course these treatments should only be emergency first aid treatments; if a doctor or hospital is available, rush the victim there as quickly as possible.

All stingrays are livebearers, giving birth to living young.

Potamotrygon laticeps

Potamotrygon laticeps

Potamotrygon motoro

Potamotrygon motoro

Potamotrygon reticulatus

Pomatotrygon reticulatus

Potamotrygon magdalenae

Potamotrygon humboldtii

Osteoglossum ferreirai Kanazawa • Black Arowana

RANGE: Rio Banco tributary of the Rio Negro in Brazil.
HABITS: Large specimens won't hesitate to swallow anything they can cram in their very spacious mouths, but neither adults nor young specimens are quarrelsome with fishes not regarded as food; rather unpredictable in temperament, frequently showing disturbance when there is no visible cause for alarm.
WATER CONDITIONS: Soft, slightly acid water desirable. Temperature 25 to 28°C.
SIZE: Wild adult specimens run up to about 40 cm; juveniles of about 8 cm most often seen.
FOOD REQUIREMENTS: Variable from individual to individual; some will take prepared aquarium foods, while others refuse all except small live fishes.

Osteoglossum bicirrhosum Vandelli • Arowana

RANGE: Guianas and most parts of the Amazon.
HABITS: Only small ones may be kept together; big ones are best kept alone.
WATER CONDITIONS: Should be moved as little as possible. Temperature 24 to 26°C.
SIZE: To about 60 cm, but usually much smaller.
FOOD REQUIREMENTS: Greatly prefers fishes which can be swallowed whole, but can be trained to take pieces of raw fish, shrimp, etc., from the fingers.

Lepidosiren parodoxus Fitzinger • South American Lungfish

RANGE: Amazon Basin, South America.
HABITS: This ancient fish is not for the home aquarium. They are very hardy and easy to keep alive, but they hardly ever move and are of little interest other than as a curiosity. They eat almost everything and have a very well-studied history since they are truly "living fossils."
WATER CONDITIONS: These very hardy fish can live under almost any conditions. Even if the water dries out, the fish can make a mud cocoon and last out the drought. Typical aquarium conditions are acceptable.
SIZE: They may grow to 120 cm.
FOOD REQUIREMENTS: These fish are very difficult to feed but may take chunks of fish. Every curator has his own "secret" for keeping lungfishes alive.

Arapaima gigas (Cuvier) • Arapaima, Pirarucu

RANGE: Entire tropical South American region, usually in the deeper, larger streams.
HABITS: Because of their size, any more than one to a large tank would be unthinkable.
WATER CONDITIONS: Water conditions are not particularly important with this species. Temperature 24 to 27°C.
SIZE: To about 4.5 m in the open; captive specimens seldom over 60 cm.
FOOD REQUIREMENTS: In captivity they will eat nothing but small living fishes.

Osteoglossum ferreirai (juv.)

Osteoglossum ferreirai (young)

Osteoglossum ferreirai (subadult)

Osteoglossum ferreirai (adult)

Osteoglossum bicirrhosum (newly born)

Osteoglossum bicirrhosum (juv.)

Lepidosiren paradoxus

Arapaima gigas

Characidium brevirostre Pellegrin • Checkered Darter Tetra

RANGE: Brazil.
HABITS: Stays on the bottom of the aquarium, darting from leaf to leaf on bottom-growing plants.
WATER CONDITIONS: Prefers shaded situations with slightly acid water between 22-25°C.
SIZE: Not too much is known about this fish. The specimens collected by the author (HRA) reached 4 cm in total length.
FOOD REQUIREMENTS: Small, fine-particle dried aquarium foods or finely sifted live foods are taken.

Characidium catenatum Eigenmann • Gray Darter Tetra

RANGE: Brazil.
HABITS: A bottom-dwelling characin that darts about in search of food.
WATER CONDITIONS: Typical aquarium conditions suit it fine.
SIZE: 4 cm.
FOOD REQUIREMENTS: Small foods including brine shrimp nauplii and most dried aquarium foods.

Poecilocharax weitzmani Meinken • Black Darter Tetra

RANGE: The Upper Amazon (Solimoes) as well as the upper Rio Negro-Orinoco in heavily vegetated, slow-moving streams.
HABITS: It stays on the bottom of the aquarium, barely rising even when it is hungry. It preys on slowly falling food particles whether they are live or not. They are extremely difficult to keep without live foods. The males are territorial even when not spawning.
WATER CONDITIONS: Warm, slightly acid water.
SIZE: 4 cm.
FOOD REQUIREMENTS: Living foods that fall to the bottom, such as daphnia, tubifex worms, live brine shrimp, etc.

Crenuchus spilurus Guenther • Sailfin Tetra

RANGE: Guyana and central Amazon region.
HABITS: Probably a predator; do not keep them with any smaller fishes.
WATER CONDITIONS: Soft, definitely acid water is required. Temperature 24 to 26°C, never lower.
SIZE: To 6 cm.
FOOD REQUIREMENTS: All sorts of live foods, preferably the larger ones like cut-up earthworms and young livebearers.

Ctenolucius huieta (Valenciennes) • Blunt-nosed Gar, Hujeta

RANGE: Tropical South America.
HABITS: Aggressive; eats small fishes and flying insects. A jumper, so keep the tank covered. A nocturnal fish.
WATER CONDITIONS: Not sensitive to changes in water conditions. Does well in water from 21 to 29°C with a pH from 6.0 to 7.6. Prefers soft water, but doesn't suffer too much in hard water.
SIZE: Up to 25 cm.
FOOD REQUIREMENTS: Loves floating insects or live baby Guppies.

Boulengerella maculata (Valenciennes) • Spotted Pike Characin

RANGE: Amazon basin.
HABITS: Predatory on small fishes. Should be kept with larger fishes or with members of its own kind.
WATER CONDITIONS: Not critical. A pH of between 6.0 and 7.5, a hardness of 6 DH or less and a temperature between 24 and 27°C are recommended.
SIZE: Attains a length of 35 to 40 cm.
FOOD REQUIREMENTS: Small live fishes such as goldfish and livebearers (guppies may be too small) are preferred.

Hoplerythrinus unitaeniatus (Spix) • Golden Trahira

RANGE: Amazon River system and probably other systems in South America.
HABITS: A nasty, predacious fish that eats fishes almost as large as itself and grows very quickly. A food fish in Brazil.
WATER CONDITIONS: Thrives under almost all aquarium conditions.
SIZE: Reaches almost 50 cm.
FOOD REQUIREMENTS: Eats everything but prefers small living fishes.

Hoplias malabaricus (Bloch) • Tiger Fish; Trahira

RANGE: Central and northern South America.
HABITS: Predatory on fishes it can swallow. Not generally regarded as a good aquarium fish.
WATER CONDITIONS: Not critical; can exist in soft to medium-hard water and prefers dim light. Temperature 24 to 26°C.
SIZE: Attains a length of about 50 cm.
FOOD REQUIREMENTS: Small fishes are eagerly hunted down. Chopped fish or brine shrimp and possibly earthworms might provide suitable substitutes.

Characidium brevirostre

Characidium catenatum

Poecilocharax weitzmani

Crenuchus spilurus

Ctenolucius hujeta

Boulengerella maculata

Hoplerythrinus unitaeniatus

Hoplias malabaricus

Characidium fasciatum Reinhardt • Banded Characidium

RANGE: South America, Orinoco region in the north to La Plata region in the south.

HABITS: Comes from streams where there is some current; therefore requires fresh, clean water in an uncrowded aquarium.

WATER CONDITIONS: Clean, well-oxygenated water, about neutral. Temperature should not exceed 24°C.

SIZE: 6 cm.

FOOD REQUIREMENTS: Not a fussy eater, but prefers living foods.

Elachocharax junki Gery • Junk's Darter Tetra

RANGE: Discovered by the author (HRA) in the Rio Madeira, Brazil.

HABITS: A bottom-dwelling fish that scoots about in short jerks from which its name darter tetra derives. Named to honor Dr. Junk of INPA in Manaus, Brazil. Junk is charged with protecting the Amazonian fishes.

WATER CONDITIONS: Clear water, shady situations. Temperature as close to 25°C as possible. Neutral to slightly acid water.

SIZE: A small, chunky fish. The specimens collected average 3.1 cm.

FOOD REQUIREMENTS: Ate small living foods; prefer newly hatched brine shrimp but accepts dry food as well.

Nannostomus espei (Meinken) • Barred Pencilfish

RANGE: Guyana.

HABITS: Peaceful and active; a skilled jumper whose tank should be covered.

WATER CONDITIONS: Soft water, neutral to slightly acid. Temperature 24 to 27°C.

SIZE: To 5 cm.

FOOD REQUIREMENTS: Not choosy as to foods, but very partial to live daphnia.

Nannostomus beckfordi Guenther • Beckford's Pencilfish

RANGE: Guianas, Parana, Rio Negro, middle and lower Amazon.

HABITS: Peaceful toward other fishes and plants; should be kept in a group of their own kind or other related species.

WATER CONDITIONS: Prefers soft, slightly acid water but is not intolerant to other types. Temperature 24 to 27°C.

SIZE: To 5 cm.

FOOD REQUIREMENTS: Prefers the smaller living foods, but can be accustomed to taking frozen or dried foods when the others are not available.

Characidium "Gery" • Gery's Characidium

RANGE: Discovered in Brazil by the author (HRA). This undescribed species is known in the trade as *Characidium* "Gery," but this is not to be taken as its scientific name; it has never been scientifically described.

HABITS: Typical habits of South American darter tetras, moving about in a jerky, darting pattern.

WATER CONDITIONS: Slightly acid, still water was used for the first fish imported; they thrived, but they were collected in fast-moving streams.

SIZE: To 5.3 cm.

FOOD REQUIREMENTS: Tubifex worms and other small live foods, but they also accept dried foods small enough to ingest whole.

Lebiasina panamensis (Gill) • Panama Pencil

RANGE: Panama, Central America.

HABITS: A devourer of mosquito larvae. This fish is always seen with a full, rotund belly if there are enough mosquito larvae in its habitat. It has been successfully transplanted for mosquito control.

WATER CONDITIONS: Thrives under most non-toxic aquarium conditions. Likes warm water between 25-30°C.

SIZE: Reaches a maximum length of 8.2 cm.

FOOD REQUIREMENTS: Seems to prefer live mosquito larvae, but accepts almost all aquarium foods.

Nannostomus harrisoni Eigenmann • Harrison's Pencilfish

RANGE: Guyana and the upper Amazon.

HABITS: Peaceful, a good community tank fish.

WATER CONDITIONS: Aged water that is slightly acid, hardness less than 10 DH and a temperature of 24-27°C. are recommended.

SIZE: Attains a length of about 5-6.5 cm.

FOOD REQUIREMENTS: Small live foods preferred but will eventually accept flake foods.

Characidium fasciatum

Characidium fasciatum

Elachocharax junki

Characidium "Gery"

Nannostomus espei

Lebiasina panamensis

Nannostomus beckfordi

Nannostomus harrisoni

111

Pyrrhulina brevis "Aguaro" • Aguaro Pencilfish

RANGE: Rio Aguaro, Venezuela.
HABITS: A typical pencilfish, waiting motionless as food comes its way. Easy to breed if given an isolated aquarium with lots of live food and warmth.
WATER CONDITIONS: Prefers a neutral to slightly acid pH (6.0-7.2) with temperatures around 24-25°C.
SIZE: Averages about 5.2 cm.
FOOD REQUIREMENTS: Prefers small live foods but eagerly accepts fine dried foods, too.

Pyrrhulina brevis "Boa Vista" • Boa Vista Pencilfish

RANGE: Collected by the author (HRA) in the Rio Branco, Brazil, area in shallow, flooded grassy plains.
HABITS: Feeds mainly on insects and prefers shallow waters. Very common in flooded plains but rare during the dry season in shallow streams.
WATER CONDITIONS: Warm, slightly acid water.
SIZE: To 5 cm.
FOOD REQUIREMENTS: Prefers floating live foods like mosquito larvae but quickly adapts to a normal aquarium diet.

Nannostomus eques Steindachner • Brown-tailed Pencilfish

RANGE: Guyana and Orinoco to lower Amazon.
HABITS: Peaceful; swims with the head tilted upward, and prefers to swim in schools.
WATER CONDITIONS: Soft, neutral to slightly acid water. Temperature 24 to 27°C.
SIZE: To 5 cm.
FOOD REQUIREMENTS: Most foods are taken from or near the surface; mosquito larvae are particularly relished by mature fish.

Nannostomus unifasciatus Steindachner • One-lined Pencilfish

RANGE: Middle and lower Amazon tributaries, Rio Negro, Guyana, Orinoco.
HABITS: Peaceful and somewhat timid; prefer to be kept in a small group.
WATER CONDITIONS: Soft, slightly acid water. Temperature 23 to 26°C.
SIZE: To 6 cm.
FOOD REQUIREMENTS: Live and prepared foods of small size, preferably food which will remain at or near the surface.

Nannostomus trifasciatus Steindachner • Three-lined Pencilfish

RANGE: Upper Amazon region.
HABITS: Peaceful toward other fishes and plants; should not be kept with active fishes.
WATER CONDITIONS: Soft, slightly acid water which has been run through peat moss. Temperature 24 to 27°C.
SIZE: To 6 cm.
FOOD REQUIREMENTS: Small live foods are best, with frozen or dried foods given only when living foods are not available.
COLOR VARIATIONS: Three black stripes at side of the body, with red markings on anal, ventral, dorsal and caudal fins.

Nannostomus marginatus Eigenmann • Dwarf Pencilfish

RANGE: Guyana to Colombia and the lower Amazon.
HABITS: Very peaceful; an excellent community fish.
WATER CONDITIONS: Neutral to slightly acid; requires heat, about 26°C.
SIZE: Maximum about 3 cm.
FOOD REQUIREMENTS: Prefers small live foods, but will take dry food if necessary.

Nannostomus bifasciatus Hoedeman • Two-striped Pencilfish

RANGE: Guyana, Surinam, French Guiana.
HABITS: Peaceful toward other fishes and plants.
WATER CONDITIONS: Soft, slightly acid water. Temperature 24 to 27°C.
SIZE: About 5 cm.
FOOD REQUIREMENTS: Small live foods are preferred, but frozen and dried foods are also accepted.
COLOR VARIATIONS: Body brown with two dark stripes, one from the top of the eye to the upper caudal base and another from the snout to the lower caudal base.

Pyrrhulina brevis "Aguaro"

Pyrrhulina brevis "Aguaro"

Pyrrhulina brevis "Boa Vista"

Nannostomus eques

Nannostomus unifasciatus

Nannostomus trifasciatus

Nannostomus marginatus

Nannostomus bifasciatus

Copella arnoldi (Regan) • Splash Tetra

RANGE: This is an aquarium strain derived from the wild
 Brazilian fishes.
HABITS: Lays its eggs out of the water on overhanging plants.
 Then uses its long fins to splash the eggs to keep them
 wet. The breeding habits of most copellas are very
 unique for characins.
WATER CONDITIONS: Warm, slightly acid water. pH 6.0-
 6.8; 24-29°C.
SIZE: 8.5 cm.
FOOD REQUIREMENTS: Prefers live foods such as daphnia
 but readily accepts a normal aquarium diet.

Copella metae (Eigenmann) • Meta Copeina

RANGE: Rio Meta, Colombia.
HABITS: Spawns like a cichlid. The photo on the facing page
 shows the pair carefully laying eggs on a leaf! This
 behavior is more typical of a cichlid than a characin
 (copellas are characins).
WATER CONDITIONS: Slightly acid water. pH 6.0-6.8; temperature 22-30°C.
SIZE: To 8 cm.
FOOD REQUIREMENTS: Prefers mosquito larvae and other
 floating live foods but readily adapts to standard
 aquarium fare.

Copeina guttata (Steindachner) • Red-spotted Copeina

RANGE: Central Amazon region.
HABITS: Peaceful; good community tank fish if not kept with
 others much smaller than themselves.
WATER CONDITIONS: Not critical; a wide range of temperatures is tolerated, with optimum temperatures around
 24°C.
SIZE: Wild specimens attain a size of about 10 cm; in captivity 15 cm.
FOOD REQUIREMENTS: Heavy eaters which will take prepared foods, but they should also be given live foods
 whenever possible.

Copella nattereri (Steindachner) • Plain Nattereri

RANGE: This is an aquarium variety that was derived from
 Copella nattereri many years ago (1925). The black
 stripe has disappeared but the pale spot in each scale remains.
HABITS: Scatters adhesive eggs in typical characin fashion,
 quite in contrast to *C. arnoldi.*
WATER CONDITIONS: Warm, slightly acid water.
SIZE: To 6 cm.
FOOD REQUIREMENTS: As with most copellas, these fish
 prefer mosquito larvae or other floating live foods, but
 they easily adapt to normal aquarium fare.

Pyrrhulina spilota Weitzman • Blotched Pyrrhulina

RANGE: South America, specific origin unknown.
HABITS: Very peaceful in the community aquarium.
WATER CONDITIONS: Soft, slightly acid water. Temper-
 ature 24 to 27°C.
SIZE: 6 cm.
FOOD REQUIREMENTS: Small live foods are preferred, but
 it will also accept frozen and some prepared flake foods.

Pyrrhulina laeta (Cope) • Long-lined Pyrrhulina

RANGE: Guyana and the central Amazon region.
HABITS: Very peaceful; can be kept in a community aquar-
 ium with non-aggressive fishes.
WATER CONDITIONS: Slightly soft, acid water is best.
 Temperature should be about 20°C but higher (to 24°C)
 for breeding.
SIZE: Attains a length of about 8 cm.
FOOD REQUIREMENTS: Will accept dry foods but has a
 strong preference for live or at least frozen foods.

Copella arnoldi

Copella arnoldi

Copella metae

Copeina guttata

Copella metae juvenile

Copella nattereri

Pyrrhulina spilota

Pyrrhulina laeta

115

SPAWNING IN *COPEINA* AND *COPELLA*

Most fishes in a single genus spawn in approximately the same fashion. If one lays adhesive eggs on leaves, so do most of the others. Yet in the single genus *Copella* and its close relative *Copeina* are found three very different spawning methods, one of which is extremely unusual to say the least.

The large, spotted *Copeina guttata* is somewhat unusual among tetras in that it clears a small depression in the substrate (fine silt or sand) and, after a rather brief spawning ritual, lays its eggs in the depression and fertilizes them. In some ways the spawning behavior is similar to that of cichlids although obviously not as "advanced" as in that family.

Most *Copella* species lay their eggs on the substrate, especially large heavy leaves. *Copella metae* is fairly representative of this type of spawning behavior, as shown in the photos.

Copella arnoldi and perhaps one or two other species are the "splash tetras" of aquarium legend. They are among the very few fishes known to spawn *totally out of the water*. The spawning pair goes through a short pre-spawning ritual just below the surface of the water and under a large leaf or similar object overhanging the water at the distance of 20-50 mm. At the peak of the "dancing" the male leaps from the water followed by the smaller female. The surface tension of the water on their bodies allows them to adhere to the surface of the leaf for a few seconds, long enough to lay and fertilize the eggs. After the clutch is completed the male stays below the leaf, occasionally splashing the eggs with sprays of water from his tail to keep them moist. The eggs develop rapidly, the fry soon leaving the eggs and dropping into the water below, where they then go through a normal "fishy" life. In the aquarium *Copella arnoldi* has been known to lay its eggs on the sides of the tank above the waterline and on the glass cover. The advantage of laying eggs out of water would seem to be that they are less subject to predators in their niche in the air but still near the water.

The male *Copeina guttata* (farther from camera in both photos above) approaches the female from the side and slightly to the rear as she enters the depression in the gravel to deposit her eggs.

A *Copella metae* pair (male is above female in photo at left, behind female in photo at right) station themselves above the leaf they've selected to receive the eggs.

At left the pair of *Copella arnoldi* (male above) are shown leaving the water; at right they are shown actually adhering to the leaf to which the eggs are being attached.

Leporinus agassizi Steindachner • Half-striped Leporinus

RANGE: Central Amazon region.
HABITS: Fairly peaceful and fond of nibbling algae from glass or plants.
WATER CONDITIONS: Neutral to slightly acid. Temperature 23 to 26°C.
SIZE: About 9 cm in the aquarium; likely to grow much bigger.
FOOD REQUIREMENTS: Will take prepared foods, but live and frozen foods are preferred; fond of nibbling a lettuce leaf.

Leporinus melanopleura Guenther • Spot-tailed Leporinus

RANGE: Eastern Brazil, between the Amazon River and Rio de Janeiro.
HABITS: Peaceful toward other fishes; a jumper which must be protected by keeping its tank covered.
WATER CONDITIONS: Neutral to slightly alkaline. Temperature 24 to 27°C.
SIZE: To 20 cm; usually sold at 8 to 10 cm.
FOOD REQUIREMENTS: All live foods and frozen foods; prepared foods are also accepted, and an addition of vegetable matter is very beneficial.

Leporinus nigrotaeniatus Schomburgk • Black-lined Leporinus

RANGE: Northern South America; regularly shipped from Guyana.
HABITS: A peaceful aquarium fish that prefers large, well planted tanks. Has never been spawned in the aquarium. A relatively rare species and one of the few longitudinally banded *Leporinus*.
WATER CONDITIONS: Warm, clear water that is heavily aerated. pH 6.0-7.0; temperature 24-30°C. Needs large aquaria.
SIZE: To 20 cm; probably larger.
FOOD REQUIREMENTS: Learns to accept standard aquarium fare but does much better on various small live foods, as do most fishes. Likes worms picked from the bottom.

Schizodon fasciatum Agassiz • Four-barred Leporinus

RANGE: Throughout the Amazon basin.
HABITS: A big jumper. Has never been spawned in the aquarium. A food fish in Brazil.
WATER CONDITIONS: Thrives in most aquarium conditions.
SIZE: Fairly large for an aquarium fish, reaching 25 cm.
FOOD REQUIREMENTS: Eats everything usually offered aquarium fishes.

Copella callolepis (Regan) • False Splashing Tetra

RANGE: Eastern Amazon in the state of Para, Brazil. Often confused with *C. arnoldi* and perhaps actually a new species.
HABITS: Found in shallow flooded plains.
WATER CONDITIONS: Warm, slightly acid water.
SIZE: To 5.4 cm.
FOOD REQUIREMENTS: Prefers mosquito larvae but quickly adapts to the normal aquarium fare.

Copella compta (Myers) • Red-bellied Copella

RANGE: Flood plains of the upper Rio Negro.
HABITS: Has never been spawned. Only imported once when it was collected by the author (HRA) along with cardinal tetras.
WATER CONDITIONS: Slightly acid, dark waters with pH on the acid side, from 4.8-6.2.
SIZE: Reaches 5.4 cm.
FOOD REQUIREMENTS: Prefers mosquito larvae and other small living foods but quickly learns to accept the usual aquarium fare.

Copella nattereri (Steindachner) • Spotted Copella

RANGE: Amazon Basin.
HABITS: Peaceful; a good community fish. Should be kept in a covered tank.
WATER CONDITIONS: Soft, slightly acid water. Temperature 22 to 28°C.
SIZE: Up to 8 cm.
FOOD REQUIREMENTS: Not too particular, but not all dry foods are accepted.

Copella "Bleher" • Red-dot Copella

RANGE: From the Rio Negro. This is probably a new species that is as yet undescribed, but it goes under the name C. Bleher in the aquarium trade.
HABITS: A typical copella that jumps rather easily from uncovered fish tanks! Has never been spawned in an aquarium.
WATER CONDITIONS: Prefers warm, acid waters, though it tolerates a great variation in pH range from 4.8-7.4.
SIZE: 6 cm.
FOOD REQUIREMENTS: Prefers small live foods but readily takes to a normal aquarium diet.

Leporinus agassizi

Leporinus melanopleura

Leporinus nigrotaeniatus

Schizodon fasciatum

Copella callolepis

Copella compta

Copella nattereri

Copella "Bleher"

119

Leporinus jamesi Garman • James's Leporinus

RANGE: This fish came from the Rio Negro, where it was collected by the author (HRA). It probably represents a new subgenus of *Leporinus*.

HABITS: Not much is known about the fish since only few specimens have been found to date. It probably needs acid, warm water since it came from the Rio Negro in Brazil.

WATER CONDITIONS: Slightly acid to neutral.

SIZE: To at least 12.5 cm in length.

FOOD REQUIREMENTS: The stomach contents contained small insects.

Leporinus pellegrini Steindachner • Striped Leporinus

RANGE: Upper Amazon, Peru and Colombia.

HABITS: This species stays small. At least no large ones have been found, though it it possible that they look different when larger than the specimen shown here.

WATER CONDITIONS: Warm, clear water with a pH of 6.0-7.2; temperature 22-28°C.

SIZE: About 10 cm.

FOOD REQUIREMENTS: Prefers small insects but gets along well on a typical aquarium diet.

Leporinus octofasciatus Steindachner • Eight-banded Leporinus

RANGE: Southeastern Brazil in larger streams and rivers.

HABITS: In cool, clear, running water. It has never been spawned in the aquarium. It belongs to a group of transverse-banded *Leporinus,* all of which probably are closely related.

WATER CONDITIONS: Water 20-26°C, clear and well aerated.

SIZE: To 15.6 cm.

FOOD REQUIREMENTS: Enjoys live daphnia but quickly adapts to an aquarium diet of prepared foods.

Leporinus striatus Kner • Striped Leporinus

RANGE: Amazon River south to the Parana in Uruguay.

HABITS: Peaceful and very active; tank should be kept well covered.

WATER CONDITIONS: Neutral to slightly alkaline. Temperature 23 to 26°C.

SIZE: About 30 cm in nature; in captivity about half that.

FOOD REQUIREMENTS: Omnivorous; likes to nibble on plants, so should be given an occasional lettuce or spinach leaf.

Leporinus pearsoni Fowler • Pearson's Leporinus

RANGE: Colombia.

HABITS: Never spawned in the aquarium. Feeds from the bottom. A jumper that should be maintained in a covered aquarium.

WATER CONDITIONS: Slightly acid to neutral water; 23-28°C.

SIZE: Aquarium specimens are about 15 cm long; in nature they reach 30 cm.

FOOD REQUIREMENTS: While they prefer daphnia, they do well on most aquarium diets.

Leporinus fasciatus (Bloch) • Banded Leporinus

RANGE: Widely distributed in South America from the Guianas to the La Plata.

HABITS: Active and peaceful toward other fishes, but inclined to be destructive to plants; keep their tank covered because they jump.

WATER CONDITIONS: Neutral to slightly alkaline water. Being active, they require a good-sized tank. Temperature 23 to 26°C.

SIZE: In their home waters to 33 cm; in captivity, seldom over 15 cm.

FOOD REQUIREMENTS: Omnivorous, with a preference for vegetable matter; crushed lettuce leaves or spinach leaves should be frequently provided.

Leporinus multifasciatus Cuvier • Many-banded Leporinus

RANGE: Rio Branco, Brazil, probably going as far north as Guyana.

HABITS: There are many look-alikes in the *Leporinus fasciatus* complex; their appearance changes as they get larger and their bands either split like the one shown here or disappear as in *L. pellegrini*. They are probably all closely related.

WATER CONDITIONS: Warm, clear water, pH 5.8-7.4. Temperature 23-30°C.

SIZE: This specimen was caught on hook and line and measured about 30 cm.

FOOD REQUIREMENTS: Insects are preferred in nature, but in the aquarium they thrive on a typical aquarium diet.

Leporinus arcus Eigenmann • Lipstick Leporinus

RANGE: Venezuela, the Guianas and parts of Brazil.

HABITS: Peaceful; likely to jump out of an uncovered tank.

WATER CONDITIONS: Neutral to slightly acid. Temperature 23 to 26°C.

SIZE: Reaches 40 cm, but only 5-10 cm when imported.

FOOD REQUIREMENTS: Live and frozen foods preferred; should have an occasional lettuce leaf to nibble on.

Leporinus jamesi

Leporinus pearsoni

Leporinus pellegrini

Leporinus fasciatus

Leporinus octofasciatus

Leporinus multifasciatus

Leporinus striatus

Leporinus arcus

Rhytiodus microlepis Kner • Pencil Anostomid

RANGE: Throughout the Amazon basin in deep waters; easily caught on a fly (like trout fishing).

HABITS: A pelagic fish that moves quickly, jumps easily, and is the thinnest of all anostomids. It has never been kept in an aquarium more than a few days, probably because it didn't have enough room.

WATER CONDITIONS: Must have lots of room; at least a 400-liter aquarium is required.

SIZE: Reaches 28.5 cm, perhaps larger.

FOOD REQUIREMENTS: Eats everything usually offered to an aquarium fish, especially live foods and small fishes. Has a tiny mouth.

Abramites hypselonotus (Guenther) • Headstander

RANGE: Upper Peruvian Amazon, Paraguay, Venezuela.

HABITS: May be aggressive, also nibble plants.

WATER CONDITIONS: Water should be soft and slightly acid. Temperature 23 to 25°C.

SIZE: About 12.5 cm; usually smaller specimens are sold.

FOOD REQUIREMENTS: Living foods are eagerly accepted, and the fish are fond of nibbling algae or a lettuce leaf.

Leporinus maculatus Mueller & Troschel • Spotted Leporinus

RANGE: These are tank-raised fish. The origin is probably Brazil. Several species have been called L. maculatus, and the ichthyological problem has not as yet been worked out.

HABITS: Most Leporinus come from small streams or rivers. This is the only species that is regularly spawned.

WATER CONDITIONS: Soft, clean, acid waters with temperatures ranging from 23-30°C.

SIZE: To 20 cm.

FOOD REQUIREMENTS: They do best on live foods, especially live brine shrimp, tubifex worms, and daphnia.

Leporinus melanostictus Norman • Silver Leporinus

RANGE: Guyana and Rio Branco in Brazil.

HABITS: This is a rare fish that hardly ever shows up in any quantity. No one has spawned the fish or knows much about it. Initial imports were fragile, and none lived more than a few months.

WATER CONDITIONS: Exact conditions are not known, but clear water, as close to neutral as possible, with a temperature about 27°C should suffice.

SIZE: Not known. Usual aquarium specimens 10 cm.

FOOD REQUIREMENTS: They eat everything, from live foods to freeze-dried aquarium foods.

Rhytiodus argenteofuscus Kner • Silver-bellied Anostomid

RANGE: Amazon area, but more available near the Rio Madeira.

HABITS: The two Rhytiodus species here were collected by the author (HRA) in the Amazon. A third species, R. elongatus, was also collected in the Rio Purus, but the author lost those specimens. They have never survived in an aquarium.

WATER CONDITIONS: Difficult or impossible. Typical aquarium conditions, but with lots of room. Specimens kept in small tanks died quickly.

SIZE: To 29.3 cm.

FOOD REQUIREMENTS: Eats small living insects and crustaceans. A deep-water fish.

Leporinus megalepis Guenther • Three-spot Leporinus

RANGE: Guyana and the Amazon, including the Rio Branco in Brazil.

HABITS: This fish is confused with at least three other fishes, namely, L. marcgravii, L. granti, and L. badueli. It is a popular aquarium fish that usually comes in with imports from Guyana.

WATER CONDITIONS: Light, almost neutral water. Temperature 23-30°C.

SIZE: To 25 cm.

FOOD REQUIREMENTS: Prefers live foods as do most characins, but easily acclimates to normal dried aquarium foods.

Leporinus granti Eigenmann • Red Leporinus

RANGE: This fish comes from the Mato Grosso of Brazil.

HABITS: The name granti is given to many Leporinus that have spots. Unfortunately the genus is a mess as far as nomenclature is concerned and there is hardly a positive identification for any of the 100-odd fishes known as Leporinus.

WATER CONDITIONS: Highly acid water with a pH about 5.4-6.6 suits them best, though they survive under most tropical aquarium conditions.

SIZE: 15 cm.

FOOD REQUIREMENTS: Prefers live foods but gets along on a normal dried food aquarium diet.

Leporinus melanopleura Guenther • Spot-tailed Leporinus

RANGE: Eastern Brazil.

HABITS: A great jumper. The identification of this fish and most fishes in the genus Leporinus is in doubt, but this fish has been called L. melanopleura in the aquarium trade since 1926.

WATER CONDITIONS: Likes slightly acid to neutral water; temperature 23-29°C.

SIZE: 26.5 cm.

FOOD REQUIREMENTS: Prefers living foods but gets along well on the usual aquarium diet.

Rhytiodus microlepis

Rhytiodus argenteofuscus

Abramites hypselonotus

Leporinus megalepis

Leporinus maculatus

Leporinus granti

Leporinus melanostictus

Leporinus melanopleura

Anostomus anostomus (Linnaeus) • Striped Headstander

RANGE: Guyana; Amazon River above Manaus.
HABITS: Mostly peaceful; prefers large aquaria which are well-planted. Likes to nibble algae.
WATER CONDITIONS: Fairly soft water is preferable, neutral to slightly acid. Temperature 24-25.5°C.
SIZE: 18 cm; usually collected and sold at 8 to 10 cm.
FOOD REQUIREMENTS: All living foods are preferred, but dried or frozen foods are also taken. Diet should be supplemented with green foods.

Anostomus trimaculatus (Kner) • Three-spotted Headstander

RANGE: Amazon Basin, the Guianas and Surinam
HABITS: Moderately peaceful; may be kept safely with fairly large fishes.
WATER CONDITIONS: Soft and slightly acid water. Temperature 25 to 26°C.
SIZE: 20 cm; specimens are usually sold at about 10 cm.
FOOD REQUIREMENTS: Live foods and dried foods, with the addition of occasional feedings of green foods such as chopped spinach.

Anostomus gracilis (Kner) • Four-spot Anostomus

RANGE: There are similar specimens to be found throughout Amazonia from the Rio Guapore, Rio Purus, and Rio Madeira all the way north to the Rio Negro and Rio Orinoco. They are always found in slow-moving streams.
HABITS: These are mid-water fish found in shallow streams about 2 meters deep at the most. They are very beautiful but have never been spawned in an aquarium.
WATER CONDITIONS: Clear water with a pH range from 5.8-7.2. Warm water is appreciated, average 28°C.
SIZE: Averages about 17.5 cm. Small specimens under 10 cm have never been found; they probably have been identified as something else.
FOOD REQUIREMENTS: Small live foods like newly hatched brine shrimp or daphnia are sought eagerly; dried aquarium diets are tolerated.

Anostomus garmani Borodin • Gray-lined Anostomid

RANGE: Rio Araguaia to most rivers in Para, Brazil.
HABITS: Found in shallow streams under 2 m deep. Only large specimens were collected by the author (HRA) in these areas. They eat insects in their natural habitat. The species has never been spawned in an aquarium.
WATER CONDITIONS: Prefer warm, clear water with a pH of 6.6-7.2, which is like the waters from which they were collected.
SIZE: To 15 cm, but probably larger.
FOOD REQUIREMENTS: Small insects, mosquito larvae, brine shrimp, and daphnia. Will probably take aquarium foods, too.

Anostomus taeniatus (Kner) • Lisa

RANGE: The Amazon from Brazil to the upper Amazon in Colombia and Peru.
HABITS: Jumps at the slightest provocation. Its tiny mouth indicates it must have small particled food.
SIZE: To 12.5 cm.
WATER CONDITIONS: Prefers warm, soft, slightly acid water. Temperature 25°C.
FOOD REQUIREMENTS: Small particles of dry food and tiny worms are accepted. Frozen brine shrimp is a favorite food.

Leporinus badueli Puyo • Golden Leporinus

RANGE: Upper Rio Branco to Guyana.
HABITS: A delicate fish that has never been kept for more than a few months in the aquarium. This is probably the juvenile of a fish that grows much larger.
WATER CONDITIONS: Warm, clear water with heavy aeration and lots of room; pH 6.0-7.2; temperature 23-30°C.
SIZE: The small fish shown in the photo is 8.4 cm long, with a lovely golden color. It has the larger, darker spots when it gets larger. Probably reaches 30 cm.
FOOD REQUIREMENTS: Prefers living foods such as daphnia and brine shrimp, but will quickly acclimate to a typical aquarium diet supplemented with freeze-dried or frozen live foods.

Anostomus proximus Garman • Banded Anostomid

RANGE: Amazon and Rio Negro in Brazil.
HABITS: Found in shallow streams and rivers; sometimes jumps for insects, but only when hungry. Prefers small, quiet environments but needs a large aquarium of 200+ liters in capacity.
WATER CONDITIONS: Water must be warm and clear with lots of aeration. Temperature between 25-30°C with pH 6.0-7.0.
SIZE: The known specimens were under 25 cm.
FOOD REQUIREMENTS: Brine shrimp and daphnia are preferred, but they take dried food when hungry.

Anostomus plicatus Eigenmann • Black Anostomus

RANGE: Northern Amazon to the Guianas.
HABITS: Never spawned in an aquarium, though this male is in obvious breeding colors. A fast-moving fish that readily jumps from an uncovered aquarium.
WATER CONDITIONS: Warm, clear water, heavily aerated. pH 6.0-7.0; temperature 23-30°C.
SIZE: To 26.5 cm.
FOOD REQUIREMENTS: Its small upturned mouth means it digs around for small living creatures like daphnia, tubifex, and the like. Difficult to acclimate to non-living foods.

Anostomus anostomus

Anostomus taeniatus

Anostomus trimaculatus

Leporinus badueli

Anostomus gracilis

Anostomus proxlmus

Anostomus garmani

Anostomus plicatus

Synaptolaemus cingulatus Myers & Fernandez-Yepez • Funny-mouthed Anostomid

RANGE: Found only in the intersection of the Upper Orinoco and Rio Casiquiare and in the Rio Xingu.

HABITS: Found in shallow streams under 1 m deep, where it pokes about on the bottom for small living crustaceans.

WATER CONDITIONS: Clear, still water. Requires a large tank with a messy bottom. Turns on its back to feed! Temperature 24-30°C; pH 6.4-7.2.

SIZE: To 17.5 cm.

FOOD REQUIREMENTS: Must be fed small live foods like newly hatched brine shrimp and daphnia. Does not live long unless it has these foods and similar living ones.

Sartor respectus Myers & de Carvalho • Peculiar-mouthed Anostomid

RANGE: Rio Xingu, Brazil.

HABITS: Found in very small creeks that are heavily laden with fallen vegetation in which they poke about for food. Has never been kept for long in an aquarium.

WATER CONDITIONS: Found in water of pH 6.4-7.0; temperature 24-30°C.

SIZE: To 22.5 cm.

FOOD REQUIREMENTS: Swims about on its back, searching the bottom for small living crustaceans.

Hemiodopsis sterni Gery • Stern's Hemiodus

RANGE: Upper Juruena River, Brazil.

HABITS: Peaceful but should be kept with other very active fish.

WATER CONDITIONS: Neutral to slightly alkaline. Temperature 23 to 26°C.

SIZE: To about 10 cm.

FOOD REQUIREMENTS: Dried foods accepted, but live or frozen foods needed occasionally. Vegetable substitutes like lettuce leaves are recommended.

Hemiodopsis immaculatus (Kner) • Silver Hemiodus

RANGE: Rio Negro and upper Amazon.

HABITS: A high-jumping fish that sailed over the seines with which the author (HRA) was trying to catch them. Must be kept in covered tanks. Never spawned. Requires lots of room.

WATER CONDITIONS: Acid water of pH 5.6-6.8; warm, between 25 and 30°C.

SIZE: To 22 cm.

FOOD REQUIREMENTS: Live small crustaceans. This is a small-mouthed fish.

Hemiodopsis gracilis (Guenther) • Slender Hemiodus

RANGE: Guyana and the middle Amazon River region.

HABITS: Peaceful toward other fishes. An active swimmer and skillful jumper.

WATER CONDITIONS: Soft and slightly acid. Temperature about 24°C.

SIZE: To about 15 cm; imported specimens about half this size.

FOOD REQUIREMENTS: Greedy eaters which should get green vegetable foods in addition to prepared and freeze-dried foods.

Hemiodopsis microlepis (Kner) • Red-tailed Hemiodus

RANGE: Taken in the Rio Madeira, near Humaita, Brazil, by the author (HRA). Probably widespread.

HABITS: This fish is called H. microlepis in the aquarium trade, but it is probably an undescribed species. It has never been kept for long in an aquarium.

WATER CONDITIONS: Clear, relatively cool water around 23-26°C. pH 6.2-7.2.

SIZE: To 20 cm.

FOOD REQUIREMENTS: Live foods; probably can be trained to other foods, but no reports have reached the aquarium literature yet.

Hemiodus unimaculatus (Bloch) • Yellow-tailed Hemiodus

RANGE: Found by the author (HRA) in Humaita, Brazil, along with Hemiodopsis microlepis. Probably more extensive in range.

HABITS: Never brought back alive.

WATER CONDITIONS: The water in which they were collected had a pH of 6.2-7.2 and the temperature varied from 23-26°C.

SIZE: About 19 cm.

FOOD REQUIREMENTS: Its stomach contained small crustaceans and insects.

Synaptolaemus cingulatus

Sartor respectus

1

2

Hemiodopsis sterni

Hemiodopsis immaculatus

3

4

Hemiodopsis gracilis

Hemiodopsis gracilis

5

6

Hemiodopsis of the *microlepis* group

Hemiodus unimaculatus

7

8

Parodon piracicabae Eigenmann • Brazilian Darter Tetra

RANGE: Tiete-Parana River basins in southeastern Brazil.
HABITS: Darts along the bottom in jerky movements. It has never been spawned, but would make a wonderful scavenger for the aquarium in which dried food is used.
WATER CONDITIONS: They thrive under almost all aquarium conditions even in unheated aquaria that stay about room temperature.
SIZE: Up to 7.5 cm.
FOOD REQUIREMENTS: Scavengers on the bottom of aquaria, picking up everything including live foods.

Parodon caliensis Boulenger • Barred Darter Tetra

RANGE: Found in the Andes Mountains in Colombia in cold water at up to 1 km in altitude.
HABITS: In fast-moving streams the fish scouts the bottom over sand and stone searching for anything edible.
WATER CONDITIONS: Prefers colder waters in an unheated tank, though it lives in warmer waters typical of tropical aquaria. The water must be highly aerated.
SIZE: To 5 cm.
FOOD REQUIREMENTS: Eats just about everything small enough to ingest.

Bivibranchia "Gery" • Spotted Sandsucker

RANGE: Surinam. An undescribed species of a poorly known genus.
HABITS: Digs its snout into the sand, where it forages for small crustaceans. It has special skeletal adaptations that enable it to sift the sand and filter it for food organisms.
WATER CONDITIONS: Likes sandy bottoms to poke around in. Tolerates most aquarium water conditions.
SIZE: To 10 cm.
FOOD REQUIREMENTS: Seems to eat everything small enough to ingest. A bottom-feeder.

Hemiodopsis goeldii (Steindachner) • Goeldi's Hemiodus

RANGE: Guianas and the Rio Xingu, Brazil.
HABITS: Peaceful and highly active; likely to jump out if the tank is not covered.
WATER CONDITIONS: Neutral to slightly alkaline. Temperature 24 to 27°C.
SIZE: To about 15 cm.
FOOD REQUIREMENTS: Prepared foods accepted, but likes to nibble on plants occasionally. Lettuce or spinach leaf should be provided for this reason.

Parodon pongoense (Allen) • Pongo Pongo

RANGE: Peruvian Amazon, Ecuador and Colombia.
HABITS: Peaceful; prefer to school.
WATER CONDITIONS: Soft acid water is preferred. Temperature from 23 to 30°C.
SIZE: About 5 cm.
FOOD REQUIREMENTS: Prefers live foods but can readily take frozen brine shrimp and prepared dry foods.

Parodon affinis Steindachner • Paraguay Darter Tetra

RANGE: La Plata, Parana, and Rio Paraguay basins. Very common in its range. Often still called *P. paraguayensis*.
HABITS: Stays on the bottom moving about in a jerky, darter-like fashion. Makes a good scavenger. The six bands on the back are hardly visible in this photo. Has never been spawned.
WATER CONDITIONS: Likes highly aerated waters and cool temperatures. Thrives in unheated tanks at room temperatures.
SIZE: To 6.5 cm.
FOOD REQUIREMENTS: Eats everything small enough to ingest. An active feeder.

Hemiodopsis parnaguae (Eigenmann & Henn) • One-spot Hemiodus

RANGE: Found in the Rio Parnagua. There are many fish that look like this found throughout northern South American waters connected to the Amazon.
HABITS: A small-mouthed fish that jumps, so keep the aquarium covered. Has never been spawned in the aquarium.
WATER CONDITIONS: Prefers warm, clear water with a pH of 6.0-7.0 and temperature of 24-30°C.
SIZE: To 20 cm.
FOOD REQUIREMENTS: Prefers small live foods but easily acclimates to any aquarium diet.

Hemiodopsis semitaeniatus (Kner) • Black-and-white-tailed Hemiodus

RANGE: Rio Guapore and Rio Madeira, Brazil.
HABITS: A middle-water fish that stays on the bottom when young (the fish in the photo is a juvenile). They are great jumpers, so keep their aquarium covered.
WATER CONDITIONS: Slightly acid waters with a pH 6.5-7.4. Temperature 23-30°C.
SIZE: Probably reaches 20 cm.
FOOD REQUIREMENTS: Prefers live foods but quickly acclimates to an aquarium diet.

Parodon piracicabae

Parodon pongoense

Parodon caliensis

Parodon affinis

Bivibranchia "Gery"

Hemiodopsis parnaguae

Hemiodopsis goeldii

Hemiodopsis semitaeniatus

Semaprochilodus taeniurus (Valenciennes) • Silver Prochilodus

RANGE: Amazon basin.
HABITS: Peaceful, but very likely to nibble at plants; tanks should be kept covered at all times, as the fish jump.
WATER CONDITIONS: Soft, slightly alkaline water. These are active swimmers, and they like a roomy tank. Temperature 23 to 26°C.
SIZE: To 30 cm.
FOOD REQUIREMENTS: Mostly vegetable foods should be offered, such as lettuce or spinach.

Semaprochilodus theraponura (Fowler) • Flag-tailed Prochilodus

RANGE: Guyana and the central Amazon region.
HABITS: Peaceful, but its vegetarian habits may lead it to nip plants; a skilled jumper, so tank must be kept covered.
WATER CONDITIONS: Soft, slightly alkaline water. Temperature 23 to 26°C.
SIZE: To 35 cm; imported specimens seldom exceed 13 cm.
FOOD REQUIREMENTS: Mostly vegetable food should be offered, such as lettuce leaves, spinach or boiled oatmeal; live foods also accepted.

Chilodus punctatus Mueller & Troschel • Spotted Headstander

RANGE: Northeastern South America between the Amazon and the Orinoco.
HABITS: Very peaceful; pays no attention to the other fishes. Rather shy, and should be moved as little as possible.
WATER CONDITIONS: Slightly acid to neutral water, very soft. Temperature should range between 24 and 27°C.
SIZE: About 9 cm.
FOOD REQUIREMENTS: Diet should be largely vegetarian; lettuce or spinach leaves are nibbled frequently. Some dried food and live food also.

Caenotropus maculosus (Eigenmann) • Slender Headstander

RANGE: The northern rivers of South America that eventually connect to the Amazon.
HABITS: The downturned inferior mouth indicates that it feeds from the bottom. A very shy fish, it should be maintained in a heavily planted aquarium.
WATER CONDITIONS: Prefers clear, aerated water of pH 6.0-7.0; water temperatures should be between 25-30°C.
SIZE: To 12 cm.
FOOD REQUIREMENTS: Requires small living foods such as daphnia, brine shrimp, and tubificid worms.

Chilodus "Black-band" • Black-banded Headstander

RANGE: Throughout Amazonia in Brazil.
HABITS: Look closely at this spotted headstander. It looks much like *Caenotropus*, but the mouth is different. This species has an upturned mouth making it a *Chilodus*, but it is as yet undescribed. If the mouth were turned down it would be *Caenotropus*.
WATER CONDITIONS: Found under most water conditions in small creeks. They do well in aquaria under normal temperatures from 23-30°C, with a pH between 6.0 and 7.2. Every white water river system has a fish that looks like this one.
SIZE: About 12 cm.
FOOD REQUIREMENTS: Must be fed living foods, which it picks off the bottom most of the time. Without live foods it dies within 90 days.

Caenotropus labyrinthicus (Kner) • Giant Headstander

RANGE: Found throughout the Amazon basin including the Rio Orinoco and the Rio Parnaiba. Widely distributed in small creeks with sandy bottoms.
HABITS: Stays mostly on the bottom. If large chunks of wood or stone are in the tank it continuously picks on them for small animal food. Note the inferior mouth.
WATER CONDITIONS: Cool, clear water. Sandy bottoms and bits of driftwood make it "feel at home." pH 6.0-7.2; water temperature should be between 23-30°C.
SIZE: Up to 12.5 cm.
FOOD REQUIREMENTS: Requires small live foods if it is to thrive. A difficult fish to keep alive for a long time.

Parodon suborbitale Valenciennes • Golden Darter Tetra

RANGE: Thus far found only in Venezuela.
HABITS: Scoots about the bottom of the aquarium and prefers a sandy bottom with many hiding places. Congregates in schools and swims in tight circles.
WATER CONDITIONS: Prefers highly aerated water that is as clear as possible. pH 6.0-7.0; temperature 25-28°C.
SIZE: To 6 cm.
FOOD REQUIREMENTS: Small living foods, especially baby brine shrimp.

Semaprochilodus taeniurus (juvenile)

Semaprochilodus taeniurus

Semaprochilodus theraponura

Chilodus "Black-band"

Chilodus punctatus

Caenotropus labyrinthicus

Caenotropus maculosus

Parodon suborbitale

131

Semaprochilodus squamilentus Fowler • Sailfinned Prochilodus

RANGE: Upper Rio Negro into Colombia and Peru; northeastern Brazil.
HABITS: A high-jumping fish that travels in schools and seems to migrate past such natural barricades as small cataracts and falls.
WATER CONDITIONS: Not fussy about water chemistry, but likes warm water. Very difficult to keep in an aquarium when they are large.
SIZE: Grows to 25 cm or larger.
FOOD REQUIREMENTS: They seem to eat anything in small quantities, but they are at starvation level in most cases under aquarium conditions.

Prochilodus ortonianus Cope • Gray Prochilodus

RANGE: Brazilian Amazon; a similar fish is found in Guyana.
HABITS: The fish shown was discovered by the author (HRA) in the Rio Urubu along with several other prochilodid fishes. It thrived for several years in a large (400-liter) aquarium that was heavily vegetated.
WATER CONDITIONS: Typical aquarium conditions. pH 6.2-7.2; temperature 23-30°C.
SIZE: To 25 cm, perhaps larger. The fish shown here is a juvenile.
FOOD REQUIREMENTS: Eats the usual aquarium diet.

Curimata lineopunctata Boulenger • Line-spotted Curimata

RANGE: Found in the Rio Calima, Colombia, by the author (HRA).
HABITS: A well-defined species that does well in the aquarium as long as it retains its juvenile teeth. A bit aggressive and a good jumper.
WATER CONDITIONS: Cool, clear water with a pH 6.0-7.0 and a temperature of 23-30°C.
SIZE: It is not known how large they grow, but the juveniles reached 10-12 cm before they lost their teeth.
FOOD REQUIREMENTS: The teeth of the juveniles enable them to accept most foods, but the toothless adults soon die because aquarists have not figured out how to feed them.

Prochilodus nigricans Agassiz • Black Prochilodus

RANGE: Wide-ranging throughout western Brazil in Amazonia.
HABITS: This is a common food fish with very firm flesh that is difficult to pierce with a harpoon and requires a very sharp knife. The meat is delicious and chewy and is a favorite of the Indians.
WATER CONDITIONS: Highly aerated, moving water. Does not thrive under aquarium conditions.
SIZE: Over 30 cm.
FOOD REQUIREMENTS: They have never been kept long in an aquarium, and nothing is known of their feeding habits.

Curimata ciliata (Mueller & Troschel) • Hairy Curimata

RANGE: Northern South America, primarily imported from Guyana by the pet trade.
HABITS: When young this species has sharp teeth and they require different handling than the adult form. Youngsters may bite and attack each other over food and territorial jealousies.
WATER CONDITIONS: Cool, clear water with a temperature of 23-29°C and a pH 6.2-7.0.
SIZE: Probably reaches 20 cm but small specimens are brought in for the aquarium trade.
FOOD REQUIREMENTS: Young fish eat a normal aquarium diet and do very well on almost everything; as they get older you must watch what they eat carefully and only offer them that diet or they will slowly starve.

Curimata isognatha Eigenmann & Eigenmann • Chunky Curimata

RANGE: The Amazon basin south to the Pantanal in Brazil.
HABITS: A large fish that is easily confused with many other curimata species because it has no significant markings and is just plain silvery. It is longer and shallower in form than most species.
WATER CONDITIONS: Very tolerable of many poor aquarium situations and thrives in waters from 22-30°C with a pH of 6.0-7.4.
SIZE: Reaches 26 cm.
FOOD REQUIREMENTS: As a juvenile it has teeth and chases live foods, including small fishes; as an adult it eats a normal aquarium diet, but they never live very long in captivity.

Curimata elegans Steindachner • Spotted Curimata

RANGE: The Amazon basin south to Rio de Janeiro area.
HABITS: This fish was collected by the author (HRA) from the same area and at the same time he collected C. isognata. They are similar in appearance until you notice the body proportions and the spot in the dorsal. All Curimata with a spot in the dorsal are said to be in the "elegans" group.
WATER CONDITIONS: Takes many different aquarium conditions. Temperature 22-30°C and pH 6.0-7.4.
SIZE: Reaches 25 cm.
FOOD REQUIREMENTS: Juveniles have sharp teeth and use them for feeding. Adults present a problem in feeding and don't last more than a few months in captivity.

Semaprochilodus squamilentus

Prochilodus nigricans

Prochilodus ortonianus

Curimata ciliata

Curimata ciliata (juvenile)

Curimata isognatha

Curimata lineopunctata

Curimata elegans

Curimatopsis macrolepis Steindachner • Shiny-scaled Curimata

RANGE: Northern South America from the Amazon to the Guianas.
HABITS: The larger the scales on a curimata the better chance you have to keep it alive. This fish lasted a long time in the author's tank, over a year. It lost its teeth and still accepted the flake food diet.
WATER CONDITIONS: Normal aquarium conditions suited it with temperature about 25°C and a pH of 6.8.
SIZE: Never grew larger than 170 mm but it probably does in nature.
FOOD REQUIREMENTS: Normal flake food suits it fine.

Curimatella alburna (Mueller & Troschel) • Common Curimata

RANGE: Very common throughout northern South America from the Amazon Basin to Rio Aguaro, Venezuela.
HABITS: For some reason or other this fish is always speckled with the encysted larvae of parasites. They don't seem to bother the fish and in time drop off and probably die.
WATER CONDITIONS: They thrive under almost all aquarium conditions, but a pH of 6.8 and water temperature of 26°C suit them well in captivity.
SIZE: To about 20 cm.
FOOD REQUIREMENTS: Eats everything, especially when young, since they have teeth as juveniles and lose them as adults.

Curimata vittata Kner • Banded Curimata

RANGE: Rio Madeira near Humaita, Brazil, but reported from all over Brazil.
HABITS: This specimen doesn't show it, but the males have elongated dorsal and caudal fins. The bands over the top half of the body number about 8; the tiny spot at the base of the adipose is important diagnostically.
WATER CONDITIONS: Thrives in clear, heavily aerated water with a pH between 6.8 and 7.2 and a water temperature of 25-30°C.
SIZE: Probably grows to 25 cm.
FOOD REQUIREMENTS: Easy to feed as a juvenile with teeth; very difficult to feed as an adult.

Curimata gilberti Quoy & Gaimard • Gilbert's Curimata

RANGE: Amazon basin. A very common fish that is imported in large quantities for the aquarium trade.
HABITS: They are very easy to care for as long as they have their juvenile teeth, but once their teeth are lost they are difficult to feed. These did well for over a year on Gordon's formula and flake food.
WATER CONDITIONS: Thrive under most aquarium conditions if they are kept in a large tank (over 200 liters) with plenty of plants and sunlight.
SIZE: Probably stays under 25 cm.
FOOD REQUIREMENTS: Juveniles take flake foods readily.

Curimatopsis evelynae Gery • Evelyn Axelrod's Curimata

RANGE: Upper Rio Meta in Colombia; probably more widespread.
HABITS: Probably the most beautiful curimata. The photo shows two males; the females are not as brightly colored, but this species seems to stay small as only toothless fish were collected by the author (HRA).
WATER CONDITIONS: Does well in ordinary aquaria with a pH about 6.8 and a water temperature about 26°C.
SIZE: About 10 cm.
FOOD REQUIREMENTS: Eats normal aquarium fare, with live food supplements.

Curimata "Lineofortis" • Black-lined Curimata

RANGE: A very rare and probably undescribed fish caught with Symphysodon discus in the Rio Negro. This is undoubtedly the juvenile of a large Curimata of the elegans group, but it has never lived long enough to find out what it will grow into.
HABITS: Loses its teeth at about 10 cm and then becomes a problem to feed.
WATER CONDITIONS: Did well at 25°C with a pH of 6.7.
SIZE: Not known, but probably grows to more than the 10 cm that this specimen reached.
FOOD REQUIREMENTS: Eats everything as long as it has its juvenile teeth, then it dies from starvation.

Curimata latior Spix • Gasterotomus

RANGE: The Amazon basin south to the La Plata of Argentina.
HABITS: A deep-water fish that grows fairly large and is a food fish all through the jungle. Its meat is delicious.
WATER CONDITIONS: Does not do well at all in the typical home aquarium as it requires lots of room. Probably needs a constant temperature of about 24°C with a pH about 6.8, as that is the condition of the water in which the author (HRA) found the fish.
SIZE: Over 25 cm.
FOOD REQUIREMENTS: Not known as they have never been kept in an aquarium long enough to find out.

Curimata rhomboides (Eigenmann & Eigenmann) • Silver Curimata

RANGE: Throughout the Amazon basin in Brazil.
HABITS: The Indians eat this fish in large quantities. The flesh is delicious and was eaten by the author (HRA) for weeks on end, but it is so tough it is almost impossible to put a hook into it (for use in catching piranhas).
WATER CONDITIONS: Amazon water that is clear and moving, with a pH of 6.2-7.0 and a water temperature between 25° and 30°C.
SIZE: About 25 cm, perhaps a bit larger.
FOOD REQUIREMENTS: This was a large specimen about 16 cm long that had already lost its teeth and was difficult to keep alive. It died after 3 months. The white spots on the sides of the fish are a reflection of the author's camera.

Curimatopsis evelynae

Curimatopsis macrolepis

Curimatella alburna

Curimata "Lineofortis"

Curimata vittata

Curimata latior

Curimata gilberti

Curimata rhomboides

Curimatopsis macrolepis Steindachner • Shiny-scaled Curimata

RANGE: From the Amazon basin north to the Guianas.
HABITS: These are two males in good color. They thrived in the author's (HRA) tank for more than one year. They might have spawned, for the female kept with them lost her girth about the time they lost their color.
WATER CONDITIONS: The usual aquarium conditions of pH 6.8 and water at 25°C.
SIZE: The males reached 15 cm and the female reached 17 cm, but they were probably stunted from growing up in an aquarium.
FOOD REQUIREMENTS: They did well on a normal aquarium diet of mostly flake foods.

Thoracocharax securis (Filippi) • Pectorosus Hatchetfish

RANGE: Upper Amazon in shallow sidestreams.
HABITS: Stays on top of the water, leaping for insects. Their aquarium must be covered. They cannot tolerate cold water.
WATER CONDITIONS: Warm, aerated water. Keep the surface film broken by an airstream.
SIZE: About 7.5 cm. A population with a much larger maximum size has been reported but never seen by any of the authors.
FOOD REQUIREMENTS: Floating vestigial-winged *Drosophila* is their best food, along with mosquito larvae and some floating dried foods.

Gasteropelecus sternicla (Linnaeus) • Silver Hatchetfish

RANGE: Peruvian Amazon, Guianas and the Orinoco Basin in Venezuela.
HABITS: A top-feeder which spends most of its time waiting quietly for a passing insect.
WATER CONDITIONS: Prefers warm, soft water with a pH of about 6.4. Temperature 24 to 26°C.
SIZE: About 6 cm maximum.
FOOD REQUIREMENTS: Floating foods, wingless *Drosophila* flies and floating bits of frozen brine shrimp.

Carnegiella strigata strigata (Guenther) • Marbled Hatchetfish

RANGE: Guyana, middle and upper Amazon region, especially in jungle streams.
HABITS: Occurs in schools near the surface. In the aquarium they are peaceful, but are likely to jump if a cover is not provided.
WATER CONDITIONS: Soft, slightly acid water. Temperature about 26°C.
SIZE: About 8 cm.
FOOD REQUIREMENTS: Will readily accept dried foods which float on the surface, but anything which falls to the bottom cannot be picked up.

Curimata spilura Guenther • Diamond-spot Curimata

RANGE: Amazon basin to Guyana; probably more widespread.
HABITS: This is a relatively small species that might do well in the aquarium under the proper circumstances. It likes to peck on wood upon which algae are growing.
WATER CONDITIONS: Typical aquarium conditions of 25°C and pH 6.8 are satisfactory.
SIZE: Under 12.5 cm.
FOOD REQUIREMENTS: Seems to do well in a heavily planted tank with a normal aquarium diet consisting mainly of flake foods and daphnia.

Thoracocharax stellatus (Kner) • Silver Hatchetfish

RANGE: Amazon, Paraguay, Orinoco basin to Venezuela.
HABITS: An extremely peaceful surface fish; a good jumper, so its tanks should be covered.
WATER CONDITIONS: Soft, slightly acid water a necessity; this fish dies easily if maintained in hard, alkaline water. Temperature 23 to 26°C.
SIZE: 8 cm.
FOOD REQUIREMENTS: Floating foods of all kinds taken, provided they can be swallowed.

Carnegiella myersi Fernandez-Yepez • Myers's Hatchetfish; Pygmy Hatchet

RANGE: Peru and Bolivia on the eastern side of the Andes.
HABITS: A top-swimming fish that is very difficult to maintain in the aquarium without small floating live foods such as *Drosophila* and mosquito larvae.
WATER CONDITIONS: Warm water with a neutral pH and a temperature about 26°C. The surface of their water must be kept clean by a constant stream of bubbles.
SIZE: A small fish about 4 cm long.
FOOD REQUIREMENTS: Must have small floating foods, preferably insects.

Carnegiella strigata fasciata (Garman) • Marbled Hatchetfish

RANGE: Guyana.
HABITS: Found in shaded pools where it leaps from the water for insects flying very close to the surface.
WATER CONDITIONS: Very sensitive to temperature and water changes. Prefers very soft, slightly acid water. Temperature 23 to 26°C.
SIZE: Under 8 cm.
FOOD REQUIREMENTS: This species must have small live food. Dropping wingless *Drosophila* flies onto the surface is an ideal way to feed this species. They also take small amounts of floating foods containing brine shrimp.

Curimatopsis macrolepis (male)

Curimata spilura

Thoracocharax securis

Thoracocharax stellatus

Gasteropelecus sternicla

Carnegiella myersi

Carnegiella strigata strigata

Carnegiella strigata fasciata

Carnegiella marthae Myers • Black-winged Hatchetfish

RANGE: Venezuela, Peru, the Brazilian Amazon, Rio Negro and the Orinoco.
HABITS: Active jumpers; have to be kept in a covered tank, preferably a long one. Peaceful; may be kept with other non-aggressive species.
WATER CONDITIONS: Soft, slightly acid water. Temperature 24 to 27°C.
SIZE: 4 cm; usually a bit smaller.
FOOD REQUIREMENTS: Floating prepared foods eaten when very hungry, but live foods like mosquito larvae or wingless fruitflies are best.

Colossoma bidens (Spix) • Red-bellied Pacu

RANGE: Brazilian Amazon basin.
HABITS: Swims in open water and is very quick at escaping from a net by jumping over it. Looks like a piranha but doesn't have the large, sharp teeth. These fish are largely vegetarians though they can eat almost anything. The black blotch on the gill plate is characteristic of the species.
WATER CONDITIONS: Needs large tanks to thrive, but gets along fairly well in 100-liter tanks if sufficiently aerated. pH 6.0-6.8 and water temperatures between 25-30°C.
SIZE: Grows fairly large, perhaps up to 36 cm.
FOOD REQUIREMENTS: Prefers softer vegetation such as spinach leaves, but also accepts flake foods.

Colossoma brachypomum (Cuvier) • Black Pacu

RANGE: This fish occurs with regularity in the Amazon basin but seems to migrate for spawning.
HABITS: This is a magnificent fish that commands a high price in the market because of its rarity. It has never been bred, but it probably will be as soon as enough specimens are available.
WATER CONDITIONS: Found in waters with an acid pH from 4.8-6.8 and with temperatures from 24-28°C.
SIZE: May grow much larger than the 20 cm known in the aquarium trade.
FOOD REQUIREMENTS: A vegetarian that quickly acclimates to an aquarium diet.

Colossoma oculus (Cope) • Red-finned Pacu

RANGE: Branches of the Amazon.
HABITS: Not to be trusted with small fishes.
WATER CONDITIONS: Soft, slightly acid water is indicated but is probably of no great importance. Temperature 21 to 27°C.
SIZE: Up to 20 cm.
FOOD REQUIREMENTS: Very reluctant to accept dry foods, but will take live and frozen foods.

Mylossoma paraguayensis Norman • Paraguayan Metynnis

RANGE: Rio Paraguay.
HABITS: A vegetarian that swims in open waters and is often caught on hook and line. A food fish for the poor river people.
WATER CONDITIONS: Cooler water from 20-26°C; pH close to normal, 6.8-7.2
SIZE: Grows fairly large, perhaps larger than 25 cm.
FOOD REQUIREMENTS: Prefers vegetation but does well on the usual aquarium diet.

Mylossoma duriventre (Cuvier) • Hard-bellied Characin

RANGE: Southern Amazon region, Paraguay, Parana, La Plata.
HABITS: Peaceful toward other fishes, but larger specimens are likely to damage plants.
WATER CONDITIONS: Soft, slightly acid water in a well-planted tank. Temperature 24 to 28°C.
SIZE: To 23 cm in their natural waters; imported specimens much smaller.
FOOD REQUIREMENTS: All kinds of live and frozen foods, supplemented with some vegetable substances like chopped spinach, etc.

Mylossoma aureum (Spix) • Silver Dollar

RANGE: Common in the Amazon basin.
HABITS: A deep-water fish usually caught by hook and line. A staple food for the river people; very delicious. Slashes about 1 cm apart are made in the sides and the fish is fried.
WATER CONDITIONS: Clear, aerated waters. pH 6.2-7.0; temperature between 24-30°C.
SIZE: May reach 25 cm.
FOOD REQUIREMENTS: A vegetarian in nature, but it thrives on a normal aquarium diet of flake foods.

Mylossoma acanthogaster (Valenciennes) • Venezuelan Silver Dollar

RANGE: Venezuela, especially Lake Maracaibo; northern Brazil.
HABITS: A nice fish when small. The fish illustrated is very small, about 3.2 cm. It keeps changing colors as it gets larger until it looks like *M. aureum* except for the shorter anal fin base.
WATER CONDITIONS: Prefers shaded, cool pools with pH 6.8-7.2 and temperatures between 22 and 26°C. Probably tolerates a much wider variety of conditions.
SIZE: Up to 18.5 cm.
FOOD REQUIREMENTS: A vegetarian, but quickly acclimates to flake foods.

Carnegiella marthae

Colossoma bidens

Colossoma brachypomum

Colossoma oculus

Mylossoma paraguayensis

Mylossoma duriventre

Mylossoma aureum

Mylossoma acanthogaster

139

Myleus pacu (Schomburgk) • Brown Metynnis

RANGE: Guianas and Amazon Basin.
HABITS: Depending upon its age, it has different colors, needs, and habits. The young fish are brown-colored as shown in the photo on the facing page, but as adults they become silver except during spawning time when the male may be flushed with red or have red splotches.
WATER CONDITIONS: Only acquire small, brown specimens, the larger ones are too difficult to maintain. The small ones are vegetarians that acclimate to a flake food diet. Normal aquarium conditions suit them fine when small: pH 6.8, temperature 25-28°C.
SIZE: Probably exceeds 200 mm.
FOOD REQUIREMENTS: Youngsters eat flake foods while adults are basically vegetarians. They like small fishes, too.

Myleus rubripinnis (Mueller & Troschel) • Redhook Metynnis

RANGE: Guyana and Surinam to Brazil.
HABITS: Peaceful and shy if kept by itself, but less so if kept in small groups; cannot be safely kept with vegetation because of their plant-eating tendencies.
WATER CONDITIONS: Clean, soft and highly oxygenated water is necessary. Temperature (at least for breeding) should be about 25 to 27°C.
SIZE: Matures at about 9 to 12 cm; maximum size not known.
FOOD REQUIREMENTS: Takes a variety of foods, but their diet must contain vegetable matter.

Myelus ternetzi (Norman) • Paramyloplus

RANGE: Northern South America; the Guianas.
HABITS: Their actions are typical. A very active fish. They have never been spawned. They require lots of swimming space in a large tank.
WATER CONDITIONS: Clear, aerated water with a pH of 6.8 and a water temperature of 26°C. These conditions can vary quite a bit because the fish are very hardy.
SIZE: They grow to over 200 mm and are eaten by the local people in the jungle.
FOOD REQUIREMENTS: They eat flake foods in the aquarium, especially the youngsters. Adults like small live foods, too.

Metynnis argenteus Ahl • Silver Metynnis

RANGE: Very common throughout northern South America. This specimen is from the Rio Aguaro, Venezuela.
HABITS: Metynnis comprise another group of species that are poorly known because of their wide range and their color changes as they mature. Almost all look alike when fully grown and not in breeding condition.
WATER CONDITIONS: Deep water is preferred when they are large. The water should be clear and aerated and with a pH of 6.2-7.0 and a temperature between 24-30°C.
SIZE: Exceeds 120 mm.
FOOD REQUIREMENTS: Flake foods are accepted by the youngsters but the adult needs more substantial dietary supplements in the form of small living fishes like baby guppies.

Myleus micans (Reinhardt) • Golden Dollar; Sheephead Metynnis

RANGE: Sao Francisco River, Brazil.
HABITS: M. pacu and M. micans are often confused with each other. Both have a characteristic "sheep look." Both are brown when small but micans has more anal and dorsal fin rays. Both are plain in adulthood (like the photo on the facing page) and males of both species are red splotched during breeding season.
WATER CONDITIONS: Normal aquarium water is fine, with a pH about 6.8 and a water temperature near 25°C.
SIZE: About 200 mm.
FOOD REQUIREMENTS: The small ones eat normal flake foods, as do the larger specimens, but the larger specimens need little fishes too.

Myleus rubripinnis (Mueller & Troschel) • Red Hook Metynnis

This is the female of the species; compare it to the male in photograph # 3. The spots and blotches on the males are only evident during the spawning season which usually occurs around Christmas time depending upon the flood conditions in their particular habitat. The identification of almost all species of Myleus, Metynni, etc. is a mess since they change color and finnage as they grow and mature. Almost all have red blotches during spawning time. But that doesn't matter since their care, feeding, and breeding are almost identical.

Myleus schomburgki (Jardine) • Black-barred Metynnis

RANGE: Throughout the rivers that run south of the Amazon. Varieties exist in the Xingu, Araguaia, and Madeira Rivers of Brazil.
HABITS: Easily recognizable by the broad vertical band on its side. There is more than one species with this characteristic but the fishes of this genus are very poorly known because they change so radically as they mature. One other species with the black band has black fins.
WATER CONDITIONS: They prefer large aquaria with heavily aerated water with a pH between 6.2 and 6.8 and a water temperature ranging from 23-30°C.
SIZE: May reach 225 mm.
FOOD REQUIREMENTS: Young fish eagerly take flake food but the adults require some live foods and lots of soft vegetation in their diets.

Metynnis luna Cope • Moon Metynnis

RANGE: Very common in northern South America.
HABITS: The red spot shown on the specimen here is the remnant of a lot of red spots characteristic of a breeding male. Normally all the fish are silver and only the roundness of their bodies is diagnostic of the species for aquarists.
WATER CONDITIONS: They require lots of aquarium space with a slightly acid to neutral water (pH 6.4-7.0) at a temperature of about 26°C.
SIZE: To 200 mm.
FOOD REQUIREMENTS: The small mouth and numerous gill rakers (60-62) indicate it feeds on small items. Appreciates vegetable matter in with its regular food. This is usually provided with certain flake foods offered by major manufacturers.

Myleus pacu

Myleus micans

Myleus rubripinnis

Myleus rubripinnis

Myleus ternetzi

Myleus schomburgki

Metynnis argenteus

Metynnis luna

1
2
3
4
5
6
7
8

141

Metynnis maculatus (Kner) • Guapore Metynnis

RANGE: Rio Guapore and Rio Xingu, Brazil.
HABITS: The fish illustrated on the facing page is a female in breeding color. A normal breeding male is blood red on its flanks and the edges of its dorsal fin plus lots of black pigmentation in the body and fins. Out of season the female only has a bit of black in its fins.
WATER CONDITIONS: It likes deep, clear water with a pH between 6.3 and 7.0 and a water temperature of between 24 and 30°C.
SIZE: Specimens up to 120 mm have been caught but it might grow larger.
FOOD REQUIREMENTS: Likes live foods but readily takes flake foods with lots of vegetable material in them. Chews up plants in the aquarium.

Serrasalmus gibbus Castelnau • Silver-scaled Piranha

RANGE: Northern South America.
HABITS: A dangerous fish in the aquarium. It eats other fishes and may bite your hand. They are more dangerous in the aquarium than in nature where they never attack people if they have enough food. The black border on the tail is complete.
WATER CONDITIONS: Not particular about water as long as it's clean and unpolluted. A pH between 6.0 and 7.2 is tolerated as is a temperature between 23-30°C.
SIZE: Probably reaches 300 mm.
FOOD REQUIREMENTS: Even though they can be trained to eat pellet foods, they do best on live fishes (goldfish in most cases). Don't feed them too many fish or they will only eat the back half!

Serrasalmus spilopleura Kner • Fire-mouth Piranha

RANGE: Amazon basin, Brazil.
HABITS: A scavenger in the Amazon and its larger streams. Easily caught on hook and line with a piece of meat or fishes as bait. Usually possible to catch 50 an hour when you find any at all. They are dangerous in the aquarium so don't put your hand in with them.
WATER CONDITIONS: Clear water with a pH of 6.0-7.0 and a temperature of 23-30°C.
SIZE: May reach 300 mm in nature but usually a bit smaller.
FOOD REQUIREMENTS: Bulky foods such as chunks of fish or bit of meat. Usually not interested in normal aquarium food.

Serrasalmus denticulatus Cuvier • Big-toothed Piranha; Pirambeba

RANGE: Mostly Guianan, perhaps also Amazonian.
HABITS: This fish is often confused by both aquarists and scientists with S. striolatus but clearly striolatus is a less elongate fish. This is not a vicious fish though you are not advised to put your hand in their aquarium. They will attack other fishes.
WATER CONDITIONS: A pH of 6.0-7.2 with water temperatures between 25-32°C prevailed in small rivers in which they were caught.
SIZE: Not a large fish, probably staying under 200 mm.
FOOD REQUIREMENTS: Small chunks of fish or meat; will eat live goldfish, too.

Metynnis hypsauchen (Mueller & Troschel) • Plain Metynnis

RANGE: Amazon region; widely distributed.
HABITS: Peaceful; fond of swimming in schools.
WATER CONDITIONS: Must be kept in a large aquarium. Water should be 10 to 15 DH and slightly acid; pH 6.8. Temperature 24 to 26°C.
SIZE: Up to 15 cm.
FOOD REQUIREMENTS: Will take and should get live or frozen foods, but the most important item is vegetable nourishment, such as lettuce leaves, etc.

Serrasalmus sanchezi Gery • Sanchez' Piranha

RANGE: Upper Amazon.
HABITS: The black border on the tail is incomplete and does not reach the tips of the caudal rays. The throat and belly may be red when the fish is in good condition, otherwise it's just rosy.
WATER CONDITIONS: A pH of 6.0-7.0 and water temperature of 23-30°C.
SIZE: To 275 mm, probably larger.
FOOD REQUIREMENTS: Live foods are required, especially goldfish or other large fish it can bite into two pieces. It can be trained to eat bits of fish and meat. In nature it is a scavenger of dead and dying animals and fishes. It rarely attacks.

Serrasalmus antoni (Fernandez-Yepez) • Anton's Piranha

RANGE: Venezuela.
HABITS: Not a dangerous fish in nature, but best kept by itself in the aquarium as it eats other fishes when it gets hungry. Not much is known except for the few brought in by the author (HRA).
WATER CONDITIONS: Cooler water, 23-28°C., with a pH 6.2-6.8.
SIZE: The specimens collected were under 175 mm.
FOOD REQUIREMENTS: Live fishes or bits of fish and meat.

Serrasalmus striolatus Steindachner • Black-tailed Piranha

RANGE: Lower Amazon and Guianas.
HABITS: Very often confused with Metynnis species until their teeth are noticed, then it is confused with S. denticulatus. Should be kept only with other large fishes and kept well fed.
WATER CONDITIONS: A pH of 6.2-7.0 and a temperature between 24-30°C.
SIZE: Reaches 200 mm.
FOOD REQUIREMENTS: Eats smaller fishes. Live goldfish or chunky bits of beef or fish. Does not get along on a normal aquarium diet.

Metynnis maculatus

Metynnis hypsauchen

Serrasalmus gibbus

Serrasalmus sanchezi

Serrasalmus spilopleura

Serrasalmus antoni

Serrasalmus denticulatus

Serrasalmus striolatus

PIRANHAS, FAMILY SERRASALMIDAE

Every aquarist knows the piranhas, the often large and always heavily toothed characoids that have inspired so much fascination and unnecessary fear. The piranhas form the subfamily Serrasalminae of the family Serrasalmidae (which also contains the pacus and silver dollars) in the classification of the characoids proposed by Gery. The true piranhas comprise only about 20 or so very similar species of the single genus *Serrasalmus* with at least five subgenera. Unlike any other tetras, the true piranhas have the large jaw teeth closely spaced and interlocked into a continuous saw; if one tooth has to be replaced, the entire set on that side has to be replaced.

For several years I (HRA) served as chairman of the Exotic Fishes Committee of the American Fisheries Society, and while in that post I had the responsibility for making recommendations to the Congress about the best means of protecting American waters from such menaces as piranhas from South America, walking catfish from Southeast Asia and tilapia from Africa. The fear with which American conservationists viewed the piranhas is amazing, and even though I argued that prohibiting the importation of piranhas would not stop their availability since they are so easy to breed, they still proposed laws that made importation illegal except under certain very special circumstances.

I'm frequently asked why piranhas are so feared if I go swimming with them in every river of Brazil, without the slightest hesitation. I'm not that brave. . .but I'm not stupid either. After spending so much time with Brazilian Indians, I've learned to do what they do. They know that piranhas never attack humans in rivers or lakes in which the fish have enough food. They are dangerous only when they are starving, such as in artificial situations (new reservoirs, aquaria) or in pools that are drying out and have been isolated from the main body of water (intermittent ponds).

In 25 years of travel and fishing in almost every river system in South America, nearly all of which had schools of piranha, I NEVER was bitten, nor did I ever meet anyone who was bitten . . .nor did I ever meet anyone who even *knew* anyone who was bitten by a piranha. . .and these are mostly Indians who live on the river and swim in it every day. But this does not mean that you can't be bitten if you stick your hand in your aquarium or grab one in a net! So be careful, but not frightened.

Serrasalmus elongatus

Serrasalmus hollandi

Serrasalmus nattereri

Serrasalmus nattereri

Serrasalmus manueli

Serrasalmus piraya

Serrasalmus rhombeus

Serrasalmus serrulatus

Plate #86

145

Serrasalmus elongatus Kner • Elongate Piranha

RANGE: Rio Madeira; very common in lakes around Humaita, Brazil, where the specimen shown in the photo on page 145 was caught.

HABITS: This is basically a lake-dwelling species that is very fast moving. It does not school in the usual sense, but large dying animals attract a lot of them. They are not to be trusted in the aquarium as they eat other fishes and may bite an aquarist's hand.

WATER CONDITIONS: Warm water between 25-32°C and a pH of 6.4-7.2

SIZE: Over 300 mm.

FOOD REQUIREMENTS: Live goldfish suits them fine, but they also take chunks of meat and fish. They do not thrive on a typical aquarium diet.

Serrasalmus nattereri (Kner) • Natterer's Piranha; Red-bellied Piranha

RANGE: Widely distributed throughout the Amazon and Orinoco basins.

HABITS: Vicious; must be kept alone in the average tank.

WATER CONDITIONS: Soft, slightly acid water. Temperature 24 to 27°C.

SIZE: Up to 30 cm in natural waters; shipped specimens usually much smaller.

FOOD REQUIREMENTS: Smaller living fishes or strips of raw fish or beef heart.

COLOR VARIATIONS: Back steel gray with many tiny shining scales; large black spots on sides; throat, belly and anal fin bright red.

Serrasalmus manueli Fernandez-Yepez • Manuel's Piranha

RANGE: Venezuela; collected by the author (HRA) in Rio Aguaro. Has never since been imported.

HABITS: Not known. Specimens were caught on hook and line, but none were collected with poison! In the aquarium they are very nasty, killing everything else in the tank.

WATER CONDITIONS: A pH of 6.4-7.0; water temperature of 24-30°C.

SIZE: To 200 mm, probably larger.

FOOD REQUIREMENTS: Live goldfish or chunks of meat and fish. Does not accept normal aquarium foods.

Serrasalmus rhombeus (Linnaeus) • White Piranha; Spotted Piranha

RANGE: Amazon river system and northeastern South America.

HABITS: Dangerous to most other fishes; perhaps smaller ones can be kept with larger fishes in a community tank.

WATER CONDITIONS: Soft, slightly acid water best. Temperature 24 to 27°C.

SIZE: To about 32 cm.

FOOD REQUIREMENTS: Does well on fishes and raw meat.

Serrasalmus hollandi (Eigenmann) • Holland's Piranha

RANGE: South of Amazon basin.

HABITS: Vicious; cannot even be kept with another of its own kind.

WATER CONDITIONS: Soft, slightly acid water. Temperature 24 to 27°C.

SIZE: About 13 cm.

FOOD REQUIREMENTS: Smaller living fishes preferred; can be trained to take strips of raw fish.

Serrasalmus piraya Cuvier • Man-eating Piranha

RANGE: Rio Sao Francisco basin.

HABITS: "Piraya" is the general word for "piranha." This is a greatly feared fish because it occurs in small streams that break down into a series of drying-out pools. The piraya in these pools eat everything, then begin starving. If a person walks into such a pool they are usually attacked.

WATER CONDITIONS: Tolerates extremes of temperature from 20-35°C.; the pH is not important, either, as long as it's between 6.0 and 7.4.

SIZE: To 320 mm.

FOOD REQUIREMENTS: Must have living fishes or chunks of fresh meat and fish.

Serrasalmus serrulatus (Valenciennes) • Serrated Piranha

RANGE: Guyana and northern South America.

HABITS: This is often shipped in as a Metynnis because of its deep body. It is a peaceful piranha and can be kept in the community aquarium if it is well fed. It has never been spawned but probably this will not be too difficult.

WATER CONDITIONS: Water should be warm, 24-30°C, with a pH between 6.0 and 7.0.

SIZE: Grows to only 165 mm, though larger specimens might be found.

FOOD REQUIREMENTS: Live foods or chunks of meat and fishes.

Hydrolycus scomberoides (Cuvier) • Tiger Characin

RANGE: Guianas and Amazon, Orinoco, and Paraguay basins.

HABITS: It is frightening just to look at their teeth but they only eat very small fishes. For some reason the Indians don't eat them and don't like them either. They have never been kept alive in an aquarium.

WATER CONDITIONS: They inhabit rivers. Nothing is known about their aquarium needs but it would have to be a large, well aerated tank. A good start would be a 2000 l aquarium with a pH of 6.8 and a temperature around 26°C.

SIZE: They grow large to almost 400 mm.

FOOD REQUIREMENTS: Small live fishes.

Charax gibbosus (Linnaeus) • Glass Headstander

RANGE: Guianas, lower and middle Amazon region and Rio Paraguay.

HABITS: Perfectly peaceful and harmless.

WATER CONDITIONS: Not critical. Temperature should average about 24°C.

SIZE: 15 cm; aquarium specimens are usually much smaller.

FOOD REQUIREMENTS: Prefers live foods, but dried foods may be fed when others are not available.

Asiphonichthys condei Gery • Glass Tetras

RANGE: Throughout the Amazon basin.

HABITS: Found in quiet, small pools, in shallow waters. They are very delicate and hard to "bring back alive." Nothing is known about their breeding or sex differences but this probably could be easily managed once they became available.

WATER CONDITIONS: Slow moving water with lots of hiding places. A pH of 6.8-7.0 is recommended with a temperature between 26-30°C.

SIZE: Under 100 mm.

FOOD REQUIREMENTS: Does well on a normal aquarium diet but should be started with live brine shrimp or daphnia.

Gnathocharax steindachneri Fowler • Biting Tetra

RANGE: Northern South America from the Amazon and Rio Negro to the Upper Orinoco and Guyana.

HABITS: A nasty fish with nasty teeth. It usually jumps for insects, especially at night, in its natural habitat, but when it gets hungry it tears up its tankmates, especially at night.

WATER CONDITIONS: A pH of 6.2-7.0; temperature 27°C. The populations of these fish in the Rio Negro are darker and tolerate acid water down to pH 5.8.

SIZE: About 80-90 mm.

FOOD REQUIREMENTS: Prefers live insects floating on the surface but quickly acclimate to adult live brine shrimp and other live foods.

Catoprion mento (Cuvier) • Wimple Piranha; Flag Piranha

RANGE: Rare in nature but usually found in rivers north and south of the Amazon, especially the Guapore and Rio Negro.

HABITS: There are probably two species in the genus, one with short fins (the one shown on the next page) and one with long fins with anal and dorsal filaments extending far beyond the tail. Their piranha-like look is misleading. They have been imported by Heiko Bleher of Frankfurt, Germany.

WATER CONDITIONS: They thrive under normal aquarium conditions. They like clear, running water but aeration is good enough. A pH of 6.4-7.0 with a water temperature of 25-30°C is sufficient for their needs.

SIZE: Probably reaches 200 mm.

FOOD REQUIREMENTS: Supposedly eats scales of other fishes but the author (HRA) has never witnessed this action even among starving fish. They do take normal aquarium foods.

Rhaphiodon vulpinus Agassiz • Skinny Tiger Characin

RANGE: Amazon and Paraguay-Parana basins.

HABITS: Not known to aquarists. The author (HRA) has never been able to bring them back alive because they seem to require more water than is available for transporting the fish. They are feared by the Indians but no one knows why.

WATER CONDITIONS: Not known, but probably a pH of 6.8 and a temperature of about 26°C would serve as this is the kind of water they were found in.

SIZE: Probably reach 500 mm.

FOOD REQUIREMENTS: Probably small living fishes.

Gilbertolus alatus Eigenmann • Dwarf Biting Tetra

RANGE: Extreme northern South America.

HABITS: Same habits as *Gnathocharax*. Both fishes, by the way, are the sole members of their genera. Since *Gilbertolus* is about half the size of *Gnathocharax* and both look so much alike, *Gilbertolus* is usually sold as the juvenile of *Gnathocharax*.

WATER CONDITIONS: pH 6.2-7.0 with a water temperature of about 27°C.

SIZE: 45 mm, perhaps a bit larger.

FOOD REQUIREMENTS: They are jumpers and like to take insects from the surface of their tanks.

Hydrolycus scomberoides

Catoprion mento

Charax gibbosus

Rhaphiodon vulpinus

Asiphonichthys condei

Asiphonichthys condei

Gnathocharax steindachneri

Gilbertolus alatus

Plate #87

148

Heterocharax macrolepis

Roeboides descalvadensis

Roeboides caucae

Exodon paradoxus

Oligosarcus argenteus

Acestrorhynchus falcatus

Acestrorhynchus heterolepis

Acestrorhynchus falcirostris

Plate #88

149

Heterocharax macrolepis Eigenmann • Blue-lined Glass Tetra

RANGE: Guyana, the Rio Negro and other dark waters of the Amazon basin.
HABITS: Shallow streams with dark water. Nothing is known about this fish in the aquarium world except for the sole importation by the author (HRA).
WATER CONDITIONS: It was kept with cardinal tetras in pH 5.8; water temperature 27°C. Never spawned.
SIZE: About 10 cm.
FOOD REQUIREMENTS: Prefers live foods but quickly adapts to dried aquarium foods.

Roeboides caucae Eigenmann • Cauca Humpback

RANGE: Colombia.
HABITS: Probably a scale-eater; the mouth and lips are full of sharp teeth that are very pointed. They are not safe for the home aquarium, and they seem to be especially aggressive at night.
WATER CONDITIONS: Water temperature between 26-30°C; pH 6.2-7.0.
SIZE: About 14 cm.
FOOD REQUIREMENTS: It is difficult to feed this fish. Because it is a scale-eater, you'll have to supply goldfish for it to chew on. Often it takes regular aquarium foods, but it never lives long in an aquarium.

Oligosarcus argenteus Guenther • Silver Fish-killer

RANGE: These are cool-water fish found throughout southern South America. They are nasty predaceous fish.
HABITS: There are now twelve species of Oligosarcus, all of which cannot be trusted in the home aquarium unless the aquarium is dedicated to this genus only. They eat fishes almost half their size in one gulp and are powerful swimmers.
WATER CONDITIONS: Clear, cool water. Do best in unheated tanks that are maintained between 15-23°C, with a pH of 6.4-6.8.
SIZE: Probably reach 10 cm.
FOOD REQUIREMENTS: Only can be kept alive on small living fishes even though they take chunks of meat and fish.

Acestrorhynchus heterolepis (Cope) • Amazonian Cachorro

RANGE: Amazon River basin, Brazil.
HABITS: A predatory fish that is often found in small streams, where it preys upon any fish that swims by. It prowls in open waters looking for food. Not safe for a community aquarium unless kept with fishes much larger than itself.
WATER CONDITIONS: A large aquarium is needed, with neutral water with a temperature between 26-30°C.
SIZE: May reach 30 cm.
FOOD REQUIREMENTS: Only living fishes, though some specimens learn to eat bits of fish and meat in between the live fishes they crave.

Roeboides descalvadensis Fowler • Humpbacked Characin

RANGE: Mato Grosso, Brazil, where it is very common.
HABITS: Found in shallow, slow-moving streams with clear water. The fish is very translucent, and specimens of all sizes had the humeral spot and the caudal peduncle mark. The fins always have a rosy hue.
WATER CONDITIONS: pH 6.0-7.2; temperature 24-30°C.
SIZE: Up to 15 cm.
FOOD REQUIREMENTS: Prefers living foods, especially brine shrimp and daphnia, but these can be bolstered with freeze-dried or flake foods. However, the fish only thrives on live foods.

Exodon paradoxus Mueller & Troschel • Bucktoothed Tetra

RANGE: Guyana and Brazil.
HABITS: Small specimens are mostly peaceful toward other fishes; bigger ones are likely to fight among themselves.
WATER CONDITIONS: Should have a large, sunny tank with plenty of vegetation. Rather high temperatures are required, not under 25°C.
SIZE: Attains a size of about 15 cm, but specimens in the aquarium seldom exceed 10 cm.
FOOD REQUIREMENTS: Should get mostly live foods, but will also take frozen foods and pieces of fish, shrimp, etc.

Acestrorhynchus falcatus (Bloch) • Spotted Cachorro

RANGE: Northern South America. As many as five different fishes are grouped under the falcatus name, and the group needs revision.
HABITS: A nasty, predatory fish. In Brazilian Portuguese the name "cachorro" means "dog," and this is a nasty dog of a fish that bites other fishes, often just for the sport of it. They are very pike-like and have teeth like a barracuda.
WATER CONDITIONS: They cannot live for long in the aquarium unless they have lots of room and heavily aerated water with a pH close to 7.0 and a water temperature that is warm, between 27 and 30°C.
SIZE: Range to 30 cm, probably larger.
FOOD REQUIREMENTS: They only thrive on living fishes, though they can be coaxed into taking bits of meat and fish.

Acestrorhynchus falcirostris (Cuvier) • Giant Cachorro

RANGE: Throughout northern South America.
HABITS: A predatory pike-like fish that is a good game fish but is rarely eaten by the people who catch it. In Guyana it is often caught by fly fishermen as well as by spoons being trawled behind slow-moving boats.
WATER CONDITIONS: A neutral pH between 6.8 and 7.2 with a water temperature between 25-30°C.
SIZE: The largest of the almost 20 fishes in this genus. It may reach 38 cm in standard length.
FOOD REQUIREMENTS: Live fishes small enough to ingest whole.

Acestrorhynchus isalinae Menezes & Gery • Isaline's
Cachorro

RANGE: Known only from specimens collected by the author
  (HRA) and colleagues near Humaita, Brazil.
HABITS: Like the other species of the genus, it is a vicious
  predator.
WATER CONDITIONS: Warm (26-30°C) water with a neutral
  pH.
SIZE: Probably reaches at least 25 cm.
FOOD REQUIREMENTS: Should do well on a diet of small
  live fishes.

Brycon melanopterus (Cope) • Common Brycon

RANGE: Throughout the Amazon; very common.
HABITS: This is the most unusual of the South American
  trout tetras imported. It is distinct because of the black
  marking that runs from the ventral fins to the upper lobe
  of the caudal. This fish has never been spawned in
  aquaria.
WATER CONDITIONS: Requires a large aquarium with lots
  of room. Prefers a pH of 6.2-6.8 with a water temperature
  of 24-30°C.
SIZE: About 27.5 cm; some reports have them larger.
FOOD REQUIREMENTS: Live fishes or chunks of fish and
  beef.

Brycon brevicauda Guenther • Short-tailed Trout Tetra

RANGE: The Amazon and its southern tributaries.
HABITS: There are almost 50 species of *Brycon* , the South
  American trout tetras, as they are called. The species
  are generally very poorly described so the species have
  been broken down into groups. Those brycons with a
  black V in the tail base are in the *falcatus* group, of which
  this species is part.
WATER CONDITIONS: Deep water and a large tank with a pH
  about 6.8 and a water temperature about 27°C. They do
  not do well in a home aquarium.
SIZE: To 25 cm.
FOOD REQUIREMENTS: Prefers live foods, but they can be
  acclimated to bits of meat or fish depending upon their
  size.

Brycon orbignyanus (Valenciennes) • Striped Brycon

RANGE: This species, which has between 27 and 31 anal fin
  rays, ranges over almost all of South America from the
  Guianas to the La Plata basin; it is even found in Central
  America!
HABITS: This fish takes on many faces depending upon where
  it is found. It has many scientific names, too, depending
  upon the country and the scientist who described it. It
  does not do well in a small tank.
WATER CONDITIONS: The preferred water temperature
  varies with the origin of the specimen. If that is unknown,
  ascertain the water chemistry from the last person to
  keep it alive. Probably about 25°C with a neutral pH of 7.0
  will do for most specimens.
SIZE: Specimens vary up to 32 cm.
FOOD REQUIREMENTS: Live fishes; also takes chunks of fish
  or meat.

Chalceus erythrurus (Cope) • Yellow-finned
Chalceus

RANGE: The Amazon basin south to the Mato
  Grosso.
HABITS: A jumper and live fish eater. It has never
  been spawned, and not much is known about their
  aquarium habits since they are so rare in the hobby, the
  reason being that they are difficult to ship.
WATER CONDITIONS: Require very large aquaria with a
  pH of 6.2-6.8 and a water temperature between 25-30°C.
SIZE: Grows to about 30 cm.
FOOD REQUIREMENTS: Live fishes or chunks of meat and
  fish.

Chalceus "Jacques Gery" • Gery's Chalceus

RANGE: Amazon basin.
HABITS: *Chalceus* was thought to be composed of only two
  species, one with red fins (*macrolepidotus*) and one with
  yellow fins (*erythrurus*). Then the author (HRA) found
  the fish shown here and Dr. Jacques Gery, expert on
  characoids, found the same variety somewhere else. He
  has not officially named it yet, but it carries his name in
  the trade and is very expensive because it is so beautiful
  when small and can be kept alive in the aquarium.
WATER CONDITIONS: Water about pH 6.8 and 27°C.
SIZE: Probably reaches 30 cm, but the maximum size is not
  known for sure.
FOOD REQUIREMENTS: Live foods or chunks of meat or fish.

Acestrorhynchus isalinae

Brycon brevicauda

1

2

Brycon melanopterus

Brycon melanopterus (juvenile)

3

4

Brycon melanopterus

Brycon orbignyanus

5

6

Chalceus erythrurus

Chalceus "Jacques Gery"

7

8

Plate #89

152

Chalceus macrolepidotus

Triportheus albus

Triportheus angulatus

Triportheus rotundatus

Triportheus rotundatus (juvenile)

Prionobrama filigera

Xenagoniates bondi

Rachoviscus crassiceps

Plate #90

153

Chalceus macrolepidotus Cuvier • Pink-tailed Chalceus

RANGE: Guyana, Surinam and French Guiana.
HABITS: Peaceful if kept in a school with no small fishes in the same tank.
WATER CONDITIONS: Not critical; best temperature about 25°C. Once they have become established, they should be moved as little as possible.
SIZE: To 25 cm.
FOOD REQUIREMENTS: Generous feedings are necessary, using earthworms, tubifex worms or chopped beef heart.

Triportheus angulatus (Spix) • Narrow Hatchetfish

RANGE: Middle and Lower Amazon, Rio Madeira, Rio Negro, Orinoco and the Guianas.
HABITS: Active and peaceful with other fishes of its own size.
WATER CONDITIONS: Not critical; tank should be in a sunny location and permit ample swimming space. Temperature about 25°C.
SIZE: Wild specimens attain a size of about 20 cm.
FOOD REQUIREMENTS: Not very fond of dried foods, so should be richly fed with living foods such as daphnia or adult brine shrimp.

Xenagoniates bondi Myers • Long-finned Glass Tetra

RANGE: Venezuela and Colombia.
HABITS: This elongated, translucent fish in many ways resembles an Asian glass catfish. Although not especially colorful, the odd shape and delicate pattern make it an interesting addition to the aquarium. It can be separated from the similar barred glass tetra by the longer body and presence of black at the base of the dorsal fin and front of the anal fin.
WATER CONDITIONS: Neutral to slightly acid pH and warm water temperatures are preferred.
SIZE: To about 10 cm.
FOOD REQUIREMENTS: Will take most small live foods and some prepared foods.

Triportheus albus Cope • Pretty Chalcinus

RANGE: Throughout the Amazon basin.
HABITS: This species is the type of the genus. It is very common but is rarely imported because it is "just another silver fish." These fish are jumpers, and their aquarium must be covered.
WATER CONDITIONS: pH 6.2-7.0
SIZE: May reach 24 cm.
FOOD REQUIREMENTS: Live foods are preferred, but they become acclimated to an ordinary aquarium diet without too much difficulty.

Triportheus rotundatus (Schomburgk) • Black-winged Triportheus

RANGE: From northern South America; usually imported from Guyana.
HABITS: The young of this fish are completely different from their elders. The fully mature fish may show a broad band from its ventral fins through the upper lobe of the caudal, mimicking in some respects Brycon melanopterus, to which it is closely related (except for the size of the scales).
WATER CONDITIONS: A jumper that likes to spend time close to the surface of the water, thus the water should be aerated to keep the temperature at the surface uniform with the rest of the tank. pH 6.8 at 27°C.
SIZE: About 16.5 cm.
FOOD REQUIREMENTS: A lover of live foods (as are most fishes), but it soon learns to accept the usual aquarium fare.

Prionobrama filigera (Cope) • Glass Bloodfin

RANGE: Tributaries of the Rio Madeira.
HABITS: Peaceful, very active fish which prefer to be in groups.
WATER CONDITIONS: Soft, slightly acid water is best; the tank should afford a good amount of swimming room. Temperature 23 to 26°C.
SIZE: To 6 cm.
FOOD REQUIREMENTS: Prepared foods accepted, but live foods should be given at least several times a week.

Rachoviscus crassiceps Myers • Golden Tetra

RANGE: Coastal blackwater streams of southeastern Brazil, from Parana perhaps to Rio de Janeiro.
HABITS: Relatively peaceful community tank species.
WATER CONDITIONS: Not critical; widely adaptable to various kinds of water, but for breeding may require a pH of about 5.0 to 5.5 and a DH of 2 to 3. Temperature 18 to 28°C; courtship occurs at the middle to upper range of these temperatures.
SIZE: Attains a length of about 4.5 cm.
FOOD REQUIREMENTS: Will accept a variety of aquarium foods, including flake food. Live foods are recommended for breeding.

Paragoniates alburnus Steindachner • Pasca

RANGE: Northern South America from the Amazon basin to Venezuela.

HABITS: A nice aquarium fish, one of only two members of the genus *Paragoniates*. This rare fish has only been imported once or twice, and there are conflicting reports about it, but generally they are peaceful, attractive members of same subfamily as *Aphyocharax*. Their bodies are much more translucent than the accompanying photograph indicates.

WATER CONDITIONS: pH 6.2-7.0; temperature 24-30°C.

SIZE: Up to about 9.5 cm.

FOOD REQUIREMENTS: Live foods are preferred, especially brine shrimp, but they are easily acclimated to flake foods and, especially, freeze-dried foods.

Aphyocharax anisitsi Eigenmann & Kennedy • Argentinian Bloodfin

RANGE: Argentina to Paraguay.

HABITS: A peaceful, colorful aquarium fish that has been around a long time under the scientific name of *Aphyocharax rubripinnis*, a synonym. It is commercially bred, but the tank-raised specimens hardly have the color of the wild ones shown in the accompanying photograph.

WATER CONDITIONS: Likes cooler water between 22-25°C, with a neutral pH.

SIZE: May reach 7.5 cm.

FOOD REQUIREMENTS: Likes live foods, especially live brine shrimp, but takes the usual flake foods fed to a community tank.

Aphyocharax rathbuni Eigenmann • Rathbun's Bloodfin

RANGE: Paraguay basin, South America.

HABITS: Peaceful and attractive. Does well in a community tank.

WATER CONDITIONS: Not critical. Temperature 24 to 27°C.

SIZE: Attains a length of about 4.5 cm.

FOOD REQUIREMENTS: Not fussy. Prepared foods accepted, but living food should be provided whenever possible.

Gephyrocharax caucanus Eigenmann • Arrowhead Tetra

RANGE: Rio Cauca, Colombia.

HABITS: In constant motion; active to the point of always having to do something, including bothering its tankmates.

WATER CONDITIONS: Temperature should range between 24 to 26°C. They prefer water that is somewhat soft and a pH that is slightly on the acid side.

SIZE: Up to 6 cm.

FOOD REQUIREMENTS: Live foods best, but will accept freeze-dried feedings; dry foods will be accepted if very hungry.

Phanagoniates macrolepis (Meek & Hildebrand) • Barred Glass Tetra

RANGE: Extreme northern South America; usually exported from Venezuela and Colombia.

HABITS: This is a very beautiful translucent fish that contains specimens (perhaps males in breeding color) that have red glowspots on their caudal peduncles. They have a set of sharp teeth but are peaceful with fishes that are as large as they themselves.

WATER CONDITIONS: pH 6.2-7.0; temperature 22-27°C, but tolerates warmer conditions.

SIZE: About 10 cm.

FOOD REQUIREMENTS: Live foods that are small enough to ingest whole, as this fish has a small mouth. Aquarium foods are generally accepted.

Aphyocharax erythrurus Eigenmann • Flame-tail Tetra

RANGE: Guyana.

HABITS: Peaceful, very active and likes to jump. Must be kept covered.

WATER CONDITIONS: Clean, well-aerated water. pH and hardness not important unless they affect spawning. Temperature 22 to 26°C.

SIZE: To 6 cm; males a little smaller.

FOOD REQUIREMENTS: Prepared foods accepted but frozen or live foods should be given occasionally.

Aphyocharax "Bleher" • Bleher's Bloodfin

RANGE: Mato Grosso, Brazil.

HABITS: A typical bloodfin, probably undescribed. The specimens collected by Heiko Bleher and photographed by the author all had very bright red markings more vivid than its sister species. Gery is working on a scientific description.

WATER CONDITIONS: Most aquarium conditions are acceptable between pH 6.2-6.9, with a temperature between 24-30°C.

SIZE: Up to 6.3 cm.

FOOD REQUIREMENTS: Live foods small enough to eat whole but quickly; learns to take the usual dried foods.

Gephyrocharax valenciae Eigenmann • Mountain Minnow Tetra

RANGE: A whole genus of *Gephyrocharax* ranges north from Bolivia along the Andes mountains at about 1,000 m; some species extend up to Costa Rica.

HABITS: In each area of their range the fish changes a bit in color, and in all populations their colors are very delicate. The fish are active swimmers and investigate every ecological niche, which makes them a nuisance in an aquarium but well dispersed in nature.

WATER CONDITIONS: pH 6.2-6.8, with water at 24-26°C. They probably can tolerate much colder water.

SIZE: To 6 cm.

FOOD REQUIREMENTS: Mosquito larvae and pupae are their principal food in nature, but they take small live foods and the usual aquarium diet as well.

Paragoniates alburnus

Phanagoniates macrolepis

Aphyocharax anisitsi

Aphyocharax erythrurus

Aphyocharax rathbuni

Aphyocharax "Bleher"

Gephyrocharax caucanus

Gephyrocharax valenciae

Plate #91

Gephyrocharax "Peeroo"

Gephyrocharax "Blotchy"

①

②

Pseudocorynopoma doriae

Pseudocorynopoma riisei

③

④

Coelurichthys microlepis

Coelurichthys microlepis

⑤

⑥

Tyttocharax madeirae

Stethaprion erythrops

⑦

⑧

Plate #92

157

Gephyrocharax "Peeroo" • Peruvian Gephyrocharax

RANGE: Peruvian Andes about 1,000 m high.
HABITS: Only once did this seemingly undescribed fish come into the U.S., and that was with a shipment of neon tetras. They were small fish and were grown up by the author (HRA). The results were not exciting, and this commonly colored fish was never again imported.
WATER CONDITIONS: Slightly acid conditions, colder water. pH 6.2-6.8, with a water temperature in the 20-26°C range.
SIZE: Barely reaches 10 cm under ideal aquarium conditions.
FOOD REQUIREMENTS: They were constantly fed live foods and dried flake foods daily, but they can subsist on either.

Gephyrocharax "Blotchy" • Blotchy Gephyrocharax

RANGE: Central America.
HABITS: A typical (and probably undescribed) *Gephyrocharax* that swims about constantly and quickly and is usually very disturbing to the peace and tranquility of a community aquarium. It has never been bred, and no one knows the sexual differences of this genus as yet.
WATER CONDITIONS: Cooler water between 22-26°C at a pH of 6.8.
SIZE: Probably reaches 7.5 cm.
FOOD REQUIREMENTS: Prefers live foods but takes dried food as well, especially if in the company of fishes that are eating the dried food.

Pseudocorynopoma doriae Perugia • Dragonfin Tetra

RANGE: Southern Brazil and the La Plata region.
HABITS: Will not annoy other fishes or chew plants.
WATER CONDITIONS: Soft, slightly acid water. Temperature 21 to 25°C.
SIZE: To 8 cm.
FOOD REQUIREMENTS: Will take any foods, but live foods are of course preferred.

Pseudocorynopoma riisei Gill • Swordtailed Characin

RANGE: Trinidad, Colombia and Venezuela.
HABITS: Peaceful and hardy; a good community fish.
WATER CONDITIONS: Not critical. Temperature between 22 to 28°C. A sunny, well-planted tank and clear water show it at its best.
SIZE: Males 6 cm; females 5 cm.
FOOD REQUIREMENTS: Will take prepared foods. Best foods are daphnia, tubifex worms and especially white worms, of which they are very fond.

Coelurichthys microlepis (Steindachner) • Croaking Tetra

RANGE: Southeastern Brazil, Rio Grande do Sul.
HABITS: Peaceful and active; does not disturb plants.
WATER CONDITIONS: Should be kept in a roomy aquarium at a temperature slightly lower than most tropical species, 21 to 24°C.
SIZE: Males about 5.5 cm; females about 4.5 cm.
FOOD REQUIREMENTS: Not a fussy eater; besides live foods, will also eat dried foods.

Tyttocharax madeirae Fowler • Bristly-mouthed Tetra

RANGE: Middle and upper Amazon basin.
HABITS: Peaceful, but because of their small size they should have a tank of their own; prefer to swim in schools.
WATER CONDITIONS: Soft, slightly acid water. Temperature 24 to 27°C.
SIZE: Up to 2 cm.
FOOD REQUIREMENTS: Smallest live foods.

Stethaprion erythrops Cope • Bumpy-back Silver Dollar

RANGE: Amazon basin, probably extending north and south from there as very similar specimens come in periodically.
HABITS: The fish of this group that come from the northern part of South America, specifically Guyana, have a dorsal spot and some very sharp but fine teeth. They dart quickly through the water and eagerly take insects from the surface.
WATER CONDITIONS: Warm water at 25-30°C with a pH of 6.4-6.8.
SIZE: To about 8 cm.
FOOD REQUIREMENTS: Prefers live foods but quickly adapts to flake foods.

Poptella orbicularis Valenciennes • Silver Dollar Tetra

RANGE: Found throughout South America from Guyana to Paraguay.
HABITS: A popular aquarium fish that flutters about the aquarium. They are the silver equivalent to the black tetra, *Gymnocorymbus ternetzi*, and are often confused with *Gymnocorymbus thayeri*. The color of the anal fin varies with the particular strain.
WATER CONDITIONS: Colder water between 22-26°C, with a pH of 6.2-7.2.
SIZE: Up to 12 cm.
FOOD REQUIREMENTS: Prefers live foods but gets along perfectly well on a good flake food.

Iguanodectes • Slender Tetras

This genus of smelt-like tetras is found throughout South America and is now thought to be closely related to the typical tetras. They are not popular aquarium fishes for they are difficult to maintain and they don't take readily to flake foods, preferring small living foods such as mosquito larvae and daphnia. The identifications of these fishes are very confused, but most seem to belong to *I. spilurus* or a very similar species. All look virtually identical, with a pale lateral band and black caudal blotch. They do well at first under normal aquarium conditions but they gradually fade away from dietary deficiencies.

Hemibrycon polydon (Guenther) • Racer Tetra

RANGE: Peru and Ecuador in fast-moving mountain streams.
HABITS: These fish are found swimming in a single spot by racing against the fast-moving mountain stream waters. The group is very poorly known, and ichthyologists sometimes identify them by assigning a name to each geographical type. They are extremely common in their range once you find their habitat.
WATER CONDITIONS: Cold, highly aerated water. pH 6.6-7.4, with temperatures from 18-26°C.
SIZE: They reach 10 cm in length.
FOOD REQUIREMENTS: These are insect eaters that will quickly take foods that are moving, even dried foods caught in a stream of air bubbles.

Boehlkea fredcochui Gery • Cochu's Blue Tetra

RANGE: Peruvian Amazon region, near Leticia, Colombia.
HABITS: Peaceful but very sensitive; best kept with other fishes with similar characteristics.
WATER CONDITIONS: Soft, slightly acid water is highly important with this species. The addition of acid peat moss in the filter is beneficial. Temperature 23 to 26°C.
SIZE: Up to 5 cm.
FOOD REQUIREMENTS: Live or frozen foods; dried foods only when there is nothing else at hand.

Piabucus dentatus (Kohlreuter) • Keel-bellied Slender Tetra

RANGE: Guyanas through the Amazon basin and the southern Amazon tributaries. This fish is one of the few Brazilian species noted as far back as the 1600's in European literature.
WATER CONDITIONS: Not choosy, but prefers somewhat acid water and temperatures above 24°C.
SIZE: Reaches at least 17.5 cm in length.
FOOD REQUIREMENTS: Prefers small living foods such as mosquito larvae, brine shrimp, and small crustaceans; often feeds near the surface.

Carlastyanax aurocaudatus (Eigenmann) • Red-finned Tetra

RANGE: Rio Cauca, Colombia.
HABITS: A peaceful aquarium fish that is imported in large numbers from time to time though it has never been spawned. This fish is quite different from its closest relatives and is the only species in the genus known so far.
WATER CONDITIONS: Hard, cool water with a pH of 7.0 and a temperature around 23°C.
SIZE: About 5.5 cm.
FOOD REQUIREMENTS: Prefers live foods but quickly acclimates to dried foods in an aquarium situation.

Nematobrycon lacortei Weitzman & Fink • Rainbow Tetra

RANGE: San Juan basin, Colombia.
HABITS: Peaceful; inclined to be a bit shy.
WATER CONDITIONS: Soft, slightly acid water is best. Temperature 24 to 27°C.
SIZE: To 5 cm.
FOOD REQUIREMENTS: Live foods are best, but the fish can be trained to accept frozen and dried foods.

Poptella orbicularis

Piabucus dentatus

Iguanodectes spilurus

Iguanodectes purusi

Hemibrycon polyodon-jelskii

Carlastyanax aurocaudatus

Boehlkea fredcochui

Nematobrycon lacortei

Plate #93

Nematobrycon "Gery"

Nematobrycon palmeri

Inpaichthys kerri

Bryconamericus loisae

Creagrutus cochui

Knodus breviceps

Creagrutus beni

Pseudochalceus kyburzi

Plate #94

161

Nematobrycon "Gery" • Gery's Emperor Tetra

RANGE: Colombia in side streams of the Rios San Juan and Atrato.

HABITS: The author (HRA) has collected all three "species" of *Nematobrycon* in various pockets of the Atrato and San Juan Rivers during the dry season when the rivers are merely dried out bottoms with intermittent pools and feeder streams. The "species" seem to freely interbreed and their fin ray and tooth counts fall into a narrow range of variation. At best they are subspecies, because each time the author found them he discovered minor variations in fin ray counts and teeth. It is usual for many fishes to show these variations within species when the waters in which they live assume different temperatures and when the fishes have different foods available, especially when they are juvenile. Care of *N*. "Gery" is the same as for the other "species."

Inpaichthys kerri Gery & Junk • Blue Emperor

RANGE: Upper Rio Aripuana, Mata Grosso, Brazil.

HABITS: Similar to the Emperor Tetra, but perhaps more timid.

WATER CONDITIONS: Water should be soft to medium hard with a pH around neutral. Temperature about 26 to 28°C.

SIZE: Reaches a length of at least 5 cm.

FOOD REQUIREMENTS: Will accept frozen or dried foods but prefers live foods.

Creagrutus cochui Gery • Fred Cochu's Tetra

RANGE: Discovered in the upper Amazon by the author (HRA).

HABITS: There are more than 20 species of *Creagrutus*, and they are very difficult to tell apart. Only an expert like Dr. Jacques Gery can be depended upon to describe a new species in this group until they are totally reworked. The only logical characters for identification are the size, shape and location of the humeral spot and the lateral band.

WATER CONDITIONS: Most of the *Creagrutus* take the same normal pH between 6.4 and 7.2 and a water temperature between 24-30°C. Even the coldwater species of *Creagrutus* thrive at this range.

SIZE: Rarely exceeds 10 cm.

FOOD REQUIREMENTS: Accepts life in the aquarium with its usual flake foods, but likes an occasional feeding of live food.

Creagrutus beni Eigenmann • Benny Tetra

RANGE: The fish illustrated is from the Rio Meta in Colombia, but the species was named from a fish found in the Rio Beni, Bolivia. So many of these fish look alike that this must also be called *C. beni*, however.

WATER CONDITIONS: pH 6.4-7.2; water temperatures between 24-30°C.

SIZE: Up to 5.2 cm.

FOOD REQUIREMENTS: Thrives under usual aquarium conditions.

Nematobrycon palmeri Eigenmann • Emperor Tetra

RANGE: San Juan basin and Atrato Rivers, Colombia.

HABITS: Peaceful and a bit shy; inclined to remain singly or in pairs rather than forming a school.

WATER CONDITIONS: Clean, soft, slightly acid water is best. Temperature 23 to 25°C.

SIZE: To 5 cm.

FOOD REQUIREMENTS: Excellent appetite; will accept dried or frozen foods, but of course live foods are preferred.

Bryconamericus loisae Gery • Pico Peixe

RANGE: Rio Meta, Colombia.

HABITS: There are about 40 *Bryconamericus* species, almost all of which have very few interesting colors and are thus rarely imported even though they are hardy, relatively peaceful and common in their ranges. This fish is typical of the genus. It has never been spawned.

WATER CONDITIONS: Harder than normal water, slightly cool, with a pH around neutral (6.8-7.2) at a temperature of 24°C.

SIZE: About 5 cm.

FOOD REQUIREMENTS: Eats normal aquarium foods but, like almost all aquarium fishes, does better on feedings of live foods every few days.

Knodus breviceps (Eigenmann) • Soap Eater

RANGE: Throughout the Amazon there are species of *Knodus*, perhaps as many as 50 different species, very few of which have been described, and those that have been described are uncertain in many cases.

HABITS: This fish got its common name from the author (HRA), who was washing himself while sitting in a small, clear-water creek. As he lathered his body and laid down for the water to rinse off the soap, he was "attacked" by thousands of *Knodus breviceps* as they pecked off the soap. He described the sensation of these tiny "bites" as "uncomfortable but not painful and they didn't draw blood."

WATER CONDITIONS: The fish thrive under most aquarium conditions.

SIZE: Probably reaches a size of 5 cm.

FOOD REQUIREMENTS: Will tackle anything small enough to chew.

Pseudochalceus kyburzi Schultz • Kyburz Tetra

RANGE: Colombia.

HABITS: Active and aggressive, even with their own kind.

WATER CONDITIONS: Soft, slightly acid water. Temperature 24 to 26°C.

SIZE: To 8 cm.

FOOD REQUIREMENTS: Various live foods including insects.

Astyanax daguae Eigenmann • Plain-tailed Astyanax

RANGE: Colombia.
HABITS: Should not be kept with smaller fishes which it may attack.
WATER CONDITIONS: Soft, slightly acid water. Temperature 24 to 26°C.
SIZE: About 8 cm.
FOOD REQUIREMENTS: Will accept most foods.

Astyanax kennedyi Gery • Kennedy's Astyanax

RANGE: Upper Amazon near Iquitos. The fish probably has a much wider distribution, but this has never been verified.
HABITS: A typical tetra with a nice glowing line on the caudal peduncle and a black spot in the tail that make it an attractive but not beautiful species. Therefore it is rarely imported except accidentally with other species from Iquitos, one of the capitals of the aquarium fish world.
WATER CONDITIONS: pH 6.2-6.9 at a water temperature of 25-30°C.
SIZE: Barely reaches 5 cm.
FOOD REQUIREMENTS: Prefers live foods but quickly acclimates to dried foods.

Astyanax abramis (Jenyns) • Confusing Astyanax

RANGE: Throughout most of temperate and tropical South America.
HABITS: Indistinguishable under aquarium conditions from *A. kennedyi* and *A. zonatus* except for the amount of black in the tail.
WATER CONDITIONS: pH 6.2-6.9 at a temperature of 25-30°C.
SIZE: To about 5 cm.
FOOD REQUIREMENTS: Prefers live foods but gets along on a typical aquarium diet.

Astyanax fasciatus (Cuvier) • Silvery Tetra

RANGE: Texas to Argentina.
HABITS: Will get along with other fishes of its size; very likely to eat plants.
WATER CONDITIONS: Not at all critical, but slightly alkaline water is best. Temperature 21 to 24°C.
SIZE: To 9 cm.
FOOD REQUIREMENTS: All foods accepted, but there should be some vegetable substances included, such as lettuce or spinach leaves.

Astyanax fasciatus mexicanus (de Philippi) • Blind Cave Tetra

RANGE: The blind form of this fish (known formerly as *Anoptichthys jordani*) occurs in caves in a restricted area in Mexico, especially La Cueva Chica.
HABITS: This is a blind fish that has been the subject of many interesting investigations, and it poses interesting problems for the scientist. Previously it was placed in the genus *Anoptichthys*, then it was discovered that it freely interbred with *Astyanax* even in nature and on this basis it was reclassified as a "form" of the fish with which it breeds in nature. If interbreeding is a test for species integrity, then many species of *Nematobrycon*, *Pterophyllum*, *Symphysodon*, platies, mollies and swordtails plus most of the small lake cichlids of central Africa would be lost and the basis of scientific classification would be in shambles.
SIZE: Barely reaches 7 cm.
FOOD REQUIREMENTS: Eats everything from flake foods to live foods, which it finds with extraordinary ease.

Astyanax zonatus Eigenmann • False Kennedy Tetra

RANGE: Very common in the upper Amazon in Brazil and Peru. This fish is almost identical to *A. kennedyi* except for the intensity of the humeral spot.
HABITS: A typical tetra that swims about peacefully, schooling with its own species (including *A. kennedyi*), occupies mid-water, and doesn't attack fishes that are smaller than itself but too large to eat in one gulp.
WATER CONDITIONS: pH 6.2-6.9 with a temperature of 25-30°C.
SIZE: About 5 cm.
FOOD REQUIREMENTS: Prefers live foods but takes flake foods, too.

Astyanax gymnogenys Eigenmann • One-spot Astyanax

RANGE: In Brazil south of the Amazon system.
HABITS: A very nice aquarium fish. Very peaceful, with a small mouth. It has never been spawned and has rarely been imported. It is usually sold as a *Ctenobrycon*, which it resembles in a very general way in many respects.
WATER CONDITIONS: pH 6.2-7.2 with a temperature between 22-28°C.
SIZE: To 12.5 cm.
FOOD REQUIREMENTS: Prefers live foods small enough to ingest like brine shrimp, but quickly adapts to a normal aquarium diet.

Astyanax daguae

Astyanax fasciatus

Astyanax fasciatus (albino)

Astyanax f. mexicanus, formerly Anoptichthys

Astyanax kennedyi

Astyanax zonatus

Astyanax abramis

Astyanax gymnogenys

Plate #95

Astyanax "Schultz"

Astyanax metae

Astyanax "Big Scale"

Astyanax bimaculatus

Astyanax "Broken Stripe"

Astyanax longior

Astyanax gracilior

Astyanax "Red Spot"

Plate #96

ASTYANAX TETRAS

If you are collecting in Central or South America and find a deep-bodied 50-100 mm silvery tetra with indistinct black markings on the shoulder and along the midsides, you probably have a species of *Astyanax*. With over 100 described species and subspecies in the genus, it is almost impossible to obtain a realistic identification of a specimen unless it belongs to one of the handful of well-marked species with odd patterns. Even the experts such as Dr. Jacques Gery, author of *Characoids of the World,* are often stumped. Not only are the old names hard to place, but there are dozens of undescribed species as well, some of which reach the petshops in America and Europe.

The author (HRA) has collected dozens of species of the genus but I've never found them especially interesting. They are usually just some of the "silvery tetras" that come up in the seine when looking for more colorful or worthwhile fishes. In the aquarium they are active and, when properly fed, usually iridescent fishes,but they tend to be fin-nippers and can drive more sedentary species crazy with their unwanted attentions. Since most of the species are cheap, hardy and adapt to many different water and temperature conditions, they can make good beginner fishes. Like other tetras, they will spawn in the aquarium if conditions are to their liking and the breeders are properly conditioned on live foods.

The most famous species of *Astyanax* is certainly the blind cave tetra of Mexico, *Anoptichthys jordani*. Yes, *Anoptichthys* is actually an *Astyanax*. Although the blind cave tetra shows modifications associated with other types of cave-dwellers, especially the absence of eyes and pigment and the strong development of sensory line organs to help it orient itself and find food, in the 1960's scientists found that the distinctive *Anoptichthys* interbred totally with *Astyanax fasciatus mexicanus* in surface streams that flowed into its caves. For this reason *Anoptichthys jordani* and the several other described species of the "genus" are now placed as synonyms of *Astyanax fasciatus mexicanus*, a non-descript silvery tetra that ranges north into the Rio Grande basin of Texas. (*Astyanax f. mexicanus* is the only tetra to be found naturally in the United States. It is often sold as fish bait in Texas!) This is one situation in which the usual rules of binomial nomenclature are hard to apply —if you call the blind cave tetra by the same name as the silvery surface fish you do nothing but confuse aquarists. Yet *Anoptichthys* just is not a real genus, so that name cannot be used in a technical sense. For convenience we are calling it by the boring and cumbersome term "*Astyanax fasciatus mexicanus,* formerly *Anoptichthys,*" but there must be a better way. Any suggestions?

Bryconops melanurus (Bloch) • Tail-light Tetra

RANGE: Middle through northern South America. Very common.

HABITS: This fish is so common it has played an important role in three taxa in which it has been assigned. It was the type species for the genus *Creatochanes* and has been placed in both the genus *Bryconops* and the subgenus *Brycochandus*. There are many fishes that look almost exactly like this one; even scientists find them difficult to distinguish.

WATER CONDITIONS: It thrives under most aquarium conditions.

SIZE: 63 mm is a large size for this fish.

FOOD REQUIREMENTS: Prefers live foods but gets along very well on a good flake food.

Moenkhausia agnesae Gery • Agnes' Tetra

RANGE: Igarape Preto (Black Stream), Brazil.

HABITS: This fish has only been imported once when the author (HRA), with Harald Schultz, brought back a dozen or so specimens for their aquariums. The fish lost the immensely outstanding colors they had in nature. They were never spawned or they would have been popular.

WATER CONDITIONS: They did well in acid water, pH 5.6-6.6, at 27°C.

SIZE: They reached about 100 mm.

FOOD REQUIREMENTS: They did well on small crustaceans and dried foods.

Moenkhausia georgiae Gery • Georgi Gery's Tetra

RANGE: Widely distributed but rare in most areas. Specimens have been found from Guyana to Mato Grosso, Brazil.

HABITS: A very pretty fish with a deep body, sparkling scales and an apparent black eye. This fish was especially suitable for naming after his wife for Jacques Gery thought this fish was beautiful, too. His wife is a stunningly beautiful blonde.

WATER CONDITIONS: Thrives in water with a pH 6.0-6.8 and at a water temperature between 25-30°C.

SIZE: About 65 mm.

FOOD REQUIREMENTS: Prefers live foods but gets along well on normal flake foods.

Moenkhausia intermedia (Eigenmann) • False Spot-tailed Tetra

RANGE: Throughout northern South America. Very common throughout its range.

HABITS: This fish and several species that look very much alike (such as *M. dichroura*) are difficult to distinguish since they are differentiated solely by the bones of their jaws.

WATER CONDITIONS: All species that have the central parts of their caudal lobes pigmented in black have the same needs: pH 6.2-6.6; temperature 25-30°C.

SIZE: Reaches about 75 mm.

FOOD REQUIREMENTS: Prefers live foods but accepts flake foods readily.

Ctenobrycon spilurus (Cuvier & Valenciennes) • Silver Tetra

RANGE: Northern South America from Surinam to Venezuela.

HABITS: Peaceful with fishes of its own size or larger, but likely to pick on smaller ones.

WATER CONDITIONS: They prefer clean water, and their tank should be large. Temperature may range from 20 to 25°C.

SIZE: About 8 cm.

FOOD REQUIREMENTS: Greedy eaters, they may extend their appetites to some of the plants. Will also take all kinds of dried foods.

Bryconops affinis (Guenther) • Red-topped Tetra

RANGE: Found along with *B. melanurus* except for Colombia. This species is not as common as *melanurus*.

HABITS: This fish is more colorful in many respects than *B. melanurus*, a fish with which it is often confused for some reason. They sometimes school together, therefore are collected and shipped together.

WATER CONDITIONS: Thrives under normal aquarium conditions, pH 6.0-7.2 and a temperature from 24-30°C.

SIZE: Up to 65 mm.

FOOD REQUIREMENTS: Prefers small live foods but gets along well on a good dried aquarium diet.

Moenkhausia collettii (Steindachner) • Collett's Tetra

RANGE: Widely ranging throughout northern South America in large numbers.

HABITS: Found in quantity in shallow, slowly moving waters that are clear and slightly cool. They have never been spawned. The juveniles lack any color whatsoever.

WATER CONDITIONS: Slightly acid, cool waters about pH 6.5 and 23°C.

SIZE: To about 55 mm.

FOOD REQUIREMENTS: Does well on dried foods, but some live food makes them more active.

Moenkhausia gracilima (Eigenmann) • Graceful Moenkhausia

RANGE: Widely scattered over northern South America. There are several fishes that look alike, once again making identification difficult. This specimen was discovered by the author (HRA) in Tefe, Brazil.

HABITS: At times, when the fish is in breeding dress, the colors are intense and striking. These colors usually are good indications of species since the normal colors of many *Moenkhausia* are so similar. A very peaceful fish that makes a nice addition to a large tank if schools of them are available.

WATER CONDITIONS: A pH of 6.2-7.0 at a temperature of 25-30°C is recommended.

SIZE: About 60 mm.

FOOD REQUIREMENTS: Prefers live foods, especially brine shrimp and daphnia, which enhances their color.

167

Bryconops melanurus

Ctenobrycon spilurus

Moenkhausia agnesae

Bryconops affinis

Moenkhausia georgiae

Moenkhausia collettii

Moenkhausia intermedia

Moenkhausia gracilima

Plate #97

Moenkhausia

Moenkhausia lepidura

Moenkhausia oligolepis

Moenkhausia sanctaefilomenae

Moenkhausia lepidura icae

Moenkhausia pittieri

Moenkhausia robertsi

Moenkhausia takasei

Plate #98

169

Moenkhausia ? • Moenkhausia Question Mark

RANGE: *Moenkhausia* ranges over northern South America but this species is nowhere abundant.

HABITS: *Moenkhausia* Question Mark isn't as funny as it sounds! It looks a lot like *Moenkhausia comma* from the Amazon Basin and may be one of the prettiest species of *Moenkhausia* with its specially marked humeral spot ringed in gold and a golden line running into the blood red tail. The author (HRA) discovered this fish and brought back some specimens that were necessarily carried in the unheated hold of the plane where they all died.

WATER CONDITIONS: They thrive in slightly acid water that's a bit cool; pH 6.4 at 25°C.

SIZE: Up to 100 mm; perhaps larger.

FOOD REQUIREMENTS: In nature they have insects as their main diet but they probably will accept any small live foods.

Moenkhausia oligolepis (Guenther) • Glass Tetra

RANGE: Guyana and the upper Amazon regions.

HABITS: Quite peaceful, but must not be kept with smaller fishes.

WATER CONDITIONS: Soft, slightly acid water and a large tank are required. Temperature 22 to 25°C.

SIZE: 11 cm, usually smaller.

FOOD REQUIREMENTS: Must be fed generously with mostly live or frozen foods; if hungry they may nip plants.

Moenkhausia lepidura icae Eigenmann

The description of *Moenkhausia lepidura* applies to this subspecies from Rio Ica as well.

Moenkhausia robertsi Gery • Iquitos Moenkhausia

RANGE: Upper Amazon. The fish shown here was discovered by the author (HRA) near Iquitos, Peru.

HABITS: A very active and hardy fish for the aquarium. It has never been spawned but it doesn't appear to be a fish that would give the serious breeder a problem.

WATER CONDITIONS: Slightly acid, about pH 6.6-7.0, at a temperature ranging from 25 to 30°C.

SIZE: About 60 mm.

FOOD REQUIREMENTS: Prefers live foods but easily acclimates to an aquarium diet.

Moenkhausia lepidura (Kner) • Half-mast Flag Tetra

RANGE: Throughout the Amazon basin north to the Guianas. Very abundant and with slightly different coloration in some forms (see *Bryconops affinis*).

HABITS: The *Lepidura*-group of *Moenkhausia* have all their color concentrated in the unpaired fins especially along the dorsal edges, including only the upper lobe of the caudal (tail) fin. Compare this coloration to *Bryconops* sp. cf. *affinis*, *B. melanurus*, and *M. l. icae*. Note that all have the same color pattern even though they do not have the same colors.

WATER CONDITIONS: They thrive in acid water, pH 6.0-6.4, at 27°C but they get along in a widely variable environment.

SIZE: To 56 mm.

FOOD REQUIREMENTS: They enjoy live food and attack it voraciously, but they can easily be trained to accept flake foods, too.

Moenkhausia sanctaefilomenae (Steindachner) • Yellow-banded Moenkhausia

RANGE: Paraguay Basin.

HABITS: Peaceful toward other fishes and very active.

WATER CONDITIONS: Not critical, but slightly acid, soft water is preferred. Temperature 24 to 26°C.

SIZE: To 7 cm.

FOOD REQUIREMENTS: Omnivorous, with a good appetite; if fed with a good amount of vegetable substances, it will not nibble plants to any great extent.

Moenkhausia pittieri Eigenmann • Diamond Tetra

RANGE: Environs of Lake Valencia, Venezuela.

HABITS: Peaceful and very active.

WATER CONDITIONS: Large, well-planted tanks are best. Temperature 24 to 27°C.

SIZE: To 6 cm.

FOOD REQUIREMENTS: A good eater which will take practically any kind of food but should have a supplement of vegetable matter, like lettuce leaves.

COLOR VARIATIONS: Body color yellowish, darker above; upper half of body gleams golden, the lower part iridescent; unpaired fins milky violet.

Moenkhausia takasei Gery • Takase's Moenkhausia

RANGE: This species was discovered and collected by Mr. Takase and Harald Schultz in the Mato Grosso region of Brazil and other areas south of the Amazon.

HABITS: Takase was a Japanese fish collector and breeder who settled in Sao Paulo, Brazil and became friends with the author (HRA) and Harald Schultz. The author frequently sent him fishes from the jungle to be held for months until it was time to return to New Jersey. Specimens were sent to Dr. Gery with the request to name it in honor of Takase. All specimens living were given to Takase but they all perished before he was able to breed them and nothing is known about their aquarium habits.

SIZE: To about 45 mm.

FOOD REQUIREMENTS: They ate flake foods in the jungle when we kept them in net traps; Takase fed them live foods.

Moenkhausia sp. • Undescribed Moenkhausia species

Throughout Brazil where the author (HRA) has spent almost 40 years collecting both fishes and fish fossils, he has discovered some 26 different *Moenkhausia*. Many (most) of them have never been described because of the complexity of the task or the lack of interest by scientists who by their very nature work slowly and carefully. Through this book you will find fishes that are simply called "species" because they have not been identified. Hopefully, in future editions of this book there will be additional information or the fishes will be described so that we can give a name to these "species." They have never been imported alive and nothing is known about their aquarium needs.

Tetragonopterus argenteus Cuvier • Silver Tetra

RANGE: Amazon and La Plata Basins.
HABITS: Generally peaceful, but larger individuals may become unsociable.
WATER CONDITIONS: Prefers mature, slightly acid water with a hardness about 10°DH. Temperature should be about 24° to 27°C.
SIZE: About 115 mm.
FOOD REQUIREMENTS: Will accept a wide variety of foods including brine shrimp, daphnia, tubifex, mosquito larvae, chironomid larvae, and flake foods.

Schultzites axelrodi Gery • Axelrod's Moenkhausia

RANGE: Discovered by the author (HRA) in the Rio Meta, Colombia.
HABITS: It closely resembles the two fishes *Moenkhausia dichroura* and *M. intermedia* but it has twice as many teeth as they do which is obvious as soon as you see them. They behave well in an aquarium but they probably are scale eaters who mimic the *Moenkhausia*.
WATER CONDITIONS: Cooler water with a pH 6.4-7.0 at 24°C.
SIZE: Reaches about 100 mm but most of the specimens are half that size.
FOOD REQUIREMENTS: They seem to accept flake foods as well as live foods. They never eat scales in the aquarium but the stomach contents of two fish collected by the author had scales in them.

Gymnocorymbus ternetzi (Boulenger) • Black Tetra

RANGE: Paraguay and Rio Guapore Basins in southern Brazil, Argentina and Bolivia.
HABITS: A fast moving fish which is responsible for some fin nipping, but it cannot do real damage to fishes larger than itself.
WATER CONDITIONS: This is not a warm water fish as so many people think. It does best in temperatures in the low 20's (°C).
SIZE: In nature specimens as large as 8 cm are found; tank-raised specimens rarely grow larger than 4 cm.
FOOD REQUIREMENTS: To be at its best this fish requires live food, but it can live for years with nothing but pelletized dry food and a bit of frozen brine shrimp now and then.

Tetragonopterus chalceus Agassiz • False Silver Tetra

RANGE: Throughout South America east of the Andes, but mostly from the Guianas and Rio Sao Francisco.
HABITS: An easily collected fish as it favors small, open slow-moving streams making netting it easy. The genus *Tetragonopterus* was once the catchall genus for some 130+ species of "tetras."
WATER CONDITIONS: Slightly acid and cool water with a pH 6.5 and a water temperature between 23-25°C.
SIZE: Reaches about 100 mm.
FOOD REQUIREMENTS: Eats everything that is normal for aquarium fishes including flake foods and live foods.

Bario steindachneri (Eigenmann) • Blotch-tailed Bario

RANGE: Peruvian Amazon.
HABITS: Peaceful toward fishes of comparable size.
WATER CONDITIONS: Prefers slightly acid, clean, soft water. Temperature 24 to 27°C.
SIZE: Specimens of 10 cm have been known.
FOOD REQUIREMENTS: Eats all kinds of foods, but is especially fond of frozen brine shrimp. Live foods should be offered once a week.

Gymnocorymbus socolofi Gery • Rio Meta Black Tetra

RANGE: Upper Rio Meta, Colombia.
HABITS: This species was discovered by the author (HRA) in the 1960's. It became quite popular when it was imported in large numbers because it was found with other valuable fish and the success of the collecting ventures depended upon filling an airplane full of fishes. Once the economic pressure disappeared the fish fell into disfavor because of its tendency to bite other fishes and it was no longer worth collecting for itself.
WATER CONDITIONS: Acid water with the pH about 6.0 and with a temperature between 25-27°C.
SIZE: Reaches over 100 mm.
FOOD REQUIREMENTS: Unless it is fed live foods it loses its red color. Insects especially (drosophila) are needed to keep this fish in color.

Moenkhausia sp.

Moenkhausia sp.

Tetragonopterus argenteus

Tetragonopterus chalceus

Schultzites axelrodi

Bario steindachneri

Gymnocorymbus ternetzi

Gymnocorymbus socolofi

Plate #99

Gymnocorymbus thayeri

Gymnocorymbus thayeri

Hyphessobrycon bifasciatus

Hyphessobrycon griemi

Hyphessobrycon minimus

Hyphessobrycon flammeus

Hyphessobrycon peruvianus

Hyphessobrycon loretoensis

Plate #100

173

Gymnocorymbus thayeri Eigenmann • Straight-finned Black Tetra

RANGE: Upper Amazon, Bolivia and Colombia in warmer waters.
HABITS: A fast swimming fish which should be well fed at all times if kept in a community aquarium.
WATER CONDITIONS: Prefers warmer, softer and more acid waters than its much blacker cousin, *G. ternetzi*. Temperature 24 to 26°C.
SIZE: Not larger than 5 cm.
FOOD REQUIREMENTS: Prefers copious feedings of live foods, but does equally well if fed frozen brine shrimp and a varied diet of prepared foods. Some live food should be offered weekly.

Hyphessobrycon bifasciatus Ellis • Yellow Tetra

RANGE: Southeastern Brazil, near the coast.
HABITS: Very peaceful; will not attack other fishes or plants.
WATER CONDITIONS: Neutral to slightly acid. Temperature 22 to 24°C.
SIZE: Up to 5 cm.
FOOD REQUIREMENTS: All foods gratefully eaten, prepared as well as live or frozen.

Hyphessobrycon griemi Hoedeman • Griem's Tetra

RANGE: Brazil, in the vicinity of Goyaz.
HABITS: Perfectly peaceful; like the other small members of the family, they also prefer to be kept in groups of at least six.
WATER CONDITIONS: Soft, slightly acid water is best but not necessarily essential. Temperature 24 to 26°C.
SIZE: About 4 cm.
FOOD REQUIREMENTS: Prepared foods are accepted, but live or frozen foods are preferable.

Hyphessobrycon minimus Durbin • False Gold Tetra

RANGE: Guyana.
HABITS: A peaceful little characin that often came in mixed with similar looking fishes from Guyana. It was never pretty enough to be spawned commercially as cheap imports were always available.
WATER CONDITIONS: Water with a pH of 6.4-7.2 and a temperature between 25-30°C.
SIZE: Up to about 65 mm.
FOOD REQUIREMENTS: Likes all kinds of typical aquarium diets.

Hyphessobrycon flammeus Myers • Flame Tetra, Red Tetra, Tetra from Rio

RANGE: Region near Rio de Janeiro.
HABITS: Peaceful; best kept with other small fishes and in a school of at least six.
WATER CONDITIONS: Not critical; water is best if slightly acid and soft, but this is not absolutely essential. Temperature of 24 to 26°C.
SIZE: To 4 cm.
FOOD REQUIREMENTS: Prepared foods accepted, but live or frozen foods are preferred.

Hyphessobrycon peruvianus Ladiges • Loreto Tetra

RANGE: Peruvian Amazon.
HABITS: Peaceful and a bit shy; should not be kept with large or aggressive fishes.
WATER CONDITIONS: Soft, slightly acid water is best but is not absolutely essential. Temperature 24 to 28°C.
SIZE: 5 cm; most specimens smaller.
FOOD REQUIREMENTS: Live foods preferred, but frozen or prepared foods are accepted without any trouble.

Hyphessobrycon loretoensis Ladiges • Tetra Loreto

RANGE: Peruvian Amazon.
HABITS: A very peaceful fish that previously was imported in huge quantities but gradually fell into disfavor. It is rarely seen any more as tank-bred specimens lose much of their purple color.
WATER CONDITIONS: Do best in acid water at a pH of 6.0-6.6 and a temperature between 26-30°C.
SIZE: A small tetra about 40 mm.
FOOD REQUIREMENTS: Likes newly hatched brine shrimp as do most fishes, but it accepts fine flake foods as well.

Hyphessobrycon saizi Gery • Saiz' Tetra

RANGE: Colombia, where it was discovered by the author (HRA) and named after an employee of TFH, Capt. Emilio Saiz.
HABITS: This is probably just a diseased form of *H. metae,* but it doesn't matter since the fish has disappeared. This strange disappearance adds strength to the conclusion that the fish is *H. metae* with the gold disease.
WATER CONDITIONS: Slightly acid water (pH 6.5) at a temperature of 25°C.
SIZE: Almost 53 mm.
FOOD REQUIREMENTS: Eats a normal aquarium diet.

Hyphessobrycon agulha Fowler • Red-tailed Flag Tetra

RANGE: Upper Amazon region.
HABITS: Peaceful; likes to swim in schools.
WATER CONDITIONS: Soft, slightly acid water. Temperature 24 to 26°C.
SIZE: About 5 cm.
FOOD REQUIREMENTS: Will accept dried foods, but live or frozen foods should be given frequently.

Hyphessobrycon herbertaxelrodi Gery • Black Neon Tetra

RANGE: Rio Taquary, Brazil.
HABITS: Peaceful toward other fishes; prefers to be kept in a group of at least six.
WATER CONDITIONS: Soft, slightly acid water preferred but not essential. Temperature 25°C.
SIZE: About 3 cm.
FOOD REQUIREMENTS: Hearty eaters; prepared foods as well as live or frozen foods are eaten with equal gusto.

Hyphessobrycon scholzei Ahl • Black-lined Tetra

RANGE: Vicinity of Para, Brazil.
HABITS: Peaceful; will not harm other fishes or plants.
WATER CONDITIONS: Soft and slightly acid water is preferable but not essential. Temperature 23 to 26°C.
SIZE: To 5 cm.
FOOD REQUIREMENTS: Prepared foods accepted readily, but they should be supplemented with frozen and live foods.

Hyphessobrycon vilmae Gery • Vilma's Tetra

RANGE: Northern and central Brazil.
HABITS: A lively nature yet not aggressive, but can be a fin-nipper.
WATER CONDITIONS: Somewhat on the acid size; a small fluctuation of DH will be tolerated. Temperature 24°C.
SIZE: To 4 cm.
FOOD REQUIREMENTS: Will accept freeze-dried foods and also dry foods; live foods are naturally relished.

Hyphessobrycon heterorhabdus (Ulrey) • Flag Tetra, False Ulreyi

RANGE: Lower and middle Amazon region.
HABITS: Peaceful and very active.
WATER CONDITIONS: A little sensitive if not given soft, slightly acid water. Temperature should be kept around 25°C.
SIZE: About 5 cm.
FOOD REQUIREMENTS: Will take dried foods readily, but should also get frequent feedings of live or frozen foods.

Hyphessobrycon georgettae Gery • Georgette's Tetra

RANGE: Surinam.
HABITS: A pretty little tetra that Dr. Jacques Gery thought was pretty enough to be named after his wife, Georgette. The fish is nicely colored when wild and the translucent flesh is rose colored, but after being bred once the fish is not very attractive unless fed heavily on brine shrimp.
WATER CONDITIONS: Acid water, about pH 6.3, and a temperature of 25-30°C.
SIZE: About 50 mm.
FOOD REQUIREMENTS: Needs live brine shrimp but subsists on the normal aquarium diet.

Hyphessobrycon saizi

Hyphessobrycon agulha

Hyphessobrycon herbertaxelrodi

Hyphessobrycon scholzei

Hyphessobrycon vilmae

Hyphessobrycon heterorhabdus

Hyphessobrycon heterorhabdus (gold?)

Hyphessobrycon georgettae

Plate #101

176

Above: Beginning the spawning ritual, the male (lower fish in both photos) pursues the female and drives her through the tank. Below: At left, the male displays before the female near the plant thicket; at right, the fish have entered the plant thicket and are shown just before the actual moment of spawning.

Plate #102

SPAWNING THE SERPAE TETRA, *HYPHESSOBRYCON SERPAE*

The serpae tetra does best in schooling groups. One should, therefore, keep 8 to 12 of them in a roomy tank. At a minimum temperature of 20°C, they feel happiest in a medium to large tank with good illumination. The water should be clear, soft (but not too soft) and slightly acid.

The sexual differences among *H. serpae* individuals are not always easy to make out. Male and female look very much alike, and their coloration is the same. The adult male is more slender, however, and—as can be seen against the light—the male's air bladder is more pointed at its rear. For breeding, it is best to select a courting male from the school. Put the male in the spawning tank one day earlier than the female. The fish spawn very readily and are content with an all-glass tank containing 10 to 15 liters of water that is not too hard. The temperature should be raised to 24-26°C. The fish use fine-leaved plants for spawning. The male starts to court by fluttering about in front of the female; he later swims around the female on the way to the spawning site, though mostly he stays in front of her, luring her on and not getting alongside until immediately before the act of spawning. Sometimes, not always, the male puts his caudal fin underneath the female's body. With a sudden jerk, the sexual products are discharged, the fish separate, and the eggs fall down. All this happens within a fraction of a second. The act of spawning is repeated about 20 times within 2 to 4 hours, and several hundred eggs are laid. A good pair often produces 300 fry.

Immediately after the spawning has ended the parents should be removed from the spawning tank. No harm is done by darkening the spawning tank. As soon as the fry have resorbed their yolk sacs they should be given the finest live food, being graduated to larger fare as soon as they can eat it.

Hyphessobrycon copelandi Durbin • Callistus Tetra

RANGE: Upper and middle Amazon basin.
HABITS: This is one of the many tetras that have the same general shape and color pattern and that are found in non-overlapping ranges. Most of them are simply called *Hyphessobrycon* "callistus" in the aquarium trade.
WATER CONDITIONS: Slightly acid water with a pH of 6.4-6.8 and a water temperature between 25-30°C.
SIZE: About 48 mm.
FOOD REQUIREMENTS: Prefers live foods but gets along well on small aquarium foods.

Hyphessobrycon socolofi Weitzman • Lesser Bleeding Heart

RANGE: Upper Amazon basin.
HABITS: A pale, sickly looking fish when compared to the rest of the *Hyphessobrycon* on this page. It is far from an aquarium favorite and it probably has no future. It has never been bred and it is doubtful that it ever will. No fish with a deep red humeral spot in the family Characidae has ever been spawned. It is distinguished from the bleeding heart tetra by the uniform width of the white anal fin band.
WATER CONDITIONS: Survives under all normal aquarium conditions. No special requirements.
SIZE: Reach 60 mm.
FOOD REQUIREMENTS: Eats a normal aquarium diet.

Hyphessobrycon takasei Gery • Coffee Bean Tetra

RANGE: Amapa Territory in northern Brazil.
HABITS: Very peaceful; will not harm plants or other fishes.
WATER CONDITIONS: Soft, acid water is optimal. Temperature 24 to 26°C.
SIZE: About 3 cm.
FOOD REQUIREMENTS: Prefers live foods, but will accept frozen, freeze-dried or dried foods as well.

Hyphessobrycon serpae Durbin • Serpae Tetra

RANGE: Amazon River (Madeira and Guapore regions) and upper Paraguay.
HABITS: Mostly peaceful, but will sometimes take a dislike to a fish and nip fins.
WATER CONDITIONS: Soft, slightly acid water.

SIZE: Up to 4 cm; usually smaller.
FOOD REQUIREMENTS: Does very well on dried foods, but of course should get occasional feedings with live or frozen foods.

Hyphessobrycon erythrostigma (Fowler) • Bleeding Heart Tetra, Tetra Perez

RANGE: Upper Amazon.
HABITS: Peaceful if kept with fishes of its own size.
WATER CONDITIONS: Slightly acid, soft water. Temperature 23 to 26°C.
SIZE: To 8 cm.
FOOD REQUIREMENTS: Live or frozen foods preferred; prepared foods taken if hungry.

Hyphessobrycon bentosi Durbin • Rosy Tetra

RANGE: Amazon Basin and Guianas.
HABITS: Peaceful; should be kept in groups of at least six.
WATER CONDITIONS: Soft, slightly acid water is best. Temperature 24 to 27°C.
SIZE: To 5 cm.
FOOD REQUIREMENTS: Prepared foods accepted, but live and frozen foods preferred.

Hyphessobrycon species • Tetra Robertsi

RANGE: There are "robertsi" found in Peru, Colombia, and Brazil.
HABITS: There are many fish, mostly of a difficult scientific group, which are sold as "callistus", "robertsi", "Perez", etc. These are all what once were called "flag-fin" tetras. If you look at photos 7 and 8 you can see the most colorful (known as "robertsi") and most plain (known as "callistus").
WATER CONDITIONS: They prefer warm, slightly acid waters at a pH of 6.4-6.8 and a water temperature between 26-30°C.
SIZE: Up to 65 mm.
FOOD REQUIREMENTS: They prefer live foods but they take to a normal flake food diet without any difficulty.

179

Hyphessobrycon copelandi

Hyphessobrycon serpae

Hyphessobrycon socolofi

Hyphessobrycon erythrostigma

Hyphessobrycon takasei

Hyphessobrycon bentosi

Hyphessobrycon sp. (callistus group)

Hyphessobrycon sp. (tetra Robertsi)

Plate #103

180

Parapristella georgiae

Hemigrammus erythrozonus

Hemigrammus levis

Hemigrammus ocellifer

Hemigrammus stictus

Hemigrammus bellottii

Hemigrammus hyanuary

Hemigrammus marginatus

①
②
③
④
⑤
⑥
⑦
⑧

Plate #104

Parapristella georgiae Gery • Plain Jane

RANGE: Upper Rio Meta.
HABITS: A simple little tetra is probably a species of *Hemigrammus*. There are two species in this genus, the other being *P. aubynei* from Guyana which is probably a *Pristella*.
WATER CONDITIONS: Warm, slightly acid water with a pH of 6.5-6.8 and a temperature of 25-30°C.
SIZE: Barely reaches 76 mm.
FOOD REQUIREMENTS: Eats a normal aquarium diet but its strong, numerous teeth indicate it is a live food eater, too.

Hemigrammus erythrozonus (Durbin) • Glowlight Tetra

RANGE: The Guianas and adjacent regions of the Amazon.
HABITS: One of the most peaceful of all tetras.
WATER CONDITIONS: Should have a clean aquarium at all times, with slightly acid, soft water. Temperature 23 to 26°C.
FOOD REQUIREMENTS: Will eat dry food, but this should often be augmented with live and frozen foods.
COLOR VARIATIONS: Body greenish and very transparent, with a brilliant, glowing red or purple line running from the upper edge of the eye to the caudal base.

Hemigrammus levis Durbin • Golden Neon

RANGE: The middle Amazon basin.
HABITS: Found in small, dark streams, this lovely fish doesn't look well in this photo but the body glistens with a metallic golden sheen that includes the dorsal, adipose, and upper caudal lobe, the lateral line, and the upper part of the eye and operculum. Add to this a peaceful hardy fish and you have the golden neon.
WATER CONDITIONS: Prefers acid water, pH 6.0-6.8, at a temperature of 26-30°C.
SIZE: A small tetra never reaching 50 mm.
FOOD REQUIREMENTS: Small live foods like brine shrimp should be given between normal feedings of flake foods.

Hemigrammus ocellifer (Steindachner) • Head and Tail Light

RANGE: Widely distributed throughout the Amazon region, especially in the southern part.
HABITS: Mostly peaceful, if kept with fishes their own size.
WATER CONDITIONS: Not critical, but warm temperatures are preferred. Temperature 25 to 26°C.
SIZE: About 4 cm.
FOOD REQUIREMENTS: Will get along very well on dry foods.

Hemigrammus stictus (Durbin)

RANGE: Throughout the Amazon basin north to the Guianas and the Rio Meta.
HABITS: A very peaceful fish which, in some habitats, is also very beautiful with a magnificent red blotch covering the caudal peduncle and the central parts of the caudal fin. The redness envelops the rear of the body including the adipose fin.
WATER CONDITIONS: Very acid water is preferred, from pH 5.8-6.4 at a temperature of 26-30°C. It loses the red when the water is not acid enough.
SIZE: To about 55 mm.
FOOD REQUIREMENTS: Prefers live foods, but this peaceful species gets along on the usual aquarium diet, too.

Hemigrammus bellottii (Steindachner) • Dash-Dot Tetra

RANGE: Upper Amazon tributaries.
HABITS: Peaceful and active; prefer to swim in a group of their own kind.
WATER CONDITIONS: Soft, acid water preferred. Temperature 24 to 27°C.
SIZE: To 2.5 cm.
FOOD REQUIREMENTS: Because of their small size, small foods of all kinds are recommended.

Hemigrammus hyanuary (Durbin) • January Tetra

RANGE: Amazon tributaries near Leticia, Colombia.
HABITS: Very peaceful; prefers to be in a school with others of its own kind.
WATER CONDITIONS: Not critical; best is water which is neutral to slightly acid in character. Temperature 23 to 26°C.
SIZE: About 4 cm.
FOOD REQUIREMENTS: Live or frozen foods are of course preferred, but dried foods are also accepted eagerly.

Hemigrammus marginatus Ellis • Bassam Tetra

RANGE: Venezuela to Argentina.
HABITS: Peaceful.
WATER CONDITIONS: Fairly soft and slightly acid. Temperature 24 to 26°C.
SIZE: To 7 cm.
FOOD REQUIREMENTS: Live or frozen foods preferred; will also accept prepared foods.

Hemigrammus rodwayi Durbin • Gold Tetra

RANGE: Guianas and the Upper Amazon.
HABITS: Peaceful; prefers to be kept in a school.
WATER CONDITIONS: Not critical, but water should be
    somewhere near neutral.
SIZE: About 5 cm.
FOOD REQUIREMENTS: Live foods preferred, but frozen and
    prepared foods are also readily accepted.

Hemigrammus pulcher Ladiges • Garnet Tetra

RANGE: Peruvian Amazon, Loreto region.
HABITS: Peaceful; will not bother plants or other fishes.
WATER CONDITIONS: Prefers a roomy, well-planted tank.
    Most important requirement is warmth, 26 to 27°C.
SIZE: About 5 cm.
FOOD REQUIREMENTS: Will not refuse dried foods, but
    should be given frequent changes to live or frozen foods.
COLOR VARIATIONS: Greenish body with a small shoulder
    spot and indistinct horizontal line. Upper half of caudal
    base deep red, with black area below.

Hemigrammus unilineatus (Gill) • Featherfin Tetra

RANGE: Trinidad and northern South America from Venezuela
    to Brazil.
HABITS: Peaceful; a heavy eater which should have plenty
    of swimming room.
WATER CONDITIONS: Should have a sunny aquarium with
    fairly high temperatures, 26 to 27°C.
SIZE: Attains a length of 5 cm; most specimens smaller.
FOOD REQUIREMENTS: Like all active fish, a heavy eater.
    If possible, should be fed several times daily. Will take
    dried foods, but live foods should also be fed.
COLOR VARIATIONS: Body silvery with a gold horizontal
    stripe. First rays of the dorsal and anal fins white, with a
    black streak behind. Brazilian variety has red fins.

Hemigrammus mattei Eigenmann • Slender head and tail light

RANGE: Paraguay, Argentina; probably more dispersed.
HABITS: A peaceful fish which during the period from 1920-
    1958 was very popular. It is now confused with every fish
    that has a shining spot over the eye and in the tail. The
    identification of this fish is tentative and it may well be a
    new species.
WATER CONDITIONS: Should be kept at   pH 6.4-7.2 and a
    temperature of 23-28°C.
SIZE: Up to 45 mm.
FOOD REQUIREMENTS: Prefers small living foods but also
    accepts a normal aquarium diet.

Hemigrammus boesemani (Gery) • Boeseman's Tetra

RANGE: Guianas and upper Amazon.
HABITS: A non descript fish that is only imported accidental-
    ly with other fishes. It has few redeeming features color-
    wise, but it is peaceful and when in superb condition does
    show a few metallic markings at the base of the upper
    caudal lobe and along the lateral line. It was formerly
    considered a subspecies of *H. micropterus.*
WATER CONDITIONS: pH 6.4-6.9 at a temperature of 25-30°C.
SIZE: To 52 mm.
FOOD REQUIREMENTS: Eats a normal aquarium diet.

Hemigrammus barrigone Eigenmann • Henn Meta Pink

RANGE: Rio Meta, Colombia.
HABITS: A robust and delightful fish for the aquarium. It
    changes colors dramatically but always in subtle shades
    of pink, gray, and white. The females (illustrated here)
    are very fat and full and have huge spawns of over 1,000
    eggs.
WATER CONDITIONS: A pH of 6.2-6.8 and a temperature of
    25-30°C.
SIZE: Barely reaches 50 mm.
FOOD REQUIREMENTS: Prefers live foods but takes flake
    foods readily.

Hemigrammus rodwayi (armstrongi var.)

Hemigrammus rodwayi

Hemigrammus pulcher pulcher

Hemigrammus pulcher haraldi

Hemigrammus unilineatus

Hemigrammus mattei

Hemigrammus boesemani

Plate #105

Hemigrammus barrigone

184

The false wimple piranha can be distinguished from the true wimple piranha mainly through a comparison of the length of the anterior rays of the dorsal and anal fins. In the photos on this page, (note especially the close up of the ventral area above right) which are of the false wimple piranha, the anterior dorsal and anal rays are seen to extend beyond the tips of the caudal lobes. Additionally, the red spot present on the cheek of many true wimple piranhas is not present on any of the false wimple piranhas.

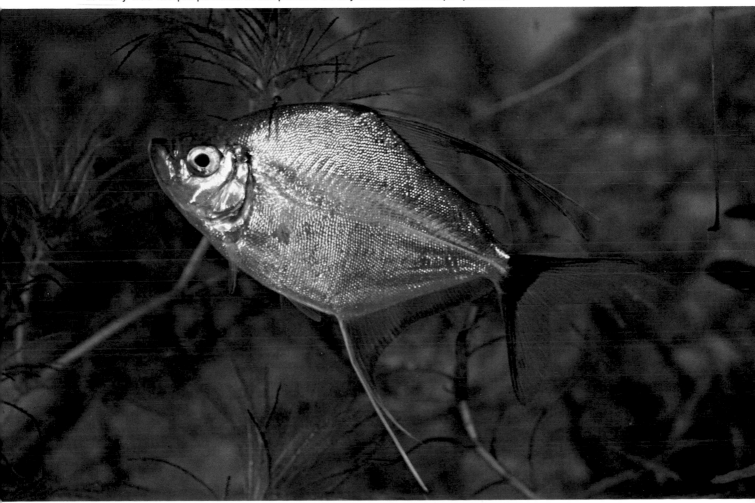

Plate #106

THE FALSE WIMPLE PIRANHA, *CATOPRION* "BLEHER"

The Mato Grosso of Brazil is a huge piece of real estate—this single Brazilian state has an area the size of Texas, Utah, Nebraska and Colorado combined. In its western corner along the Bolivian border is a virtually unexplored system of rivers, streams, and swamps that are part of the Rio Guapore drainage. Few collectors—or even scientists—have ventured into this country, but it was here that Heiko Bleher, German fish collector and dealer *extraordinaire,* collected the regal false wimple piranha. Seemingly an undescribed species, its graceful finnage puts it in a class with only the angelfish among freshwater fishes when it comes to length of fins. Heiko was able to collect only 17 specimens after days of intensive diving in the dense caiman-infested aquatic gardens of the Guapore, also making this one of the rarest and most desirable of recent aquarium imports.

Even the true wimple piranha, *Catoprion mento,* is far from being a common fish in the aquarium hobby, and there are few specimens in museum collections. The oddly undershot lower jaw of the wimples is a specialization for scale-eating, although this unusual habit was only confirmed a bit over 30 years ago. In the aquarium the wimples take most normal aquarium foods as well as small fishes and seldom bother their neighbors for a bite of scales.

The most obvious difference between the true wimple piranha and the undescribed false wimple is of course the length of the anterior rays of the dorsal and anal fins. In fully developed specimens of the new species these rays extend beyond the tips of the caudal lobes. The red spot on the cheek that is so prominent in at least many true wimples seems to be lacking in *Catoprion* "Bleher," and there are probably consistent small differences in structural characters. Dr. Jacques Gery, eminent authority on the taxonomy of the characoid fishes, is studying the status of the false wimple and will eventually clarify the situation.

Heiko Bleher reported in full on his trip to the Mato Grosso in the June, 1983, issue of *Tropical Fish Hobbyist* magazine, an article well worth reading.

Hemigrammus schmardae (Steindachner) • Schmard Tetra

RANGE: Upper Rio Negro River, Brazil.
HABITS: Very peaceful.
WATER CONDITIONS: Soft, acid water preferred, but not essential. Temperature 24 to 27°C.
SIZE: Up to 5 cm.
FOOD REQUIREMENTS: Dried as well as live foods.

Hemigrammus rhodostomus Ahl • Rummy-nose Tetra

RANGE: Lower Amazon region, around Aripiranga and Para.
HABITS: Peaceful; is most at home with lively fishes of about its own size.
WATER CONDITIONS: Best kept in a well planted, well established, well heated tank. Temperature about 26°C.
SIZE: 4 to 5 cm.
FOOD REQUIREMENTS: Will get along fairly well on dried food, but should get an occasional meal of live or frozen food.

Hemigrammus caudovittatus Ahl • Buenos Aires Tetra

RANGE: Region around Buenos Aires.
HABITS: Fairly peaceful with fishes about its size; should not be kept with thread-finned fishes, whose fins it nips.
WATER CONDITIONS: Neutral to slightly acid. Can withstand temperatures around 21°C for a time; should be kept about 25° normally.
SIZE: About 10 cm.
FOOD REQUIREMENTS: Seems to like dried foods as well as live foods; has a good appetite and should be fed generously.

Axelrodia lindeae Gery • Lindy Tetra

RANGE: Amazon basin near Obidos and Porto Velho.
HABITS: An extremely peaceful fish, as are all fishes of the genus. *Axelrodia* was named in honor of the author (HRA) by Dr. Jacques Gery. Only a few specimens of this species were brought out alive by the author, and they did not survive to be bred.
WATER CONDITIONS: Normal water at a pH of 6.4-7.2; temperature 25-30°C.
SIZE: Mostly less than 4 cm.
FOOD REQUIREMENTS: Does best on brine shrimp but accepts any aquarium diet small enough for it to ingest.

Hemigrammus coeruleus Durbin • Coerulean Tetra

RANGE: Manacapuru, Brazil.
HABITS: Peaceful when kept with fishes of its own size.
WATER CONDITIONS: Neutral to slightly acid. Temperature 23 to 26°C.
SIZE: To about 7.5 cm.
FOOD REQUIREMENTS: Will accept prepared foods, but should also get live and frozen foods.

Hasemania nana (Reinhardt) • Silver-tipped Tetra

RANGE: Rio S. Francisco basin, southeastern Brazil.
HABITS: Very peaceful; should be kept in a school of not less than six.
WATER CONDITIONS: Slightly acid and soft water. Temperature 24 to 26°C.
SIZE: To 5 cm.
FOOD REQUIREMENTS: Prepared foods accepted, but live or frozen foods are preferred.

Hemigrammus "Goldi" • Red-finned Hemigrammus

RANGE: Amazon basin; extends north and south but very rare in all ranges.
HABITS: This is, unfortunately, a poor picture of a great fish discovered by the author (HRA). All fins except the caudal and pectorals are red with red spots at their bases. There is a large humeral spot, the tail is dark, and the centers of the scales are pigmented and dark.
WATER CONDITIONS: This specimen was gill-netted and lost many scales. It is found in very small streams with slightly acid, clear water with a pH of 6.2-6.8 at 23-28°C.
SIZE: Reaches over 5.5 cm.

Hemigrammus schmardae

Hemigrammus rhodostomus

Hemigrammus caudovittatus

Hemigrammus caudovittatus

Axelrodia lindeae

Hemigrammus coeruleus

Hasemania nana

Hemigrammus "Goldi"

Plate #107

188

Thayeria obliqua

Thayeria boehlkei

Phenacogaster pectinatus

Vesicatrus tegatus

Hyphessobrycon bifasciatus var.

Phenacogaster pectinatus

Petitella georgiae

Stichonodon insignis

Plate #108

189

Thayeria obliqua Eigenmann • Short-striped Penguin

RANGE: Middle Amazon region.
HABITS: Active swimmers and peaceful; may be kept in the community aquarium.
WATER CONDITIONS: Water should be soft and slightly acid. Best temperature 24 to 26°C.
SIZE: 8 cm.
FOOD REQUIREMENTS: Will take dried foods, but these should be alternated frequently with live foods.

Thayeria boehlkei Weitzman • Boehlke's Penguin

RANGE: Amazon region of Brazil (especially near Obidos).
HABITS: Peaceful, active fish that do well in a small group or school.
WATER CONDITIONS: Not critical but do better in neutral to slightly acid water; lights should not be too bright. Temperature 22 to 24°C.
SIZE: Maximum size is about 8 cm.
FOOD REQUIREMENTS: Not critical; will eat most of the usual foods.

Phenacogaster pectinatus (Cope) • Pectinatus

RANGE: Middle and upper Amazon basin.
HABITS: Generally peaceful at all times.
WATER CONDITIONS: Soft, slightly acid water. Temperature 22 to 27°C.
SIZE: About 5 cm.
FOOD REQUIREMENTS: This species is omnivorous and should be given a mixed diet of plant and animal matter; it will accept prepared flake food but prefers small live or frozen foods.

Vesicatrus tegatus Eigenmann • Tegatus

RANGE: Upper Paraguay basin.
HABITS: This is a single-species genus. The fish looks and acts like most of the small tetras of the genus *Hemigrammus*. The only ones brought in were imported by the author (HRA), who kept them for more than a year but was unable to spawn them. They are from colder waters and do well in an unheated aquarium.
WATER CONDITIONS: Water between pH 6.4-7.2 at 20-25°C.
SIZE: Reaches about 5 cm.
FOOD REQUIREMENTS: Prefers live foods but does well on a normal aquarium diet.

Hyphessobrycon bifasciatus Ellis • Copper Bifasciatus

RANGE: Southeastern Brazil.
HABITS: This is one of the copper tetras that have been identified as parasitized forms of *H. bifasciatus*, but this is doubtful since the two black humeral bands of *H. bifasciatus* are missing. This is probably another new species.
WATER CONDITIONS: Prefers warm, acid water with a pH of 6.0-6.6 at a temperature of 26-30°C.
SIZE: Reaches 5.2 cm.
FOOD REQUIREMENTS: Survives on a normal aquarium diet.

Petitella georgiae Gery and Boutiere • False Rummy-nose

RANGE: Upper Amazon basin.
HABITS: Peaceful; best kept in schools.
WATER CONDITIONS: Soft, acidic water is preferred but is not crucial. Best temperature is 23 to 25°C.
SIZE: To 8 cm.
FOOD REQUIREMENTS: Accepts all standard aquarium foods and especially relishes live freshwater crustaceans like daphnia.

Stichonodon insignis Steindachner • Tefe Gymnocorymbus

RANGE: The author (HRA) collected this specimen at Tefe, Brazil, but they are reported throughout the Amazon.
HABITS: The rounded body that resembles the black tetra in form is responsible for its popular name. There is only one species in the genus, and it was only imported once by the author. It has never been spawned.
WATER CONDITIONS: Acid, warm water with a pH of 6.0-6.8 at about 28°C.
SIZE: Reaches to at least 8 cm.
FOOD REQUIREMENTS: A voracious eater that likes falling foods.

Brittanichthys axelrodi Gery • Blood-red Tetra

RANGE: Found in Rio Negro streams near Manaus by Dr. Martin Brittan, one of the world's greatest experts on *Rasbora*. It has never been brought in alive. Dr. Brittan's description of the living fish is the only basis for reports about this legendary fish. This is the only photo known, too. Dr. Brittan says the fish is blood-red. . . "It looks like it's really bleeding!" The fish shown here had been dead for a day or so.

WATER CONDITIONS: Prefers acid water, as the stream in which it was found had a pH of 6.0 at 28°C.

SIZE: Probably reaches about 6 cm.

FOOD REQUIREMENTS: Not known exactly, but probably eats a normal diet.

Megalamphodus "Rubra" • Red Megalamphodus

RANGE: Throughout Peru and Colombia in very small pockets; nowhere abundant. Several importations were made by the author (HRA), but they were never spawned.

HABITS: A very beautiful species occupying the ecological niche of *M. sweglesi* where *sweglesi* doesn't exist. Much prettier than *sweglesi*. There are two vertical humeral bars not quite evident in this photo.

WATER CONDITIONS: Warm acid waters at a pH of 6.0-6.4, with the water at a temperature of about 28°C.

SIZE: Barely reaches 4.5 cm.

FOOD REQUIREMENTS: Likes live foods, as do most tetras, but gets along on a normal aquarium diet. Loses color if not fed brine shrimp or daphnia once in a while.

Megalamphodus sweglesi Gery • Swegles' Tetra

RANGE: Amazon region near Leticia, Colombia.

HABITS: Peaceful; like the other tetras, they prefer to be in schools.

WATER CONDITIONS: Soft, slightly acid water is preferred. Temperature 24 to 26°C.

SIZE: About 4 cm.

FOOD REQUIREMENTS: Easily fed; prefers live foods, but frozen and prepared foods also accepted.

COLOR VARIATIONS: Body reddish brown with a large lateral spot of black. Male's dorsal fin is high and pointed, the female's smaller and round.

Megalamphodus megalopterus Eigenmann • Black Phantom Tetra

RANGE: Brazil.

HABITS: Peaceful and active.

WATER CONDITIONS: Soft, acid water is best, especially for breeding. Temperature 23 to 26°C.

SIZE: 4 cm.

FOOD REQUIREMENTS: Accepts live, frozen and dried foods.

Megalamphodus axelrodi (Travassos) • Calypso Tetra, Red Pristella

RANGE: Trinidad.

HABITS: Peaceful; likes to swim in schools.

WATER CONDITIONS: Soft, slightly acid water. Temperature 24 to 27°C.

SIZE: About 3 cm.

FOOD REQUIREMENTS: Takes all foods eagerly, including dried flakes, but should have an occasional meal of live or frozen food.

Pristella maxillaris (Ulrey) • Pristella

RANGE: Northern South America.

HABITS: Peaceful and active; swims in schools.

WATER CONDITIONS: Soft, slightly acid water. Temperature 24 to 26°C.

SIZE: To 5 cm.

FOOD REQUIREMENTS: Not at all choosy; live foods should be offered as often as available.

COLOR VARIATIONS: Sides silvery to yellowish; dorsal and anal fins each have a large black spot on a white background; tail reddish to bright red.

Cheirodon insignis Steindachner • Insignificant Tetra

RANGE: Venezuela and Colombia.

HABITS: Discovered by the author (HRA) and imported, but it never became a hit. It was never spawned and was never imported again.

WATER CONDITIONS: Gets along in clear streams with a pH between 6.8-7.4 at a temperature of about 28°C.

SIZE: The specimens collected by the author barely reached 50 mm.

FOOD REQUIREMENTS: They eat everything usually offered to aquarium fishes and small enough to ingest.

Brittanichthys axelrodi

Megalamphodus "Rubra"

Megalamphodus sweglesi

Megalamphodus sweglesi

Megalamphodus megalopterus

Megalamphodus axelrodi

Pristella maxillaris

Cheirodon insignis

Plate #109

The eager-to-spawn male positions himself across the path of the heavily egg-laden female.

Having coaxed the female into the plant thicket, the male approaches her from the side.

Actively entwining their bodies, the spawning pair hover quiveringly above the plants.

Momentarily stupefied by their spawning ecstasy, the dazed spawning partners begin to separate; note the eggs in the water.

Plate #110

SPAWNING THE NEON TETRA
PARACHEIRODON INNESI

Neon tetras have long been one of the best known and most popular of all tropical fishes. They inhabit the streams of the Peruvian Amazon near Iquitos and the Yarapa River, where they travel about in schools sometimes reaching into the hundreds of thousands. Neons come from water that are nearly void of minerals, being derived to a large extent from rain water. Their colors are brought out to the fullest in water that is soft, clear and slightly acid, with a temperature between 22° and 25°C. They reach a maximum length of 37 mm, but the majority are 25 mm or less.

When attempting to breed this species, choose an attractively colored pair that is over nine months old. (Females will be filled with eggs.) Condition on ample helpings of live and freeze-dried foods. A 20-liter all-glass breeding tank that is dimly lit should be provided with several bunches of rinsed plants.

Water conditions are particularly important at this time. The water should be very soft, no more than 3 DH, acid (pH 6.5), with a temperature ranging about 23-24°C with the addition of half a teaspoon of salt to each liter. The tank must be kept clean, and there should be light aeration.

When the female has become swollen with roe, place the pair into the breeding tank. If there aren't any spawning activities within two days, remove and condition them a few more days on more generous feedings of live foods. Spawning consists of an active chase through the plant thickets. About 60 to 130 non-adhesive eggs are scattered throughout the tank.

Remove the breeders when spawning is completed and cover the tank until the eggs hatch, since they are very sensitive to light. They hatch in about a day. Keep the fry covered until the fifth day, when they are free-swimming, then increase the light gradually. Feed them the yolk of hard-boiled eggs squeezed through a porous cloth.

Paracheirodon axelrodi Schultz • Cardinal Tetra

RANGE: Upper Rio Negro and Colombian waterways.
HABITS: Perfectly peaceful and active. Likes to swim in schools, and therefore it is best to keep at least 6 of them together.
WATER CONDITIONS: Water should be soft, clean and on the acid side, about pH 6.5 or lower, in order to show the fish in its brightest colors. Temperature 21 to 24°C.
SIZE: 5 cm.
FOOD REQUIREMENTS: All foods, either live or prepared, should be given with their small size in mind. Not a fussy eater.
COLOR VARIATIONS: Back is brown on top. Horizontal stripe a brilliant blue-green. Lower part of body bright red, belly white.

Paracheirodon simulans Gery • False Neon

RANGE: Rio Negro, Brazil.
HABITS: Peaceful; likes to travel in schools.
WATER CONDITIONS: Water should be acid and very soft. Temperature 24 to 26°C.
SIZE: About 2.5 cm.
FOOD REQUIREMENTS: Small living foods preferred; probably would accept prepared or frozen foods readily.
COLOR VARIATIONS. Bright blue iridescent streak from opercle to caudal base, with an area of red above the anal fin.

Catoprion mento (Cuvier) • Wimple Piranha

RANGE: Nowhere is it abundant, but many are to be found in the Mato Grosso streams.
HABITS: Small specimens are found in shallow waters. This is a specimen that grew very long dorsal and anal fins and may be a species different from *mento*.
WATER CONDITIONS: Young fish like a pH of 6.2-7.0 and water at 28-29°C, but they get along well in the usual aquarium environment.
SIZE: They reach 200 mm.
FOOD REQUIREMENTS: They are reputed to eat scales by scraping them from other fishes, but they also eat tubificid worms and normal aquarium fare when they are small. The fish shown here is 52 mm long.

Curimata lineopunctata Boulenger • Spotted Curimata

RANGE: The author (HRA) collected this specimen in the Rio Calima, Colombia.
HABITS: This is a very rare species and only a few were caught. They might well be identified by the small black dot in the center of most of their scales.
WATER CONDITIONS: A pH of 6.2-6.8 at 27-29°C.
SIZE: Reach about 100 mm but only rarely; perhaps larger specimens are found in the rivers; this one was caught in a shallow stream.
FOOD REQUIREMENTS: Does well on a normal aquarium diet of flake foods.

Paracheirodon innesi (Myers) • Neon Tetra

RANGE: Upper course of the Rio Solimoes (= Amazon) and Rio Purus.
HABITS: Very peaceful; should be kept only with small fishes or in a tank of their own.
WATER CONDITIONS: Soft, clear, slightly acid water is preferred and brings out their best colors. Best temperature about 24°C.
SIZE: Maximum 4 cm; most specimens seen are about 2.5 cm or less.
FOOD REQUIREMENTS: Medium or finely ground dried foods, with occasional feedings of small live foods.

Bryconops "Gold" • Golden Bryconops

RANGE: Amazon Basin north to Venezuela.
HABITS: Prefers a shallow, slowly moving stream with aerated water. Only a few specimens were brought back by the author (HRA). The fish shown here had a huge parasite on its back that wasn't apparent at the time of collection.
WATER CONDITIONS: Normal aquarium water, pH 6.4-7.2 at temperature 23-30°C.
SIZE: Reaches almost 100 mm.
FOOD REQUIREMENTS: Ate a normal aquarium fare, including live foods.

Bryconops "Rose" • Rosy Bryconops

RANGE: The Amazon basin yields this fish, which is found mostly in shallow, heavily weeded shorelines and more open waters where the fish occur in large schools. They are a fast-moving species.
HABITS: This is another fish discovered by the author (HRA) that has not as yet been described. It does very well under normal aquarium conditions and always has a heavy rosy glow.
WATER CONDITIONS: Slightly acid water about 6.4 pH at a temperature of about 28°C.
SIZE: May reach 80 mm.
FOOD REQUIREMENTS: Eats a normal aquarium diet but much prefers living, moving foods.

Moenkhausia "Dusky" • Dusky Moenkhausia

RANGE: Individual specimens were caught in many areas in the northern Amazon basin, including Colombia and Venezuela.
HABITS: This fish is a very small *Moenkhausia*; perhaps it is the juvenile of a larger fish, but it has adult coloration and ripe gonads at 50 mm. Note the orange markings in the unpaired fins and the black edge on each scale that gives it the dusky appearance.
SIZE: Up to about 70 mm. Larger specimens were never found in the creek habitat in which these fish were found.
FOOD REQUIREMENTS: They thrived on a normal aquarium diet.

Paracheirodon axelrodi

Paracheirodon innesi

Paracheirodon simulans

Bryconops "Goldi"

Catoprion mento (juv.)

Bryconops "Rosy"

Curimata lineopunctata

Moenkhausia "Dusky"

Plate #111

? Deuterodon

? Boehlkea

?

?

?

? Axelrodia stigmatias

Phoxinopsis typicus

Vesicatrus tegatus

Plate #112

TETRA CONFUSION

No matter how hard you try, no matter how much material is available, and no matter how familiar you are with the literature, there will always be some tetras that defy identification. If series of adult specimens are available they must be placed in subfamilies and genera based on often weak and variable characters of the teeth (how many, how many rows, how many lobes, etc.) and scalation (extent of lateral line, number of scales on caudal peduncle, scaling of the lobes of the caudal fin, etc.). Some of the most common and largest genera are almost impossible to define, so several hundred species and synonyms—many known only from one or two small, poorly preserved specimens—cannot even be adequately grouped into distinctive genera. For instance, the differences between *Hemigrammus* and *Hyphessobrycon* are extremely minor (mostly scalation of the caudal area) and there are problems with the generic status of the type species.

All this is presented as a reason for the lack of identifications of most of the small tetras on this plate. All share a similar color pattern of a distinctive dark blotch, bar, diamond, etc., on the caudal peduncle, but they differ greatly in head and fin characters and may not be at all closely related. The two species we can be fairly sure of, *Phoxinopsis typicus* (from the Rio de Janeiro area) and *Vesicatrus tegatus* (from the Upper Paraguay system), have been present in the hobby since the 1930's, though they have never been truly popular. The fish tentatively identified as *Axelrodia stigmatias* is occasionally imported, as is the blue tetra seemingly related to *Boehlkea*. One very distinctive species may belong to the confusing genus *Deuterodon*. The others, although each distinctive in their own way, have not been identified with any certainty. Although the possibility exists that they are new species, they could equally well be members of obscure taxa that are seldom seen in the hobby and that have never been illustrated in a manner to show the color patterns.

New and unidentified fishes are constantly being imported for the tropical fish hobby, just one more of the reasons to visit your petshop frequently.

THE GYMNOTID EELS

The aquarium trade, especially public aquaria, have been fascinated by the gymnotids since Georg Marcgraf described the first "carapo" discovered in Brazil. "Carapo" is a Brazilian Indian name for these fishes. *Gymnotus*, meaning naked back, is the scientific name for one of the larger genera; Gymnotidae is the family. The scientific name refers to the missing dorsal fin in the group, though some species have a single dorsal spine or filament. All the gymnotids have slippery, elongated, eel-like bodies. Some have small scales. They have no ventral fins and very degenerate pectorals, but they all have huge anal fins. The ray count within each species varies considerably. Some species have teeth. The electric eel, which the author has seen well over 2.1 meters in length, is a member of a closely related family, and it is the only gymnotoid species with strong electrical discharge capabilities. All the other gymnotoids have very weak electrical discharges that take sophisticated electronic equipment to detect. These weak discharges are used to sense their surroundings like radar. Only the electric eel is dangerous to handle, though it has never been known to kill anyone.

In the aquarium they are a nuisance. Unless you supply them with something to hide in, such as half a coconut shell inverted to form a cave, they will dig into the sand, uprooting plants and stirring up the mulm on the bottom. They all require small live foods, which are hunted at night. During the day they hide.

While they have fantastic powers of regeneration, often being able to regenerate substantial portions of their bodies, they also chew each other up unmercifully. In dealers' tanks it is not uncommon to see 100 gymnotids of about 12-20 cm all trying to hide under the same shell. The next morning they will each have a chunk bitten out of their tail! Antibiotic treatment will hinder the infection, but the fish will have to be separated.

Most gymnotids also have wonderful powers to change color. While many of them have translucent flesh through which their viscera are plainly visible, their skin does contain tiny chromatophores that give them the ability to change to a stark black or gray at times. Their muscles sometimes show a lot of blood, and this colors the fish pink or red.

Most of the gymnotids grow large, at least averaging 200 mm in length. They are therefore merely curiosities and are not to be considered for the community tank.

Not much is known about their external sexual differences or their breeding habits.

Gymnotus anguillaris

Gymnotus anguillaris

Gymnotus sp. nov.

Gymnotus carapo

Sternarchus hasemani

Sternarchorhamphus muelleri/Sternarchorhynchus oxyraynchus

Rhamphichthys rostratus

Rhamphichthys rostratus

Plate #113

Steatogenys elegans

Steatogenys elegans

Steatogenys elegans (juv.)

Eigenmannia virescens

Sternopygus macrurus

Rhabdolichops troscheli

Distocyclus conirostris

Plate #114

Hypopomus artedi

201

Steatogenys elegans (Steindachner) • Mottled Knife Fish

RANGE: Northeastern South America, Barra do Rio Negro, Guyana, lower Amazon River and northern tributaries of the middle Amazon.
HABITS: Nocturnal; rarely seen during the daytime.
WATER CONDITIONS: Not critical; neutral, slightly soft water with a temperature between 24° and 29°C is good.
SIZE: Grows to a length of 18 to 20 cm.
FOOD REQUIREMENTS: Readily accepts live brine shrimp as well as other live foods; will also eat prepared foods, chopped fish and shrimp, etc. with a little coaxing.

Sternopygus macrurus (Bloch & Schneider) • Variable Ghost Knife Fish

RANGE: Much of South America from Colombia to the Guianas, south through the Amazon basin to Patagonia.
HABITS: A common, secretive fish that is used for food by the natives. Very variable in color from almost transparent to solid blue-black. Peaceful, but its large size could cause trouble in the aquarium.
WATER CONDITIONS: Not choosy, although prefers acid water. Must have cover to retreat from the light.
SIZE: Reaches at least 500 mm in length.
FOOD REQUIREMENTS: Will take any small live foods, including shrimp and fishes. Can be weaned onto prepared meaty foods.

Distocyclus conirostris (Eigenmann & Allen) •Yellow Knife Fish

RANGE: Iquitos, Peru, and vicinity; probably throughout the Amazon system.
HABITS: Like other small gymnotids, it is seen only at night, spending the day hiding. Peaceful, but may form weak territories.
WATER CONDITIONS: Likes densely planted, warm, acid waters.
SIZE: Only about 200 mm in length.
FOOD REQUIREMENTS: Although it may adapt to prepared foods such as beefheart, it fares best on appropriate sizes of live foods such as small crustaceans and fishes.

Eigenmannia virescens (Valenciennes) • Green Knife Fish

RANGE: Widely distributed all over northern South America.
HABITS: Mostly nocturnal; very greedy eaters which are best kept by themselves.
WATER CONDITIONS: Water should be well aged and clean. Temperature 24 to 27°C. This fish is very sensitive to fresh water.
SIZE: To 45 cm.
FOOD REQUIREMENTS: Almost any food is taken greedily; preferred of course are the larger live foods, but they also eat chunks of beef heart and oatmeal.

Rhabdolichops troscheli (Kaup) • Short-headed Knife Fish

RANGE: Found throughout the Amazon system.
HABITS: Shy, nocturnal. Its small size and tendency to hide make it hard to maintain in the aquarium.
WATER CONDITIONS: Warm, acid water. Must have plants or pots in which to hide.
SIZE: Usually only 100 mm in length, but reaches at least 180 mm.
FOOD REQUIREMENTS: Small live foods are preferred.

Hypopomus artedi (Kaup) • Spotted Knife Fish

RANGE: Brazil and the Guianas.
HABITS: Peaceful toward other fishes which are not small enough to be swallowed; likely to be belligerent toward their own kind.
WATER CONDITIONS: Not critical, but the fish is sensitive to fresh water. The tank should be well planted and offer a number of places to hide. Temperature about 24°C.
SIZE: To 43 cm.
FOOD REQUIREMENTS: Prefers large live foods or chopped lean beef.
COLOR VARIATIONS: Yellowish to brownish with darker spots.

Gymnorhamphichthys rondoni Miranda-Ribeiro • Mousetail Knife Fish

RANGE: River systems of Venezuela.
HABITS: Peaceful and shy; should not, however, be put with very small fishes.
WATER CONDITIONS: Soft, slightly acid water. Temperature 24 to 27°C.
SIZE: Up to 15 cm; usually 10 cm.
FOOD REQUIREMENTS: Small live or frozen foods.

Apteronotus leptorhynchus Ellie in Eigenmann • Long-nosed Black Ghost

RANGE: Northern South America from Iquitos, Peru, to the Guyanas.
HABITS: A shy, peaceful, nocturnal fish that must have a hiding spot.
WATER CONDITIONS: Warm, clean, slightly acid to neutral water is best, but the fish is not too choosy.
SIZE: 100-260 mm or more.
FOOD REQUIREMENTS: Will take most live foods that reach the bottom and will also adapt to some prepared foods.

Polycentrus schomburgki Mueller & Troschel • Schomburgk's Leaf Fish

RANGE: Northeastern South America and Trinidad.
HABITS: Aggressive and capable of swallowing fishes almost as large as themselves; should not be kept in a community tank.
WATER CONDITIONS: Neutral to slightly acid and soft. Temperature 24 to 26°C.
SIZE: To 10 cm.
FOOD REQUIREMENTS: Smaller fishes and pieces of earthworm preferred, but can be trained to take pieces of beef heart or other lean meat, shrimp or fish.

Monocirrhus polyacanthus Heckel • Leaf Fish

RANGE: Tropical South America; Amazon, Rio Negro, Guianas.
HABITS: Occurs in sluggish streams, where it feeds on smaller fishes and aquatic insects; peaceful in the aquarium toward anything it cannot swallow.
WATER CONDITIONS: Soft, slightly acid water. Temperature about 26°C.
SIZE: Up to 10 cm.
FOOD REQUIREMENTS: Small ones may be fed with the usual live foods; larger ones must get living smaller fishes.

Electrophorus electricus (Linnaeus) • Electric Eel

RANGE: Middle and lower Amazon basin.
HABITS: Because of this species's electric properties it is not suitable as a community tank fish. More than one specimen can sometimes be kept in a tank, but this is risky.
WATER CONDITIONS: Soft, slightly acid water is optimal, but not important.
SIZE: Up to 1.8 meters; aquarium specimens much smaller.
FOOD REQUIREMENTS: Live fishes are preferred; small specimens will take worms and may be taught to accept liver and similar foods.
COLOR VARIATIONS: Young specimens olive-brown with yellowish markings. Adults olive-brown with orange throat. Eyes emerald green.

Apteronotus albifrons (Linnaeus) • Black Ghost

RANGE: Amazon River and Surinam.
HABITS: A peaceful, friendly fish.
WATER CONDITIONS: Soft, slightly acid water best, but this is not too important, as variations in water composition are taken in stride.
SIZE: Up to 47 cm.
FOOD REQUIREMENTS: Not a fussy eater; will take dry, frozen and live foods. Tubifex eagerly accepted.

Gymnorhamphichthys rondoni

Electrophorus electricus

Apteronotus leptorhynchus

Apteronotus albifrons

Polycentrus schomburgki (juv.)

Polycentrus schomburgki (adult male)

Monocirrhus polyacanthus

Monociirhus polyacanthus

Plate #115

Platystacus cotylephorus

Aspredo aspredo

Platystacus cotylephorus

Bunocephalus amaurus

Bunocephalus kneri

Agmus lyriformis

Bunocephalus coracoideus

Bunocephalus coracoideus

Plate #116

205

FAMILY ASPREDINIDAE,
The Rough-Skinned or Banjo Catfishes

In the central Amazon basin, in almost every stream and creek feeding the Amazon or its many tributaries, are very weird-looking catfishes that look as if their heads had been flattened with a hammer and their bodies stretched on a rack! They are so well camouflaged that their eyes are even difficult to find at times, and the various armies of the world might have used their skin coloration as patterns for combat uniforms.

The family has two rather distinct subfamilies, the brackish water, long anal fin species of Aspredininae, and the more familiar freshwater, short anal fin species of Bunocephalinae. The banjo cats or bunocephalids are commonly sold in petshops, but only recently have aspredinids been imported.

In Brazil, the origin of most of these species, the bunocephalids can be found lying among fallen leaves that have blown into the shallow creeks. You simply dig into a mass of leaves with your net and look for things that move (you find snakes this way, too). More than likely it will be a bunocephalid.

There are about 10 genera and over 31 species in this family, but undoubtedly there are many more, as they are very difficult to collect unless you keep searching for them specifically. Nothing is known about their sexual differences or about how they breed. But since they are often found buried in the sand of their aquarium, it is not impossible that they may even bury their eggs—but this is pure conjecture.

These are small catfishes, hardly ever reaching 200 mm in total length. Their skin is covered with a rough coating of tubercles; the coating almost looks like ich. The fishes are very hardy and thrive under most aquarium conditions, providing their minimum needs of pH 6.4-7.2, temperature 22-30°C, and well aged water are provided. They are not to be trusted with fishes that are small enough for them to swallow. They are strictly nocturnal, as their tiny, beady eyes demonstrate, and at night they easily can surprise a fish that would be impossible for them to catch during the day.

They require a large, well planted tank with a mulmy bottom and soft sand into which they can burrow. Catfishes like this are a problem in the aquarium, for should they bury themselves and then die they might really foul up a tank and necessitate a complete tear-down of the system.

FAMILY DORADIDAE, the Spiny Catfishes

Aquarists are seeing more and more of this very interesting family, and it is only a matter of time before successful spawning is reported. The doradids are like medieval warriors. Their heads are protected above with a thick bony shield, and their bodies are protected with thorny spines, at least one row on each side of the body. These spines are dangerous to man and fishes. . . and crocodiles, many of which have died after swallowing a catfish that locked its dorsal and pectoral spines in an open position. These fin spines are also armed with serrations that are similar to the thorny spines on the sides.

This is a family of fishes that needs a lot of study. Our late, dear colleague Dr. Agustin Fernandez-Yepez, with whom the author (HRA) made many doradid collecting trips to Venezuela, wrote a monograph describing four new genera and many new species of doradids from the collections made in Venezuela. This only confused things more (for aquarists), for many of his genera were rediscovered by the author in Colombia and Brazil. When everything is considered, this narrows the differences between the known fishes of Amazon South America and the fauna of Venezuela, and it becomes likely that doradids described from Venezuela may have been described earlier from the Amazon. The species called *Pseudodoras holdeni* is one of Fernandez-Yepez' species. In Spanish it is called "sierra cachimba." It is very close to *Pseudodoras niger* except for the coloration. *P. holdeni* is gray with black fins, while *P. niger* is all black. The accompanying photos show that clearly.

In the aquarium all doradids are equal. They are generally peaceful, though nocturnal. They only eat small things, including fishes small enough to ingest whole, but they prefer scavenging at the bottom for daphnia and other small crustaceans.

They have never been spawned, but the author (HRA) has observed spiny catfishes (probably doradids) that built bubblenests under large floating leaves, assumedly to deposit their eggs like *Callichthys*, another South American catfish. But this discussion must await a more suitable arena (books on breeding aquarium fishes), for this book is large enough just dealing basically with identification of fishes and how to keep them alive.

Hassar iheringi richter

Hemidoras microstomus

Trachydoras paraguayensis

Trachydoras paraguayensis

Pseudodoras niger

Pseudodoras niger

Pseudodoras holdeni

Anadoras grypus

Plate #117

Doras eigenmanni

Doras eigenmanni

Amblydoras hancocki

Amblydoras hancocki

Autanadoras milesi

Amblydoras hancocki

Agamyxis pectinifrons

Agamyxis pectinifrons

Plate #118

Platydoras armatulus

Platydoras armatulus

Platydoras costatus

Platydoras costatus

Platydoras costatus

Acanthodoras cataphractus

Acanthodoras cataphractus

Acanthodoras spinosissimus

Plate #119

FAMILY DORADIDAE: SUBFAMILY AUCHENIPTERINAE
AND FAMILY AGENEIOSIDAE

The members of the family Doradidae are called the spiny or thorny catfishes, yet some have neither spines nor thorns and at first sight might be placed with the naked catfishes. These naked doradids are the auchenipterids, which form a distinct subfamily of the Doradidae. In fact, many of the more recent works on catfishes give them full family rank as the Auchenipteridae. For the moment we will follow a more conservative course and just recognize a subfamily Auchenipterinae. These fishes, basically of the genera *Tatia, Pseudepapterus, Trachelyopterichthys, Trachycorystes, Liosomadoras, Centromochlus, Pseudauchenipterus,* and *Auchenipterichthys,* are often imported as aquarium oddities. These are closely related to the fishes of the family Ageneiosidae, which are also scaleless.

There are about 135 species of known doradids, if we include the auchenipterids, but there are only 27 ageneiosids, all of which are naked-skinned.

For some reason, these naked-skinned catfishes do not really thrive in an aquarium environment. They do not live long but gradually die off. Perhaps it is because we do not truly understand their needs, as many of the more streamlined species of *Centromochlus, Pseudauchenipterus,* and *Ageneiosus* have relatively large eyes and good swimming ability, indicating that they might chase their food rather than scrounge it from the bottom.

Most aquarists treat all catfishes like scavengers and pay hardly any attention to their particular needs. Much more work needs to be done with all catfishes, except the armored catfishes of the family Callichthyidae, which adorn the tanks of just about every aquarist with a community aquarium.

Parauchenipterus

Parauchenipterus

Entomocorus benjamini

Auchenipterichthys thoracatus

Auchenipterichthys thoracatus

Parauchenipterus galeatus

Tatia perugiae

Tetranematichthys quadrifilis

Plate #120

Tatia creutzbergi

Tatia aulopygia

Tatia aulopygia

Pseudepapterus hasemani

Trachelyopterichthys taeniatus

Trachelyopterichthys taeniatus

Auchenipterus demerarae

Auchenipterus demerarae

Plate #121

213

Liosomadoras oncinus

Liosomadoras oncinus

Liosomadoras oncinus

Liosomadoras oncinus

Centromochlus heckeli

Pseudauchenipterus nodosus

Ageneiosus caucanus

Ageneiosus caucanus

Plate #122

FAMILY PIMELODIDAE, the Naked Catfishes

Everywhere in tropical America and much of subtropical America as well, there are catfishes with long, thin barbels that look like whiskers (thus the name "cat" in the "catfishes"); they have neither scales nor bony armor. They almost always have three pairs of long barbels and have the dorsal fin protected by a very sharp, strong spine; this dorsal fin is usually placed very far forward. In these catfishes the tail fin is almost always forked.

For the most part these catfish are not well known, and many have still not been kept in an aquarium. TFH, as a matter of fact, sent an investigating team to the cataracts near Porto Velho, Brazil (Cachoeira Teotonio, Rondonia), to investigate reports of a large new catfish that has stripes like a tiger. This was a huge fish that was described only as recently as 1981 (by Dr. Heraldo Britski). Small specimens might well make wonderful aquarium inhabitants.

None of the pimelodids have been spawned in the home aquarium, though it shouldn't be too difficult once the special hormones are available to assist ripe fishes in spawning in their unnatural surroundings.

The author (HRA) has studied hundreds, perhaps even thousands, of these pimelodids in Brazil and Venezuela trying to ascertain sexual differences and trying to find breeding habitats, without any success at all. Many of these catfishes grow very large, upwards of one meter in some cases, but only small ones have a chance in the home aquarium—thus chances of breeding successes with these are low.

In all cases, naked catfishes are nocturnal and, in most cases, very hardy if given the basic requirements. Their water needs are simple. A pH of 6.2-7.2 at 22-30°C is suitable. Their water must be aged well, as they do very poorly in fresh (new) water. Even though they have no scales to protect their bodies and skin, they fall prey to precious few external parasites like ich.

Their aquarium should be large and extremely well planted with lots of mulm on the bottom and places to hide. Small artificial caves suit them well; halves of coconut shells are successfully used in many aquaria. Feeding them is no problem, as they are scavengers and eat just about any aquarium diet including your tank inhabitants if they are not fed well. Pimelodids have teeth, but their teeth are not too highly developed. Their food of preference is tubifex worms, which they eat from the bottom of the tank, but they also do well on flake foods that fall to the floor of the tank.

Pinirampus pirinampu

Pinirampus pirinampu

Callophysus macropterus

Callophysus macropterus

Pimelodella gracilis

Pimelodella gracilis

Pimelodella linami

Pimelodella laticeps

216

Plate #123

Pimelodella parnahybae

Pimelodella dorseyi

Pimelodella metae

Pimelodella hartwelli

Duopalatinus goeldii

Duopalatinus barbatus

Gouldiella eques

Heptapterus mustelinus

Plate #124

Pimelodus clarias

Pimelodus albofasciatus

Pimelodus maculatus (juv.)

Pimelodus sp. (clarias?)

Pimelodus maculatus

Pimelodus pictus

Duopalatinus peruanus

Pimelodus pictus

Plate #125

Sorubim lima

Sorubim lima

Sorubim lima

Platystomatichthys sturio

Sciades pictus

Sciades pictus

Pimelodus ornatus

Sciades marmoratus

Plate #126

219

Phractocephalus hemiliopterus

Phractocephalus hemiliopterus

Microglanis poecilus

Microglanis poecilus

Pseudopimelodus albomarginatus

Pseudoplatystoma fasciatum

Pseudopimelodus nigricauda

Pseudoplatystoma fasciatum

Plate #127

MERODONTOTUS TIGRINUS, THE TIGER-STRIPED CATFISH

New fishes are being discovered all the time in South America, but admittedly most are small tetras or cichlids. Thus it was most unusual for a new species of meter-long catfish belonging to a new genus to be described in 1981. Not only was this new fish, *Merodontotus tigrinus* Britski, large, but it was strikingly patterned with oblique black stripes. When described, the fish was known from a single specimen.

In late 1984, T.F.H. was able to organize an expedition to the Teotonio Cataract on the Madeira River near Porto Velho in Rondonia, western Brazil, where the original specimen was taken. By questioning the native fishermen and following them on their trips to the cataract, several specimens of this striking catfish were found and photographed. You can see for yourself the incredible color pattern of the tiger-striped catfish and imagine how it would look in an aquarium. Because of the large size of even the smallest specimens known, *Merodontotus tigrinus* is obviously a candidate only for the largest private aquaria and for public aquaria, but there is still hope that the species will eventually be imported alive at sizes small enough to allow it to enter the aquarium hobby.

The Teotonio Cataract is a steep drop-off in the Madeira River where the river falls about 30 meters in a distance of 90 meters. Many species of large catfishes and characoids ascend the torrents of the cataract to spawn in the quieter upstream sections of the river, much as salmon ascend rivers in the Northern Hemisphere. Unfortunately the area is now being exploited for gold dredging, leading to an increased human population and its associated pollution. Perhaps even meter-long catfishes will not be able to survive for much longer in this region of Brazil unless more concern is given to stabilizing the environment. Who knows what other curious and sensational fishes exist in the area and may never even be seen by scientists before they become extinct?

Left: *Merodontotus tigrinus* with head removed; this fish had been captured by commercial fishermen.
Right: freshly caught *M. tigrinus* individual.
Below: Views of the Teotonio Cataract, at which the tiger-striped catfish was caught. The Teotonio Cataract is situated about 20 miles from Porto Velho in the Brazilian state of Rondonia.

Plate #128

Above and immediately below: Views of tiger-striped catfish, with unstriped belly of fish visible in photo at lower left. The big question is: are all of these individuals of the same species?

Below: Members of the 1984 T.F.H. Expedition display their finds. Left to right: Adolpho Schwartz, Heiko Bleher, and Dr. Howard Groder; Dr. Groder holds the first specimen found.

Plate #129

THE ARMORED CATFISHES:
FAMILIES CALLICHTHYIDAE AND LORICARIIDAE

The fishes of these two families are very easily distinguished from most other aquarium fishes by their being protected by a double or multiple series of "armor" plates. These dermal plates meet along the middle of the sides. Many of the armored catfishes belonging to the Callichthyidae and Loricariidae are popular aquarium fishes because they are so peaceful in the aquarium and are quite hardy if given some basic considerations. They are also very easy to spawn for the people who know their "secret": these fishes all seem to spawn after a heavy rainfall. Imitate a rainfall in your aquarium by spraying the surface with water, using an overflow device, until about 30% of the water has been changed.

FAMILY CALLICHTHYIDAE

The family Callichthyidae is composed of three main genera, *Callichthys, Hoplosternum,* and *Corydoras,* plus three or four minor genera.

KEY TO THE GENERA (after Gosline, 1940)

1a. Snout depressed, the interorbital width greater than or equal to the depth of the head at the forward margin of the orbit.

2a. Eye more or less superiorly situated, i.e., not equally visible from above and below, its diameter contained two or more times in its distance from the lower end of the bony opercle.

3a. Foremost plates of the upper lateral series, i.e., nuchal plates, fused across the midline between the supraoccipital and the dorsal.

4a. Abdomen between the pectoral fins completely covered with flesh; suborbital covered with flesh . . . . .1. *Callichthys.*

4b. Coracoids expanded on the surface of the abdomen between the bases of the pectorals; suborbital bones not covered with flesh . . . . .2. *Hoplosternum.*

3b. Nuchal plates not meeting along the mid-dorsal line; coracoids expanded on the surface of the abdomen between the pectoral bases; eye contained 3.8 in the interorbital . . . . .3. *Cascadura.**

2b. Eye laterally situated, i.e., equally visible from above and below, its diameter contained 1.3 times or less in its distance from lower end of bony opercle.

5a. Foremost plates of upper lateral series, i.e., nuchal plates, fused across the midline between the occipital and the dorsal . .4. *Dianema.*

5b. Nuchal plates not meeting along the mid-dorsal line . . . . .5. *Cataphractops.**

1b. Snout compressed or rounded, the interorbital width considerably less than the depth of head at the forward rim of orbit; barbels at either end of the mouth, i.e., rictal barbels, not reaching much beyond gill opening; lower lips reverted to form a single pair of short barbels.

*3. *Cascadura* is now known to be based on a juvenile *Hoplosternum.*

*5. A doubtful genus known from one or two poor specimens.

Callichthys callichthys

Hoplosternum thoracatum

Hoplosternum pectorale

Hoplosternum thoracatum (var.)

Dianema longibarbis

Dianema longibarbis

Dianema urostriata

Dianema urostriata

Plate #130

6a. Foremost plates of upper lateral series, i.e., nuchal plates, meeting along the midline between occipital and dorsal; abdomen between pectoral bases entirely covered with flesh; fontanel small, roundish ....6. *Aspidoras.**
6b. Nuchal plates not meeting along the mid-dorsal line; coracoids usually more or less expanded on the abdomen between pectoral bases; fontanel elongate.
7a. Dorsal fin with a spine and seven or eight, possibly nine, rays ....7. *Corydoras.*
7b. Dorsal fin with a spine and ten to twelve rays ....8. *Brochis.**

*6. Very close to *Corydoras*; the key characters may not provide a full separation of the genera.

*8. *Brochis* species with up to 17 dorsal rays are now known.

The spawning habits of *Callichthys* and *Hoplosternum* are interesting. As soon as fresh water is introduced into their aquarium in sufficient quantities to imitate a heavy rainfall and the beginning of the rainy season, these fishes build what amounts to a bubblenest. In Nature they select a strong leaf or a floating, but anchored, joint of a branch as a nest substrate. They amass bits of small vegetation that they cause to adhere to each other by slightly sticky mucus that they spit into the nest until it is quite large, perhaps as much as 200 mm in diameter. Then the eggs are put into the nest, which may rise as high as 50 mm out of the water.

The author (HRA) has had considerable experience in spawning both *Hoplosternum* and *Callichthys*. For commercial purposes a male and two bulging females are placed into a large, relatively deep (500 mm) aquarium of about 200 liters capacity. The fish are heavily fed on white worms and flake food and then a piece of *Elodea* or *Cabomba* is introduced. Only slightly browned dying plants are used. Shortly after their introduction the male begins to "sniff" them and soon begins tearing leaves from them with his pectoral fins. Using his movable barbels, he begins to accumulate the leaves in one corner of the aquarium. At this stage a floating piece of styrofoam, which has been hollowed out to resemble a soup plate, is introduced quietly onto the surface of the tank *and the water temperature is lowered.* The temperature at which the fish were prepared for spawning was between 25 and 30°C. Now the temperature is lowered to between 20 and 23°C. Soon the male begins to accumulate bubbles and bits of vegetation under the floating styrofoam. When the nest is fairly massive, about 200 mm in diameter, the female(s) begin to take interest in the male's actions, but their interest is merely sightseeing, nothing more.

The male keeps up his work until the nest actually lifts the styrofoam almost out of the water, then he begins a rather informal mating dance by nudging the female continually until she begins to spawn. She does this without the male; she merely expels a few eggs (2-6), which she manages to hold in a pocket formed by her pelvic fins just for the purpose of carrying eggs. Normally the pelvic fins are separated, but she can move them to hold the eggs. Then she swims under the bubblenest, turns on her back, and releases them into the nest. This goes on for many hours until hundreds of eggs are deposited in the nest. After each egg deposit by the female, the male follows her and showers the eggs with bubbles to ensure that they stay floating. It is not certain at which stage fertilization takes place. The author has tested the eggs and found them not to be fertile if taken from the female before she deposits them in the nest; eggs taken from the nest were always fertile even if removed before the male had showered them with bubbles. Perhaps they are fertilized by sperm already on the bubbles. No one as yet knows for sure even though what has been described above has largely been known since Hancock (the original describer of *Hoplosternum littorale*) described the nest building in an article in the *Zoological Journal*, Volume IV, page 244, in 1828.

The male cares for the nest and developing young. The female can be left with the male, but the non-breeding female(s) should be removed and the pair kept together as they are peculiarly monogamous! The nest stays together for a long time, usually about a month, and the fry keep growing without visible efforts to eat. Perhaps they eat the slime in the bubbles like baby *Symphysodon* eat the body slime from their parents, but after a month the fry emerge from the nest. . .all at once. . .at about 20 mm in length. At this stage they eat frozen baby brine shrimp and microworms, but they soon learn to scrounge other uneaten particles from the bottom of the tank.

The same mysteries surround the *Corydoras*. The female carries the eggs in her pelvic "pouch" and glues them to a spot that previously had been cleaned by the male. Each batch of eggs is attached to a different spot. Just where fertilization takes place is not exactly known.

CARING FOR THE CALLICHTHYIDAE
The aquarium care for all of these catfishes is the same. They are peaceful and almost never bother other aquarium fishes. They scrounge along the bottom for food, but if they are hungry and only floating foods are available, they assume a belly-up position and take food from the surface. This is an unnatural position for them and they only assume it for eating and spawning purposes. The generalizations above are true for all Callichthyidae.

HABITAT
The author (HRA) has collected more than 72 different species of Callichthyidae in South America. These armored catfishes are to be found from Trinidad through to Paraguay and Uruguay; they even live under the ice in the winter at the southern edge of their range. They all are air-breathers and can tolerate very heavy population densities. In Brazil, on many occasions the author (HRA) has found hundreds of thousands of *Corydoras* in intermittent pools, trapped by receding waters. Near

Aspidoras pauciradiatus

Aspidoras pauciradiatus

Aspidoras lakoi

Aspidoras fuscoguttatus

Brochis splendens (juv.)

Brochis splendens

Corydoras acutus

Corydoras osteocarus

Plate #131

Corydoras aeneus

Corydoras aeneus

Corydoras aeneus

Corydoras aeneus

Corydoras aeneus

Corydoras aeneus

Corydoras latus

Corydoras aeneus

Plate #132

229

Humaita, Brazil, the author found almost 100,000 *Dianema urostriata* in a pool barely 50 meters across and 1 to 2 meters deep. With them, by the way, were only *Pterophyllum* (angelfish).

In the aquarium all callichthyids do well in water between 20 and 30°C. The more room the better, and the more mulm on the bottom the better they appreciate it.

MASS PRODUCTION

Corydoras and other callichthyids are mass produced in outdoor dirt ponds in Florida and probably in areas in Southeast Asia. The small ponds measuring roughly 30 meters in diameter and barely one meter deep have their edges decorated with pieces of flat wood or slate barely sticking out of the water. After each rain the plates are inspected for egg deposits. The spawning mass of fish in such a pond may be 2,000 fish, and not necessarily of the same species, either. The eggs are removed and artificially hatched.

MANY SPECIES

There are over 100 species of callichthyids, mostly *Corydoras*. The author has collected many new species of *Corydoras* (more than 25), and their habitat is not always the same. In general, *Corydoras* can be found in very shallow streams that are neither very slow nor very fast-moving. The usual water depth may be only 15 cm. The author collects them at night using a square net measuring about 50 cm wide by 25 cm high and 50 cm deep. When the fish are hit by the beam of a flashlight they seem to be stunned by the light and don't move. The author then places the net in back of them, about 15 cm from their tails, and with his foot chases them into the net. They are caught the same way in the daylight, too, but at night you never miss one once you learn the technique.

The author has also collected them deep in large rivers while seining for other fishes, and of course they are also found in quiet, still pools. In pools they are usually found in huge quantities, tens of thousands at a time, while in streams they are spaced out about one per square meter of bottom.

Many years ago, when ichthyologists were often restricted in their vision of fish classifications to political boundaries rather than zoogeographical boundaries, the relationships between fishes were often obscured and many families, subfamilies, tribes, genera, species, and subspecies were constructed on an artifical basis. As more and more "holes" are filled in the evolutionary charts, the differences between these groups narrow and the groups themselves lose significance. This is especially true of the small fishes that are kept in the aquarium, fishes of the family Callichthyidae included.

One grouping that probably will persist is the separation of the almost identical looking fishes of the genus *Dianema* (tribe Dianemini) from the genera *Hoplosternum* and *Callichthys*. The tribe Dianemini contains only two genera, *Dianema* and *Cataphractops*. These fishes all look alike and are difficult to distinguish for most aquarists, but since there are only two known species of *Dianema* at present and only three or so species of *Hoplosternum*, plus one species of *Callichthys,* a few differences in color and fin position are sufficient to keep this group straight.

CATFISH HEALTH

An experienced aquarist can tell at a glance how well a fish is in terms of health. His experienced eye quickly checks drooping fins, bloody spots, parasites, and the fish's swimming action. This is especially true of the Callichthyidae. Most normal Callichthyidae are bottom-dwellers and are constantly on the move. Even when a batch of *Corydoras* is sitting on the naked glass bottoms of a wholesaler's tanks, they immediately move into action when food is put into the tank. If you see a tankful of *Corydoras, Callichthys* or *Hoplosternum* swimming in mid-tank, you know the fish are not acting normally and disaster is imminent. Not so with *Dianema.* For some reason this catfish spends a lot of time swimming in mid-water, and this can be interpreted as their normal action.

SEX DIFFERENCES

Several authors have suggested differences between the sexes that can "easily" be recognized. They point out that males of most *Hoplosternum* can be differentiated by their being more pointed than females. In a general sense this is true. If a scientist were to lay out 100 *Hoplosternum* and sort them out by the width of their mouths or noses, the widest specimens probably would all be females. The problem is that live catfish don't lie on their backs, and making a comparison is difficult since viewing the fish from the top doesn't always make it easier. So for all practical purposes there isn't any way to tell young, unripe catfishes of the family Callichthyidae apart sexually.

With ripe fishes in spawning condition there is a difference. When viewed from above, the bulging sides of the female are very noticeable, allowing females to be distinguished from males.

Both *Hoplosternum* and *Callichthys* have been spawned often, but *Dianema* has not. Most of the known species of *Corydoras* have not been spawned either, but this is only a matter of time for the species spawned so far all spawn in the same manner.

THE TRIBE CORYDORADINI

Almost every aquarist knows a *Corydoras* when he sees one. . .or does he? There are some fishes belonging to the genus *Brochis* that look very much like *Corydoras* except they have longer dorsal fins and are deeper

Corydoras garbei

Corydoras treitlii

Corydoras semiaquilus ?

Corydoras semiaquilus

Corydoras melanotaenia

Corydoras melanotaenia (juv.)

Corydoras zygatus

Corydoras sp. eques ?

232   *Plate #133*

Corydoras barbatus

Corydoras barbatus (male)

Corydoras macropterus (female)

Corydoras macropterus (male)

Corydoras nanus

Corydoras elegans

Corydoras pygmaeus

Corydoras hastatus

Plate #134

233

bodied. The dorsal fin in *Brochis* has 10 or more rays, while *Corydoras* normally has fewer than 10, usually 7 to 9. Except for these small differences, the two genera are virtually identical and what has been said about *Corydoras* applies equally to *Brochis*. One species, *Brochis splendens,* looks very much like *Corydoras aeneus,* especially in the olive-green metallic flanks, except it appears like a misformed giant. Another group of similar looking fishes is *Aspidoras.* Only scientists can really tell them apart, for the opening in their parietal bone is round while *Brochis* and *Corydoras* have oval-shaped apertures.

FAMILY LORICARIIDAE, THE SUCKER-MOUTHED CATFISHES

The major groups of fishes in the family Loricariidae can be differentiated by the following key, which was constructed by Eigenmann for *The Fishes of British Guiana* in 1912. While there have been many changes since, the key is still valid for tropical fish hobbyist purposes.

KEY TO THE GUIANA GENERA OF LORICARIIDAE

a. Tail short; caudal peduncle compressed, cylindrical, or moderately depressed; haemal spines all simple; lower and fourth upper pharyngeals not toothed; belly naked, or with minute granular plates; intestinal canal very long. (*Plecostominae.*)

  b. Premaxillaries and dentaries nearly equal in length.

    c. Opercle and interopercle little and not independently movable; snout granular to its margin.

      d. Adipose fin present.

        e. Sides and back covered with plates; dorsal with seven rays . . . . *Plecostomus.**

        ee. Sides and back covered with plates; dorsal with thirteen rays . . . . *Pterygoplichthys.*

        eee. Sides and back mostly naked, with a few minute plates near the tail . . . . *Lithogenes.*

      dd. No adipose fin; a low crest between the dorsal and caudal; margin of snout and head granular . . . . *Corymbophanes.*

    cc. Interopercle movable, usually with spines or bristles.

      f. Snout granular to its margin, or with bristles; D. I, 6 or 7.

        g. Sides of the head without bristles . . . . *Hemiancistrus.*

        gg. Sides of the head with bristles, short in the female, much longer in the male . . . . *Pseudancistrus.*

      ff. Snout naked.

        h. No tentacles . . . . *Xenocara.**

        hh. Snout with tentacles . . . . *Ancistrus.*

*e. Plecostomus is now *Hypostomus.*

*h. Xenocara is now considered a synonym of *Ancistrus.*

    bb. Premaxillaries much shorter than the dentaries and with fewer teeth, not united. Much depressed, of small size . . . . *Lithoxus.*
  aa. Tail long, depressed, with a single series of plates on the sides; intestinal canal usually not much longer than the body. Haemal spines of the vertebrae above the anal bifid; lower and fourth upper pharyngeals toothed. (*Loricariinae.*)
    i. Teeth in the jaws in small or moderate number, not setiform; a more or less distinct orbital notch.
      j. Snout rounded or pointed, not much produced.
        k. Lips with numerous cirri and marginal fringes; no distinct anal plate. . . . . *Loricaria.*
        kk. Lips papillose; a distinct anal plate . . . . *Loricariichthys.*
      jj. Snout produced, with a long rostrum.
        l. Snout expanded at the tip, with recurved hooks. . . . . *Hemiodontichthys.*
        ll. Snout not expanded . . . . *Reganella.*
    ii. Teeth numerous, setiform; orbit circular, without a distinct notch.
      m. Dorsal opposite the ventrals.
        n. Snout rounded, not produced as a rostrum . . . . *Harttia.*
        nn. Snout produced into a rostrum. Sides of the head in the male margined with bristles . . . . *Sturisoma.*
      mm. Dorsal opposite the anal. Very slender . . . . *Farlowella.*

The major change of concern to aquarists is that the genus *Plecostomus* as used by aquarists will now be referred to as the genus *Hypostomus* based upon Dr. M. Boeseman's paper published in 1968 entitled "The genus *Hypostomus* Lacepede, 1803, and its Surinam representatives," published by the Royal Museum of Leiden, Holland.

For many aquarists, this is the most interesting family of fishes in the whole kingdom. The loricariids contain something for everyone. To begin with, they have beautiful eyes. Not only are their eyes very attractive, but they are interesting scientifically, for they are among the very few fish eyes that possess an iris flap. Like a diaphragm, it controls the amount of light that enters the eye. Thus, if you look carefully at the accompanying photographs of the various fishes in this family, especially the *Hypostomus*, you'll be able to recognize the various "settings" at which the iris is open. Irises that are fully open mean that the photo was taken while the fish was in a darkened environment; if the iris is almost closed, then the fish was taken in full daylight or its equivalent. For the aquarist, loricariids do best in a medium light situation, where the irises of the fishes are partially closed.

But loricariids have many other interesting characteristics. These fishes are found throughout most of South America, from Panama to Argentina; from sea level or below to up to 3,000 meters high in the mountains; from pure freshwater streams to brackish tidal pools; and from

Corydoras axelrodi

Corydoras axelrodi

Corydoras habrosus

Corydoras gracilis

Corydoras loxozonus

Corydoras pastazensis orcesi

Corydoras (cf aeneus)

Corydoras septentrionalis

Plate #135

236

Corydoras elegans

Corydoras rabauti

Corydoras simulatus

Corydoras adolfoi (imitator)

Corydoras adolfoi

Corydoras adolfoi

Corydoras narcissus

Corydoras robustus

Plate #136

237

still ponds to rushing torrents. They can live well in torrential mountain streams that are devoid of most other fishes because they can eat and breathe where most other fishes cannot. Their sucker mouths are, in reality, vacuum cups by which the fishes can adhere to almost anything found in nature that is solid. In the aquarium they attach themselves to the aquarium glass, to large leaves, or to sticks and stones. As they adhere to this medium they sometimes assume weird positions. . .sideways, upside down, head down, tail up, etc. So fast is their adherence that they frequently cannot be removed by pulling them off without tearing their mouthparts. But how can they breathe with such an airtight mouth? Simple. Their gills operate in both directions. If you count the gill movements of a fish that is not using its mouth for attachment purposes you will find it moves between 100 to 150 times a minute. The oxygen-containing water is usually brought in through the mouth and passed over the gills, which take the oxygen out of the water and give up the carbon dioxide waste gas at the same time. These sucker-mouthed catfishes cannot bring in water through their mouths, so their gills work as an inhalant device, bringing water in and then exhaling it, thus having twice the opportunity of extracting oxygen and giving up carbon dioxide. But the mystery is why do their gills move twice as fast, from 200-300 times a minute? In theory their gills should only move half as fast. The movements clocked, by the way, were gill openings and closings, assuming that the gills work automatically as the water passes over them.

Their mouths are armed with strong, hooked teeth. These teeth, which are only found on the jaws and not the palate of the mouth, require assistance from the fish's movement to function. As the fish scoots or slides over the aquarium glass, for example, it scrapes off the algae growing on the glass and eats it. Their very long intestine that is rolled into many coils fills their soft, sometimes unprotected undersides. The skin on their bellies is very often translucent, and if the fish has been eating algae, the green can often be seen through the skin.

BODY SCUTES
Inasmuch as the fish has its mouth under its head, thus making it difficult to defend itself with its mouth, and has a soft belly that is very vulnerable to attack, almost its sole protection is the skin covering the other parts of its body. Since it almost always assumes an attached position with its belly tight against something solid, its back, head, and exposed body parts are covered with "armor." The word "lorica" means armor, and this name refers to the very hard bony scutes that cover the exposed body parts. The scutes are so well constructed and put together, like the chain mail that covered the knights of old, that the fish is barely hampered in its wriggling and swimming movements. Ingenious slits in the armor allow for the insertion of the adipose and ventral fins. Each fish has four or five rows of these bony scutes (Callichthyidae has two rows). The head is also protected with a hard covering, and it is the construction of these head bones that in part separates the loricariids one from the other.

The body scutes are usually further protected with small denticles (tooth-like projections that aren't really teeth). All in all, the fishes in the family Loricariidae are rarely eaten by other fishes, but they are a favorite food for members of the crocodile family and turtles; and many mammals eat them, too, because they are easy to catch.

The author (HRA) had a routine on jungle collecting trips. Fish from morning until the sun was high enough in the sky to light the photo tank over his shoulder. This was usually 2 p.m. Then two hours of photography, a two-hour siesta, and then dinner in the twilight. Another two hour siesta, then two hours of night fishing. During the last siesta a large animal approached us fearlessly. We didn't take guns to the jungle for this frightened the Indians with whom we worked, so we had almost no protection from large animals and snakes except long knives (machetes). Fortunately the animal was a large dog, and it became our pet because we fed him. What did we feed him? *Hypostomus*.

One of the greatest delicacies of the world is caviar. The author (HRA) is very familiar with all types of Russian, Iranian, and American caviars since he visits Russia twice annually, but the best of all caviar is *Hyposto-mus* caviar. You get it by tearing off the heads of the *Hypostomus*. The ripe fish will have huge red eggs like the Russian salmon caviar. You drop the eggs into some salt water for a few minutes and then eat them. When washed down with cachaca (ka-sha-sa), the Brazilian firewater, it is unbelievably delicious. The Indians taught the author that one. But the bodies of the *Hypostomus* were unceremoniously tossed aside and they laid dried up and covered with flies all around us. The lost dog made a meal of them. . .spines, scutes, and all!

There are many other characteristics that make this family so interesting. They are endowed with a very peaceful disposition and are never the attackers. They are not territorial, and about the only problem an aquarist might have with them is when they try to attach themselves to the side of a larger fish. But this is a harmless bit of fun.

What really makes them interesting is their ability to grow different parts of their bodies at different rates during different times of their lives. The *Hypostomus* and their close relatives in the subfamily Hypostominae have offspring whose dorsal fin is larger (in proportion) than in the adults. Thus very young fish would have a sailfin; but as the fish grow larger their dorsal fins stay the same size and thus, proportionately, their fins lose size. In the subfamily Loricariinae, in many members, especially *Pterygoplichthys*, the opposite occurs and the dorsal fin outgrows the body of the fish and appears tremendous in a very old fish. In all loricariids, the pectoral fins keep growing, even after the body growth almost ceases.

As if this weren't enough to make for an interesting body, many of these fishes have heads and mouths covered with bristles and/or tentacles. In all cases where this is a species characteristic, the males have longer ones or more complex ones than do the females. Other sexual characteristics of some loricariids include the more pointed head and the broader lip flap on the underside of the mouth (lower lip) to be found in males of some genera of whip-tails, such as *Loricariichthys*. This lip adaptation enables the male to carry the eggs from one place to another.

HOW LORICARIIDS SPAWN

There are basically two different kinds of spawning habits. *Otocinclus* and some of its close relatives lay eggs exactly the way cichlids lay them. The pair may or may not prepare a spot upon which the adhesive eggs will be attached. The female then places her eggs in the area, making a dozen or more trips to the site to deposit all her eggs there. The male visits the spot after every visit by the female and fertilizes the eggs at that time. Then the pair leave the eggs on their own. They only lay about 50 eggs. The eggs are clear when laid and oval. The only way this differs from a cichlid's spawning habits is that the female tries to lay her eggs in exactly the same spot each time. This results in a huge sticky mass of eggs, one atop the other. The eggs hatch in two to four days, with the youngest eggs hatching first. If the oldest eggs hatched first they would be trapped under the egg mass. The young grow quickly if suitable food is available to them. They do well on dead freshly hatched brine shrimp, thus frozen nauplii are usually used for feeding these fry.

The larger loricariids such as *Loricariichthys, Loricaria, Hypostomus,* and the like have a very strong cichlid-like brood care ritual. They usually dig a hole or find a cave in which to hide their eggs. The male usually moves the eggs from the spawning site to the cave where he actually sits on them like a chicken, protecting them until they hatch. Sometimes the catfish lay their eggs on a leaf or stone and the male guards them in the open tank. Most of the fishes that "sit" on their eggs and guard them have colored eggs. The color may range from light brown to bright red. The fry need lots of soft algae. This problem has been solved by Dr. P. A. Lewis, who reported (*Tropical Fish Hobbyist* magazine, February, 1983) that he successfully spawned and raised *Sturisoma panamense* fry by feeding them green bean induced infusoria, followed by mashed green peas, followed by mashed cooked green beans.

Many back issues of *Tropical Fish Hobbyist* magazine contain illustrated articles about the spawnings of these highly interesting fishes.

Corydoras nattereri

Corydoras nattereri

Corydoras xinguensis

Corydoras polystictus

Corydoras sanchesi

Corydoras polystictus

Corydoras atropersonatus

Corydoras osteocarus

Plate #137

Corydoras guapore

Corydoras caudamaculatus

Corydoras panda

Corydoras melini

Corydoras metae

Corydoras metae

Corydoras sp. (arcuatus/evelynae)

Corydoras arcuatus

242

Plate #138

Corydoras n. sp.

Corydoras nanus

Corydoras undulatus

Corydoras nanus

Corydoras paleatus

Corydoras paleatus

Corydoras ehrhardti

Corydoras paleatus? (albino)

Plate #139

243

Corydoras robineae

Corydoras pulcher?

Corydoras blochi blochi

Corydoras osteocarus

Corydoras bondi

Corydoras bondi

Corydoras nanus

Corydoras nanus

Plate #140

Corydoras agassizi

Corydoras agassizi

Corydoras sp.

Corydoras julii

Corydoras ornatus

Corydoras sp.

Corydoras trilineatus

Corydoras trilineatus

Plate #141

Corydoras acutus

Corydoras sychri

Corydoras melanistius melanistius

Corydoras melanistius brevirostris

Corydoras delphax?

Corydoras orphnopterus?

Corydoras reticulatus

Corydoras reticulatus

Plate #142

Corydoras ornatus

Corydoras schwartzi

Corydoras evelynae

Corydoras leucomelas

Corydoras haraldschultzi

Corydoras sterbai

Corydoras reticulatus

Corydoras reticulatus

Plate #143

SPAWNING *CORYDORAS AENEUS*

Of the about 100 species of corydoras catfishes, probably the most regularly spawned is *Corydoras aeneus*. As far as known, all *Corydoras* species spawn similarly, the female mouthing the male's vent, placing her eggs in a pouch formed by the ventral fins, cleaning the substrate with her mouth, and then pressing the eggs into position on the substrate. As usual with this family, it is not certain when fertilization occurs.

SPAWNING *HOPLOSTERNUM THORACATUM*

The species of *Hoplosternum* spawn very much like the species of *Corydoras* except that the male blows a bubblenest into which the female places the eggs. The bubblenest is often a massive structure much larger than the spawning pair.

SPAWNING *"LORICARIA"*

Most loricariids spawn in hidden nests (in caves, hollow plant stems, under debris, or under large leaves). The eggs are large and often bright orange or even red in color. Usually one or both parents guard the nest and young. "*Loricaria*" of the hobby includes very similar-appearing species of *Dasyloricaria*, *Rineloricaria*, and probably other genera.

SPAWNING *ANCISTRUS*

The large, often colorful eggs are guarded by the parents, as are the fry. In most *Ancistrus* the males have larger and more numerous bristles or tentacles on the snout than do the females.

MOUTHS AND EYES

The sucking mouths of loricariids vary greatly and are important in identification. The fine teeth and very broad lips of the *Ancistrus* contrast with the narrower lips and very large teeth of the *Panaque*. Both fishes have the typical loricariid filament or lappet over the eye that serves as a sun screen to protect the iris, expanding and contracting with light intensity.

The male (upper fish in this photo) of this spawning pair of *Corydoras aeneus* is only slightly smaller than the female; most spawning males are a good deal smaller than the females.

The female has placed herself into the typical "T" position athwart the genital region of the male.

With eggs clasped within her ventral fins, the female slides along the glass side of the tank near the bottom; she has already stuck a number of eggs onto the glass.

Rising to near the water surface, the female continues to attach eggs to the side of the tank. The eggs of *Corydoras* catfishes are comparatively large and hard-shelled.

Plate #144   249

The spawning pair of *Hoplosternum thoracatum* maneuver under the bubblenest that has been constructed by the male.

The female *H. thoracatum* has begun to take up the position in which her mouth will be close to the vent of the male, with their bodies forming a "T" shape.

The male has rolled onto his side, and the female is approaching his vent with her mouth.

The female is now upside down beneath the nest, and the eggs have started to emerge from the pocket formed by the female's ventral fins.

Here the male *Rineloricaria filamentosa* has taken up a position outside the bamboo shaft and shares guard duty with the female.

The eggs of this pair of spawning *Rineloricaria filamentosa* were laid within a section of bamboo that had been hollowed out to form a "cave."

Male *Ancistrus* guards large yellowish eggs at mouth of plastic cylinder.

Baby *Ancistrus* huddle with one of their parents within the hollowed-out tube used as a spawning and rearing chamber by the parent fish.

Plate #146

Close-up of the head of *Panaque suttoni,* the "blue-eyed plecostomus."

The *Ancistrus* species shown in this close-up exhibits the typical "omega-shaped" pupil to the eye. The number of bristles on the head is not necessarily a reliable indicator of sex; the number can vary from fish to fish regardless of sex.

Left: The relatively large teeth are visible in this view of the underside of *Panaque nigrolineatus;* they contrast with the smaller teeth of the *Ancistrus* species at right.

Plate #147

Hypostomus sp.

Hypostomus sp.

Hypostomus sp.

Hypostomus sp.

Hypostomus sp.

Hypostomus sp.

Hypostomus sp.

Hypostomus sp.

Plate #148

253

Hypostomus sp.

Hypostomus sp.

Hypostomus sp. (color sport)

Hypostomus sp. (color sport)

Hypostomus sp. (albino)

Hypostomus sp.

Hypostomus sp.

Hypostomus sp.

Plate #149

Cochliodon sp.

Cochliodon sp.

Cochliodon juvenile

Pterygoplichthys cf. *gibbiceps*

Pterygoplichthys cf. *gibbiceps*

Pterygoplichthys cf. *gibbiceps*

Monistiancistrus sp.

Monistiancistrus sp.

Plate #150

255

Peckoltia sp.

Peckoltia sp.

Peckoltia sp.

Peckoltia sp.

Peckoltia sp.

Peckoltia sp.

Peckoltia sp.

Peckoltia sp.

Plate #151

256

Ancistrus sp.

Ancistrus sp.

Peckoltia sp.

Ancistrus sp.

Ancistrus sp.

Pseudacanthicus leopardus

Hypostomus sp.

Pterygoplichthys sp.

Plate #152

Ancistrus sp.

Ancistrus sp.

Ancistrus sp.

Ancistrus sp.

Ancistrus sp.

Ancistrus sp.

Ancistrus sp.

Ancistrus sp.

Plate #153

Ancistrus sp.

Ancistrus sp.

Ancistrus sp.

Ancistrus sp.

Panaque nigrolineatus

Panaque nigrolineatus

Panaque suttoni

Panaque suttoni

Plate #154

259

Panaque nigrolineatus

Panaque suttoni

Otocinclus affinis

Parotocinclus maculicauda

Farlowella acus

Pterygoplichthys aff. multiradiatus

Plate #155

Otocinclus sp.

Otocinclus sp.

Otocinclus sp.

Otocinclus sp.

Otocinclus sp.

Otocinclus sp.

Otocinclus sp.

Otocinclus sp.

Plate #156

261

Hypoptopoma sp.

Hypoptopoma sp.

Rineloricaria castroi

Rineloricaria

Rineloricaria cf. *hasemani*

Rineloricaria cf. *hasemani*

Cteniloricaria sp.

Rineloricaria fallax

Plate #157

262

Rineloricaria castroi

Rineloricaria sp.

Rineloricaria sp.

Rineloricaria lanceolata

Rineloricaria lanceolata

Rineloricaria lanceolata

Plate #158

263

Farlowella sp.

Farlowella sp.

Farlowella sp.

Farlowella sp.

Hemiodontichthys acipenserinus

Hemiodontichthys acipenserinus

Sturisoma sp.

Sturisoma sp.

Plate #159

Cynolebias antenori

Cynolebias minimus

Cynolebias boitonei (male)

Cynolebias boitonei (female)

Cynolebias wolterstorffi

Cynolebias wolterstorffi

Cynolebias bellottii (male)

Cynolebias bellotti (female)

Plate #160

265

Cynolebias antenori Tulipano • Red-Finned Pearl Fish

RANGE: Ceara, Rio Grande do Norte, Brazil.
HABITS: Peaceful toward other fishes, but best kept by themselves.
WATER CONDITIONS: Soft, slightly acid water. Temperature about 72-76°F. best.
SIZE: Reaches a length of about 2-2½ inches.
FOOD REQUIREMENTS: Prefers live foods. Will take frozen foods also but will only take dried food if very hungry.
COLOR VARIATIONS: Grayish blue anteriorly, more purplish posteriorly, the body spotted with white. White spots in vertical fins and reddish to orange stripe in anal fin fading posteriorly; anal fin also with black border.

Cynolebias boitonei (Carvalho) • Brazilian Lyrefin

RANGE: Near Brasilia, Brazil at altitudes of 1000 m.
HABITS: A typical "annual" species which prefers muddy water holes that may dry out during the dry season. A good jumper so keep the tank covered.
WATER CONDITIONS: The temperature of the water in its native habitat ranges from 5 to 37°C. It is found only in rain water with a pH of about 5.8 to 7.2.
SIZE: Very small; not much larger than 2.5 cm; males larger than females.
FOOD REQUIREMENTS: Prefers mosquito larvae, freeze-dried worms and brine shrimp.

Cynolebias wolterstorffi Ahl • Wolterstorff's Pearl Fish

RANGE: Southeastern Brazil.
HABITS: Aggressive and pugnacious. Not adaptable for community tanks. Should be given their own well planted tank.
WATER CONDITIONS: Neutral to slightly acid. Temperature 24 to 26°C.
SIZE: Males to 10 cm; females slightly smaller.
FOOD REQUIREMENTS: Frequent feedings with live or freeze-dried foods.

Cynolebias bellotti Steindachner • Argentine Pearl Fish

RANGE: La Plata region.
HABITS: Should have a good-sized aquarium to themselves.
WATER CONDITIONS: Not critical; tank should stand in a sunny spot. A wide variety of temperatures is tolerated, but 22 to 24°C is best.
SIZE: 7 cm; female a little smaller.
FOOD REQUIREMENTS: A heavy eater; should be generously fed with live foods whenever possible, but will also accept dried foods occasionally.

Cynolebias minimus Myers • Myers's Gaucho

RANGE: Northwest of Rio de Janeiro in pools which dry out seasonally.
HABITS: Must be kept by themselves.
WATER CONDITIONS: Soft, slightly acid. Temperature 24 to 26°C.
SIZE: To 4 cm.
FOOD REQUIREMENTS: Small live foods.
COLOR VARIATIONS: Body green with bright red bars which extend into the vertical fins. Eyes are a beautiful green. Females plain greenish brown.

Cynolebias adloffi (pair)

Cynolebias adloffi (old male)

① ②

Cynolebias alexandri

Cynolebias alexandri (male)

③ ④

Cynolebias nigripinnis (female)

Cynolebias nigripinnis (male)

⑤ ⑥

Cynolebias viarius

⑦ ⑧

Cynolebias nigripinnis

Plate #161

267

Cynolebias adloffi Ahl • Banded Pearl Fish

RANGE: Southeastern Brazil.
HABITS: Should be kept by themselves. Males become scrappy.
WATER CONDITIONS: Tank should have a layer of about an
    inch of peat moss on the bottom. Temperature 22 to 25°C.
SIZE: Males to 5 cm; females a little smaller.
FOOD REQUIREMENTS: Live foods of all kinds which are
    small enough for easy swallowing.

Cynolebias alexandri Castello and Lopez • Entre Rios
Pearl Fish

RANGE: State of Entre Rios, Argentina.
HABITS: Pugnacious with members of its own species;
    generally peaceful with other fishes.
WATER CONDITIONS: Not critical.
SIZE: To about 5 cm.
FOOD REQUIREMENTS: Accepts most meaty foods.

Cynolebias nigripinnis Regan • Black-finned Pearl Fish

RANGE: Parana River in Argentina, above Rosario.
HABITS: Peaceful toward other fishes, but does best when
    kept with only their own kind. Annual.
WATER CONDITIONS: Soft, slightly acid water. Temperature
    22-25°C.
SIZE: Adult males to 4 cm; females smaller.
FOOD REQUIREMENTS: Small live foods are best. Frozen
    foods are accepted, but only as a second choice.

Cynolebias viarius Vaz-Ferreira, Sierra, & Pauletter •
Blue Pearl Fish

RANGE: Vicinity of Rocha, Uruguay, near the Brazilian
    border.
HABITS: Found in temporary pools and ditches like most
    pearl fishes. Eggs hatch in 3 to 4 months. Annual.
WATER CONDITIONS: Not overly choosy about conditions,
    but seems to prefer slightly acid water of about 20-24°C.
    Subject to shock from sudden water changes.
SIZE: 3 to 4.5 cm long; females seldom over 3.5 cm.
FOOD REQUIREMENTS: Prefers small live foods such as
    brine shrimp and mosquito larvae and pupae.

Cynolebias whitei

Cynolebias whitei

Cynolebias whitei (albino)

Cynolebias whitei (variety)

Cynolebias dolichopterus

Cynolebias dolichopterus

Cynolebias melanotaenia

Cynolebias brucei

Plate #162

209

Cynolebias whitei Myers • White's Pearl Fish

RANGE: Savannah ponds of the Mato Grosso region, Brazil.
HABITS: Peaceful toward other fishes, but best if kept to
   themselves.
WATER CONDITIONS: Soft, slightly acid water. Temperature
   22 to 24°C.
SIZE: To 8 cm; females slightly smaller.
FOOD REQUIREMENTS: Live or frozen foods. Dried foods
   accepted only when very hungry.

Cynolebias dolichopterus (Weitzman & Wourms) •
Sicklefin Killie, Saberfin

RANGE: Venezuela.
HABITS: Timid, easily spooked.
WATER CONDITIONS: Soft, acid water best for breeding,
   but neutral to slightly alkaline water suitable.
   Temperature 20 to 23°C.
FOOD REQUIREMENTS: Live foods preferred.
SIZE: 4-6 cm.
COLOR VARIATIONS: Females much less spotted than males,
   especially on fins. Bluish sheen that overlies belly area
   (and sometimes fins) of male entirely lacking in female.

Cynolebias melanotaenia (Regan) • Fighting Gaucho

RANGE: Southeastern Brazil.
HABITS: Do not put two males in the same tank or they will
   fight until one or both are badly mutilated or dead.
WATER CONDITIONS: Occurs in ditches and water holes,
   some of which dry out in the hot season; can adapt to
   almost any water.
SIZE: Males about 5 cm; females slightly smaller.
FOOD REQUIREMENTS: Should be given live foods of all
   kinds. Dried foods are accepted, but not willingly.

Cynolebias brucei (Vaz-Ferreira & Sierra) • Turner's
Gaucho

RANGE: Parana, southeastern Brazil.
HABITS: A sluggish annual fish found in ditches and pools,
   rare. The anterior anal fin rays of the male are set slightly apart from the other rays and serve as a primitive
   gonopodium. Should be kept alone.
WATER CONDITIONS: Not choosy. Some populations are
   found close to the sea, but it probably prefers acid water.
   Sex determination may be pH-dependent, as aquarium
   strains tend to throw only one sex.
SIZE: Small, seldom over 3 cm.
FOOD REQUIREMENTS: Small insect larvae such as bloodworms and mosquito larvae, plus brine shrimp.

Rivulus ornatus Garman • Red-flecked Rivulus

RANGE: Amazon basin, Brazil, to Iquitos, Peru.
HABITS: Typical of other *Rivulus,* preferring backwaters.
WATER CONDITIONS: Warm, acid water is preferred.
SIZE: 3-4 cm.
FOOD REQUIREMENTS: Mosquito larvae and small crustaceans are readily eaten.

Rivulus atratus Garman • Butterfly Rivulus

RANGE: Amazon of Peru and Brazil.
HABITS: The strongly countershaded color pattern (the belly is darker than the back) shows this to be a surface-dweller. In fact, the caudal fin and general appearance greatly remind one of the African freshwater butterfly fish, *Pantodon.*
WATER CONDITIONS: Should have clean, clear, acid water.
SIZE: 2.5- 4 cm.
FOOD REQUIREMENTS: Perhaps more selective than most *Rivulus,* so try feeding floating foods and insect larvae that stay on the surface.

Rivulus beniensis Myers • Reticulated Rivulus

RANGE: Rio Beni, south at least to the Tingo Maria area of northern Peru. Occurs as several different color patterns, some of which have been given separate names. The status of these populations is very uncertain.
HABITS: Typical of most other small *Rivulus.*
WATER CONDITIONS: Vegetated backwaters with slightly to strongly acid conditions.
SIZE: 3-5 cm.
FOOD REQUIREMENTS: Like other *Rivulus,* prefers live insects and crustaceans but can often be adapted to prepared foods.

Rivulus limoncochae Hoedeman • Rio Napo Rivulus

RANGE: Rio Napo system of Ecuador, perhaps ranging into Peru.
HABITS: A colorful species from lakes and streams. Very similar to *R. rubrolineatus.*
WATER CONDITIONS: May need a little cleaner, more aerated water than most *Rivulus,* but otherwise typical of the genus.
SIZE: 4-6 cm.
FOOD REQUIREMENTS: Live foods are taken readily, but it will eventually take flakes.

Rivulus agilae Hoedeman • Agila Rivulus

RANGE: The Guianas of northern South America.
HABITS: A peaceful little aquarium fish that adapts readily to the aquarium. Often found in cooler, flowing water in nature. Some specimens develop a pattern very like *R. strigatus.*
WATER CONDITIONS: Not too choosy; perhaps will take a bit cooler water than most species of *Rivulus.*
SIZE: 4-5 cm.
FOOD REQUIREMENTS: Mosquito larvae, other insects, brine shrimp, and other live foods are taken readily.

Rivulus amphoreus Huber • Guianas Rivulus

RANGE: The Guianas of northern South America.
HABITS: Reported to be very easy to keep in the aquarium, requiring very little maintenance. Prefers a planted tank, like most other *Rivulus.* Spawns readily, only the dominant male fertilizing the eggs. The eggs hatch in two weeks and the young mature in four months.
WATER CONDITIONS: Warm (22-25°C), somewhat acid water is preferred.
SIZE: 5-7 cm. perhaps larger.
FOOD REQUIREMENTS: Adapts to aquarium diets readily but still prefers live foods.

Rivulus ornatus (male)

Rivulus ornatus (female)

1

2

Rivulus atratus

Rivulus beniensis

3

4

Rivulus limoncochae

Rivulus agilae (male)

5

6

Rivulus amphoreus

Rivulus agilae (female)

7

8

Plate #163

272

Pterolebias longipinnis

Pterolebias longipinnis

Pterolebias peruensis

Pterolebias peruensis

Pterolebias zonatus

Pterolebias peruensis

Trigonectes strigabundus

Trigonectes balzannii

Plate #164

273

Pterolebias longipinnis Garman • Common Longfin

RANGE: Northern Argentina northward into southeastern Brazil.

HABITS: Peaceful with other species, but males fight among themselves.

WATER CONDITIONS: Acidity and hardness factors of the water are not very important, provided the water is clean. Temperature 17 to 22°C; higher temperatures to be avoided.

SIZE: Males about 8 cm; females 6 cm.

FOOD REQUIREMENTS: Does best on live foods; will accept meaty prepared foods but will quickly go off feed if maintained on monotonous diet of dry foods.

Pterolebias peruensis Myers • Peruvian Longfin

RANGE: Upper Amazon region.

HABITS: Usually peaceful, but should be kept by themselves.

WATER CONDITIONS: Soft, considerably acid water; for spawning, a layer about 2 cm deep of peat moss should be provided on the bottom. Temperature 18 to 23°C.

SIZE: About 7 cm for males; females about 5 cm.

FOOD REQUIREMENTS: Live foods of all kinds.

Pterolebias zonatus Myers • Lace-finned Killie, Banded Longfin

RANGE: Venezuelan drainage of the Orinoco River.

HABITS: Males not overly aggressive, but in close quarters they may nip at each other's fin ray extensions.

WATER CONDITIONS: Does well in soft acid water but will readily adapt to neutral or slightly alkaline water. Best maintained between 20 and 24°C.

SIZE: Males grow to 15 cm in the wild and females reach half that size; aquarium-raised fish are not quite this long.

FOOD REQUIREMENTS: Feeds heavily on mosquito larvae and other surface-dwelling insects, but will adapt well to frozen or prepared foods.

Trigonectes strigabundus Myers • Brazilian False Panchax

RANGE: Rio Tocantins, Brazil.

HABITS: Peaceful with fishes it cannot swallow.

WATER CONDITIONS: Soft, slightly acid water. Temperature 24 to 26°C.

SIZE: To 6 cm.

FOOD REQUIREMENTS: Live foods of all kinds; can be trained to take frozen foods.

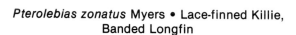

Trigonectes balzanii (Perugia) • Rivulichthys

RANGE: Paraguay drainage, Matto Grosso, Brazil.

HABITS: Generally peaceful, but will attack smaller fishes. Rather delicate.

WATER CONDITIONS: Soft, acid water is preferred; temperature 22-24°C.

SIZE: 5 to 7 cm.

FOOD REQUIREMENTS: Eats any small invertebrates or fish fry it can find.

Rachovia brevis (Regan) • Magdalena Spot-finned Killie

RANGE: Rio Magdalena basin of Colombia to the Maracaibo basin of Venezuela.
HABITS: Rather sluggish but generally peaceful. Annual. Males aggressive when spawning.
WATER CONDITIONS: Soft, very warm (25-32°C) water. Prefers neutral to slightly acid conditions, but not too choosy.
SIZE: Males reach 7.5 cm, females about 6.5 cm.
FOOD REQUIREMENTS: Omnivorous predator feeding on anything small enough and sluggish enough to grab.

Rachovia hummelincki DeBeaufort • Coastal Spot-finned Killie

RANGE: Coastal deserts and plains of northern Colombia and Venezuela.
HABITS: Found in stagnant temporary ponds, even cow tracks. Sluggish. An annual fish. Males may be aggressive.
WATER CONDITIONS: Not choosy. Will tolerate very warm (to 32°C), soft, acid water best. Tolerant of pollution.
SIZE: Females to about 6.5 cm, but males a cm larger.
FOOD REQUIREMENTS: Prefers live foods of appropriate size, but will take some prepared foods. Remember that this tends to be a sluggish fish.

Rachovia maculipinnis (Radda) • Venezuelan Spot-finned Killie

RANGE: Venezuela.
HABITS: Peaceful, but like other killifishes should be kept in a tank by themselves.
WATER CONDITIONS: Not critical, but does best in soft, slightly acid water that is clear and clean. The best temperature range is 18-24°C.
SIZE: Attains a length of up to 10 cm in their natural habitat but only about 7.5 cm in captivity.
FOOD REQUIREMENTS: Live foods are preferred, but it will accept frozen foods. Will not accept dried foods.

Rachovia pyropunctata Taphorn & Thomerson • Red-spotted Spot-finned Killie

RANGE: Eastern Maracaibo basin, Venezuela.
HABITS: Inhabits temporary ponds and ditches that are often badly polluted. Annual.
WATER CONDITIONS: Soft, acid water is preferred. Like the other species of this genus and *Austrofundulus*, it can tolerate a good deal of pollution and high water temperatures.
SIZE: Males about 7 cm long, females smaller.
FOOD REQUIREMENTS: Small insect larvae, worms, beefheart. Not choosy.

Austrofundulus limnaeus Schultz • Schultz's Spot-finned Killie

RANGE: Northern Colombia to Guyana, including Venezuela.
HABITS: Found in stagnant temporary ponds and ditches. An annual fish. Males often aggressive.
WATER CONDITIONS: Very flexible in its requirements, as long as the water is somewhat soft, acid, and warm.
SIZE: 4 to 6 cm in length, the males longer.
FOOD REQUIREMENTS: Like most annual killies, it will take almost any small invertebrates and many prepared foods.

Rachovia brevis (male)

Rachovia hummelincki

Rachovia brevis

Rachovia maculipinnis

Rachovia brevis

Rachovia pyropunctata

Austrofundulus limnaeus

Austrofundulus limnaeus

Plate #165

Austrofundulus limnaeus (female)

Austrofundulus limnaeus (male)

Cynolebias porosus

Cynolebias porosus

Rivulus cylindraceus (pair)

Rivulus punctatus

Rivulus holmiae

Rivulus holmiae

Plate #166

277

(See Plate #165)

Cynolebias porosus Steindachner • Big-lip Pearl Fish

RANGE: Coastal Brazil. The identification of this fish is very uncertain, as the larger, fine-scaled species of *Cynolebias* are poorly studied.

HABITS: Large for a killifish and can be a serious threat to smaller fishes.

WATER CONDITIONS: Not choosy. Will tolerate almost any combination of warm, moderately soft, acid to neutral water. Tolerant of pollution.

SIZE: Males to at least 15 cm, females smaller. One of the larger species of American killifishes.

FOOD REQUIREMENTS: Will eat almost anything small enough to swallow, including insects, worms, brine shrimp, fish fry, and prepared foods.

Rivulus cylindraceus Poey • Cuban Rivulus

RANGE: Cuba.

HABITS: Fairly peaceful in the community aquarium.

WATER CONDITIONS: Soft, slightly acid water preferred. Temperature 24 to 26°C.

SIZE: Males slightly under 5 cm; females slightly larger.

FOOD REQUIREMENTS: Should get live foods only, but will accept dried foods if hungry.

Rivulus punctatus (Boulenger) • Spotted Rivulus

RANGE: Paraguay, Bolivia and western Brazil.

HABITS: Generally peaceful, but shy with other fishes.

WATER CONDITIONS: Soft, slightly acid water. Temperature 24 to 27°C.

SIZE: To 8 cm.

FOOD REQUIREMENTS: All sorts of live foods; dry foods taken only when very hungry.

Rivulus holmiae Eigenmann • Golden-tailed Rivulus

RANGE: Guyana.

HABITS: Adept at jumping through the smallest opening; peaceful, but will eat small fishes.

WATER CONDITIONS: Soft, slightly acid water optimal, but not necessary. Temperature 22 to 25°C.

SIZE: About 10 cm.

FOOD REQUIREMENTS: Will accept living, frozen or freeze-dried foods.

Rivulus magdalenae Eigenmann & Henn • Bar-tailed Rivulus

RANGE: Colombia. Usually called *R. milesi* in the hobby, but this name is now considered a synonym by most workers.
HABITS: Relatively shy and sluggish. Typical of slow-water fishes in its behavior. Spawns readily in the aquarium.
WATER CONDITIONS: Likes the usual soft, slightly acid water, but quite tolerant of most aquarium conditions.
SIZE: About 6-8 cm.
FOOD REQUIREMENTS: Prefers live foods, but takes many of the common prepared aquarium foods.

(See Plate #166)

(See Plate #166)

Rivulus xiphidius Huber • Band-tailed Rivulus

RANGE: Oyapok drainage, French Guiana. The most distinctively patterned *Rivulus*.
HABITS: A shy, delicate species found in backwaters and stagnant pools.
WATER CONDITIONS: In nature takes very acid water, down to a pH of 5. Temperature 23°C.
SIZE: A dwarf species, seldom exceeding 3 cm.
FOOD REQUIREMENTS: Small live foods such as brine shrimp and daphnia are preferred, but will eventually take fine flake foods.

Rivulus strigatus Regan • Chevron Rivulus

RANGE: Found in various forms and color varieties over much of the Amazon area.
HABITS: Rather sluggish but nippy. Found in small backwaters and temporary forest pools.
WATER CONDITIONS: Warm, slightly acid water, pH 6-7, temperature 22-25°C.
SIZE: 5-6 cm.
FOOD REQUIREMENTS: Likes live foods, but will adjust to many aquarium diets.

Rivulus peruanus (Regan) • Perimparoo Rivulus

RANGE: Northeastern Peru. One of several very similar species from this area.
HABITS: Like most other species of *Rivulus*, this is a species of sluggish drainages and forest pools.
WATER CONDITIONS: Typically 22-25°C, pH 6-7.
SIZE: 6-7 cm.
FOOD REQUIREMENTS: Small crustaceans such as the daphnids and copepods form much of the natural food, along with mosquito larvae and other insects.

Rivulus urophthalmus Guenther • Golden Rivulus

RANGE: Guianas to the lower Amazon region.
HABITS: Prefer to be kept by themselves, but a large tank is not essential; they like to hide in plant thickets and are very active jumpers.
WATER CONDITIONS: Soft, slightly acid water is best. A temperature around 24°C is best, but it is not sensitive to gradual drops.
SIZE: 6 cm.
FOOD REQUIREMENTS: Live foods are essential, preferably those which remain near the surface, like mosquito larvae.

Rivulus magdalenae

Rivulus cylindraceus

Rivulus punctatus

Rivulus punctatus

Rivulus xiphidius

Rivulus strigatus

Rivulus peruanus

Rivulus urophthalmus

Plate #167

Blue snakeskin delta flagtail (Variegated snakeskin delta)

Blue snakeskin delta flagtail (Variegated snakeskin veil)

Blue snakeskin delta flagtail (Solid snakeskin veil)

Blue snakeskin delta flagtail (Variegated snakeskin delta)

Blue snakeskin fantail (Variegated snakeskin delta)

Yellow snakeskin fantail (Variegated snakeskin delta)

Yellow snakeskin delta flagtail (Variegated snakeskin veil)

White snakeskin fantail (Variegated snakeskin delta)

Plate #168

I doubt that there is any other fish besides the guppy that almost EVERY aquarist has kept at one time or another, for one reason or another. Many keep guppies merely as foods for other fishes, while some keep ONLY guppies. For whatever reason, guppies are the best-selling of all aquarium fishes. They come in many varieties, including different colors and finnage shapes. Some strains are larger than others. In some strains females are more colorful than in others, but in no strain is the female more colorful than the male.

One of the reasons that guppies are so popular is that they are easy to keep and, with a minimum of care, thrive in most aquarium situations regardless of the pH, DH, food, or water temperature. Of course the limits of these generalizations must be within reason. Even so, winter "freezes" in Florida, where many tropical fishes are raised, hardly ever kill the guppies that are kept outside in pools.

In 1859, a scientist by the name of Wilhelm Peters described a fish from the Rio Guaire in Caracas, Venezuela, as *Poecilia reticulata*. Peters was a German and published his findings in a Berlin scientific publication. Because of the very variable colors in which the guppy is normally found, other scientists also described this abundant fish, and in short order four or five descriptions of this same fish appeared under as many different names. The name "guppy" became attached to the fish when an English botanist, Robert John Lechmere Guppy, brought some preserved specimens back from Trinidad, an island lying off Venezuela. The British Museum's able ichthyologist, Dr. Albert Guenther, mistakenly identified the fish as a new species and gave it the name *Girardinus guppyi,* in honor of Robert Guppy. It was under this name that the fish became a popular pet, being so hardy, so easy to breed, and so relatively inexpensive for the wild varieties.

Because the guppy male is such a variable individual, its genetic structure has been the study of several dedicated scientists, especially Dr. O. Winge of Denmark. As Dr. Winge's results became available and more and more laboratories stocked guppies as experimental animals, it wasn't long before the aquarium pioneers began keeping guppies for their very own pleasure and profit. Most well-known of all "fathers of the guppy" is Paul Hahnel, a German cabinet-maker who emigrated to the United States in the late 1930's. He first kept wild type guppies, but instead of just keeping them alive, he treated them with the most dedicated care. You must remember that during the 1930's aquarium-keeping was hardly at its zenith. Heaters and pumps were practically unknown, and aside from goldfish and a few other hardy fishes, tropicals were kept mostly by Germans who seemed to have a knack for attention to details and difficult projects.

Hahnel, instead of feeding and keeping his guppies the way other people kept goldfish, treated his guppies to living foods and as varied a diet as he could find. He carefully aged water and changed 20% of the water in the guppy tanks each week. Soon his plain wild guppies began to grow larger...and larger. In a few years, after Hahnel kept selecting the larger and more colorful male guppies to cross with the largest and most colorful female guppies, he developed the "Hahnel guppy," one of the first strains of fancy guppy.

Beautiful guppies just don't happen...they are cultivated. In Paul's own words, "I don't care what guppy you start with; give me any guppies. Just feed them good live foods and dried foods when you pass them from the left, and siphon off 10% of their water when you pass them from the right. Replace the water with aged good water. Throw away the bad males and just keep the good males. In a few years you'll have beautiful guppies." (Good aged water is pH 6.8 and very soft.)

The original Hahnel fancy guppies had long tails, were usually intensely colored, and swam with strong strokes as their long tails waved in undulating motions as the males danced before their enchanted mates. Hahnel's fish had mostly blues and reds predominant in them, but every strain of fancy guppy has some "blood" that came from Hahnel's tanks...because Paul Hahnel invented beautiful guppies!

If Hahnel could do it, so can you. There is no great problem involved if you are willing to give it the time and effort...and have patience. You don't need a great knowledge of genetics. You just need good eyes.

Find a pet dealer having a nice variety of tropical fishes. Tell him your needs. His should be the shop from which you bought your original equipment, for when you bought it you could have ordered a few pairs of good guppies. There are many, many kinds of fancy guppies available today. Select the guppies that appeal to your own taste. Buy at least two pairs; four pairs would be even better.

Through error or otherwise, fancy males have been sold with common females as their "mates." The young that you will get from these females will be nothing like the beautiful males that came with the pairs. This is why you should buy your fish from a knowledgeable source.

Once you have acquired good stock, take them home and float them in your aquarium in the container in which they came. Allow a little time until the temperature of the water in the container is the same as the water in the 10-gallon aquarium. Check the pH of the two waters and be sure that they are within .2 of each other. Now add the fish to the 10-gallon aquarium. Allow your guppies a day or so to become accustomed to their new surroundings before you feed them or the food will go uneaten and decay.

Daily or more frequently, you should check your guppies to look for babies hiding among the plants. Immediately start to hatch brine shrimp eggs and feed the baby guppies newly hatched brine shrimp for the first few weeks of their lives. Supplement this with fine dry food. Keep the babies on this diet for one month, feeding brine shrimp every day, supplemented with other foods. By the end of the month you can begin to feel safe enough to isolate some of the fish.

Into another 10-gallon aquarium that has no filter and no gravel, put four small (one-gallon) bowls. Add water to the aquarium so that each bowl is submerged up to 1" below the neck of the bowl. Place small bowl filters in all the bowls, attaching them to the airline by means of four 3-way valves and plastic tubing. Also attach an airstone to a piece of plastic tubing and a 2-way valve at the end of the airline, and place the airstone into the 10-gallon aquarium containing the four bowls. Attach the heater, but do not plug it in until fish are about to be added. The idea of this setup is to use one heater to heat the four bowls; the airstone will circulate the water around the bowls so the heating will be uniform. In the summertime the bowls can be removed from the 10-gallon aquarium and it can be used for extra fish. Aquarium dividers are available at your petshop to separate the guppies from each other if you want to keep males and females apart.

Take the four largest fish from among the month-old babies and put one each into the jars in the other 10-gallon aquarium. Keep your eye on these fish, for your purpose here is to eventually end up with some virgin females. If you look closely at their anal fins as they grow, you'll find that fish that are males will begin to have thickened anal fins that develop into an intromittent organ called a "gonopodium." Females have "normal" anal fins that are fan-shaped and look like fins. Males, of course, can be kept together, and females can be kept together, too. But try as much as possible to keep your babies sorted out according to sex.

After a few months, as your fish become larger and more colorful, begin sorting them out. Give away your smaller males and females to others interested in the hobby (or feed them to larger fishes). Only keep the best one or two males and females from each brood. In six months you'll have about a dozen fish, each being the very best that your breeders have to offer. Some of the females can go back in with their parents, to breed with their father or uncle. Others can be crossed with their brothers in their own small jars. From this point on, luck and chance take over. If the odds were on your side and you picked the right fish, you might have a superior strain of guppies on their way to development. Regardless, keep inbreeding your fish for a few generations; this is the way new varieties spring up. Breed those fish which you like the best with virgin females. But check the virgins first with the following hormone test.

Female guppies are normally uncolored, though certain strains have some hint of coloration. Even in the most highly colored females, there is never any strength of coloration as can be found in males of the same strain. In order to check the coloration that the females might pass on to their male offspring I have found the following hormone test to work very well. This test brings out the full colors of the female, colors she should never have normally. If you ever find highly colored females offered for sale, you should consider the possibility that they have been treated with a hormone. Look at their anal fin carefully for indications of thickening. A female with a thickened anal fin is useless for breeding purposes.

Have your druggist dissolve 0.1 gram of methyl testosterone in 100cc of 70% methyl or ethyl alcohol. To this solution add 900cc of distilled water. This will make 1000cc or about one quart. This is your stock solution. To test a female guppy she must be put into one of the one-gallon jars. You can test more than one female at a time, of course. To the jars add two drops of the stock solution. Every other day add another two drops. Once the females begin to show color (from two to six weeks after you have started the test), stop adding hormone. As soon as you have ascertained which females have the most desirable color, remove them and place them in another container with fresh water. Now carefully wash the one gallon jar so that no traces of the hormone are left, or it might sterilize future females placed in the water. In a few weeks or a month, the color will leave the females and they will look normal again. Don't place them with the males until all abnormal coloration has faded.

As soon as you have set up your aquaria with guppies, you should regulate yourself into a routine. Set up a few gallons of water in some empty bottles that have been cleaned thoroughly with water and not soap or detergent. Set the bottles where they will be at room temperature and away from strong sunlight. This you will need in

Red lyretail

Red fantail (Multicolored delta)

Red delta flagtail (Half-black red delta)

Red common roundtail

Wild fantail (Red delta)

Wild delta flagtail (AOC delta)

Wild square flagtail (Multicolored delta)

Plate #169

Wild delta flagtail (Red bicolor delta)

284

Black square flagtail (Half-black red)

Black delta flagtail (Half-black blue veiltail)

Black round flagtail (Purple delta)

Black fantail (Delta)

Black snakeskin flagtail (Solid delta)

Black fantail (Delta)

Black flagtail (Purple veiltail)

Plate #170

Black fantail (Half-black AOC delta)

order to change about 10% of the water in the aquaria every week. The more strictly you adhere to this, the better off will be your guppies.

The guppy urinates. The urine collects in the water and in time builds up a poisonous environment for the guppy. These poisons must be constantly diluted with fresh water or the guppies will be stunted.

Your feeding routine should be as follows:

Early A.M.: Newly hatched brine shrimp for the babies and adults.

Noon: Dry food for babies and adults.

Early evening: Newly hatched shrimp for babies; adult frozen brine shrimp for breeders.

Late evening: Newly hatched brine shrimp for both.

Of course you don't *have* to feed your fish four times a day. It is ideal to do so, but they will get along very well on two or three meals a day. The people who raise champion fish are those who devote a great deal of time to their stock.

Guppies are very hardy aquarium fish. As a matter of fact, they are about the strongest of all tropical fishes, and if they get sick then you are doing something very wrong! Aside from some very rare ailments, your guppies are most likely to fall prey to the following diseases.

ICH

Ich (pronounced variously as "itch" and "ick") is an abbreviation of the scientific name of a parasitic protozoan known as *Ichthyophthirius*. These are microscopic organisms that bore through the slime covering of the guppy and build themselves a little home in the guppy's flesh. The parasite causes white spots to form all over the guppy's body. Usually the first spots appear on the fins, especially the tail. At the first sign of the disease, increase the temperature of the water to 85° F. This speeds up the life cycle of the parasite and the white spots will hatch out into larvae. Get some ich remedy from your petshop. Ich remedies kill the larvae, not the adults. The main ingredient of a good ich cure is malachite green, so be sure that the label says the remedy contains malachite green. The white spots should disappear in a few days and the guppies will be cured without ill effect. Follow label instructions. It may be necessary to continue treatments for two weeks or more to be sure all the parasites are killed. You can expect ich if your room temperature dropped suddenly and the aquarium heater was unable to cope with the drop in temperature. Ich also may appear any other time your fish are stressed.

WHITE MOUTH DISEASE

White mouth disease is a bacterial infection that usually begins by eating away the mouth of the fish. This bacterial infection can be cured with any of the broad-spectrum antibiotics like tetracycline, Terramycin or Aureomycin. Use 500mg per gallon of water. Change the water after the cure. This disease is brought on by bad water conditions, a chilling, or by adding unaged water to the aquarium.

FIN AND TAIL ROT

This disease is manifested by the fins of the guppy beginning to fray and disintegrate. It should be treated the same as white mouth disease.

For a much more detailed description of diseases of fishes, ask your petshop to refer you to a good disease book.

KINDS OF GUPPIES

Lots of books and articles have been written about guppies. Their care comes down to the best general care for all fishes: change the water as often as possible using the drip-siphon method. A change of 10% of the water per day with good, aged water is best. Feedings of live foods (brine shrimp is best) twice a day supplemented with a good dry food are highly recommended. Actually, guppies like to feed continuously, as they do in nature. The more often you can feed them, the better they will grow...but never feed them more than they will eat in one minute if you feed them more than once a day. Also, if you only feed them once a day (and that is not at all recommended), feed them mainly live foods one day with dry foods the next day. Never feed more than they can clean up in three minutes.

All guppies require about the same basic care: water quality as close to pH 7.0 (neutral) as possible; water temperatures about 75° F.; and good strong light at least 12 hours a day (more light makes them grow faster).

There are basically two kinds of guppies: *wild guppies,* which have little color compared to the fancy varieties (males, while looking similar, are almost never colored exactly alike and females all look the same); and *fancy guppies,* of which there are many strains. Fancy guppies are what this listing is all about.

While there are many aquarium clubs and guppy clubs, few have had the commanding authority to establish a name for each strain of guppy. There is really no need to name each strain except for commercial purposes and as an editorial convenience. But people who read about a "swordtail" guppy should have some idea of what a swordtail guppy looks like, so I (HRA) am therefore presenting a list of guppy strains, proposing names for them. These names are mostly derived from the literature. Each one has been illustrated with a photograph of a live fish. Fish will be categorized first by their being "wild" or fancy," and then on their finnage and their coloration.*

FINNAGE OF GUPPIES

There are the following kinds of tail shapes: round, veil, and pointed. Each of these shapes has subdivisions as follows:

ROUNDTAILS
1. Common roundtail.
2. Spadetail, sometimes called coffertail.

VEILTAILS
1. Flagtial: A variety where the long tail is narrower than it is long.
2. Fantail: A variety where the long tail is wider at the end than its length.
3. Bannertail: A variety where the long tail is equal in length and breadth.

POINTEDTAILS:
1. Speartail: A single spike coming from the center of a basically round tail.
2. Lyretail: A tail with a top spike and a bottom spike. This is also called a "double" swordtail at times.
3. Upper swordtail: A tail with a single spike growing out of the top rays of the tail.
4. Lower swordtail: A tail with a single spike growing from the bottom rays of the tail.
5. Crowntail: A tail with three spikes evenly disposed.
6. Fake swordtail: A fish whose tail rays are not extended but the top or bottom rays are colored, thus giving the fish the appearance of being a swordtail when in fact it is a veiltail.

DORSAL FIN SHAPES

The dorsal fin shape should be related to the tail fin, and in most cases they naturally occur that way. A fish with a long, flowing tail should have a long, flowing dorsal fin. The colors, too, of the dorsal fin should match the colors of the tail. It is almost impossible to have a fish of one color with its tail and dorsal different colors. This linked characteristic depends upon the closeness of the genes for dorsal fin and tail fin coloration. As soon as the genetic engineers get their hands on guppies, we can expect some remarkable achievements.

COLORS OF GUPPIES

Almost every color of the rainbow is to be found in guppies. It might be safe to say that the colors to be found in guppies are more varied than the colors to be found in any other single species of living thing, including plants and butterflies. For the sake of clarity, I am proposing the following color categories. I have not listed the combinations of, say, yellow and red where almost equal amounts of each are to be found in a single fish. In all cases, the basic color of the majority of the body and fin is what determines the color variety under which a fish can be classified.
1. Black
2. White
3. Yellow
4. Blue
5. Red
6. Green
7. Wild

PATTERNS

Guppies in many colors are found to have uniform patterns. Thus far the only patterns to be readily recognized are the snakeskins, though there are many popular patterns such as fishes with red tails and almost blue-black bodies. Albino guppies have never been favorites, and their appearance on the aquarium market is spotty and causes little excitement. Many new patterns might soon be developed as breeders concentrate on serious inbreeding.

The ideal for which most guppy breeders strive is color enhanced with finnage. This is due to the fact that "color sells," so petshops want colorful fish regardless of how beautiful their fins are. The ideal, then, is a fish with uniformly bright color throughout its body...with a thousand fish that look exactly the same in the same tank from the same breeder from the same strain. That's the ideal. It is certainly possible.

*Note: On the accompanying pages of guppy photos, two names have been applied to most of the fish shown. In all cases the first name is the commercial name derived from the literature, and the second name is the official description of the fish according to the International Fancy Guppy Association, the world's leading guppy society. Where only one name is given, the name derived from commercial literature and the IFGA classification are the same.

Red common roundtail (Common)

Red spadetail (Common)

Red delta flagtail (AOC bicolor delta)

Red delta flagtail (Red bicolor delta)

Red delta flagtail (Half-black red delta)

Red delta flagtail (Red veiltail)

Red fantail (Red bicolor delta)

Red fantail (Green delta)

Plate #171

288

Black fantail (Half-black AOC delta)

Black delta flagtail (Half-black blue delta)

Black fantail (Half-black AOC delta)

Black delta flagtails (Half-black red deltas)

Black lower swordtail

Black spadetail

Black square flagtail (Red bicolor veiltail)

Black fantail (Blue delta)

Plate #172

289

Yellow fantail (AOC bicolor delta)

Yellow fantail (Red delta)

Yellow common roundtail (Common)

Yellow delta flagtail (Half-black pastel delta)

Wild and yellow lyretails

Yellow delta flagtail (Red delta)

Yellow snakeskin fantail (Variegated snakeskin delta)

Yellow bannertail

Plate #173

Yellow lyretail

Yellow spadetail and upper swordtail (Bronze common)

Wild lower swordtail (Single swordtail)

Wild lower swordtail (Single swordtail)

Black lower swordtail

Red lower swordtail (Veil with poor tail shape)

Blue lower swordtail (Single swordtail)

Plate #174

Wild lower swordtail (Single swordtail)

291

Wild upper swordtails (Single swordtail)

Wild lyretail (Double swordtail)

Wild lyretail (Double swordtail)

Wild lyretail (Double swordtail)

Yellow lyretail

Yellow lyretail

Blue spadetail

Blue crowntail

Plate #175

Blue fantail (Red delta)

White square flagtails (Bronze veiltails)

Blue common roundtail (Common)

Blue fantail (Red bicolor delta)

Wild common roundtail (Common)

Blue fantail (Delta).

Wild delta flagtail (AOC bicolor delta)

Wild delta flagtail (Red bicolor delta)

Plate #176

293

Yellow upper swordtail female (Bluegreen female)

Black delta flagtail female (Half-black AOC female)

Yellow round flagtail female giving birth (Gold)

Black male lyretail (Common)

Yellow delta flagtail female (Blue/green female)

Female yellow common roundtails

Black delta flagtail female (Half-black AOC female)

Female yellow round flagtail (Bronze female)

Plate #177

Red common roundtail female (Red female)

Female black bannertail (Black female)

Yellow fantail female (AOC)

Wild common roundtail females and males (Common)

Red common roundtail female (Red female)

Red snakeskin delta flagtails (AOC female)

Female yellow flagtail (AOC female)

Yellow female roundtail above, red snakeskin lyretail male below (AOC female above)

Plate #178

PLATIES

For some reason the platies have always lagged behind the swordtail and guppy in popularity, although they are certainly among the top five or six species of popular livebearers. There are now at least 7 species of platies known from Mexico (*Xiphophorus maculatus* ranges south as far as Guatemala and Honduras), but only *X. maculatus*, the common platy, and *X. variatus*, the sunset platy or platy variatus, are currently found in the aquarium. The other species are restricted to minor drainage basins in Mexico and are certainly not very colorful in their wild form.

Both the platies in the hobby have been widely hybridized with each other and with the swordtails, resulting in a total mess as far as telling which species is which. In fact, some authorities flatly state that there are no pure strains of swordtails or platies being bred commercially at this time. Even the distinction between platies as a group and swordtails as a separate group is now hazardous. Platies were once in the genus *Platypoecilus* and were told from *Xiphophorus* by lacking the sword, having a different body shape, and by details of the gonopodium of the male. With the discovery of the sword-platy, *X. xiphidium,* in 1932, these distinctions began to break down, for this fish is obviously a platy by body shape and color pattern, but its males have a distinct sword. Later obvious swordtails lacking the swords were discovered, and eventually the genus *Platypoecilus* was dropped. For convenience, today platies are *Xiphophorus* without any swords, while any *Xiphophorus* with even a small sword is best called a swordtail.

The genetics of the platies was studied by Dr. Myron Gordon and his students, and the variation and systematics of these fishes (especially the two species in the hobby) are perhaps better known than for any other fishes. Many of the color and finnage varieties popular today are the direct and indirect results of careful breeding by Myron Gordon between the 1930's and the 1950's. Although wild platies are rather colorless, plainly spotted fishes, their genetic background includes the ability to develop and pass on traits for brilliant red, blue, and yellow colors, as well as distinctive patterns on the caudal peduncle and caudal fin. Additionally, they have the ability to pass these traits on to their hybrids with swordtails if carefully bred, with the major disadvantage being the shortening of the sword of the offspring. The platy variatus also has a strong tendency toward a greatly enlarged and brightly colored dorsal fin, making some of its varieties among the most colorful of all aquarium fishes.

Platies are very easy to keep and breed, and they are usually regarded as beginner fishes. Yet their extreme variability, much of it carefully documented many years ago, combined with their bright colors make them worthy of the respect of all hobbyists, beginner and specialist alike. Without them aquaria would be much less brilliant.

Gold variegated "Mickey Mouse" platy

Gold platy female

Gold tuxedo platy female

Gold salt and pepper platy male

Gold salt and pepper platy

Red salt and pepper platies

Milk and ink or leopard platy

Plate #179

Gold salt and pepper platies

297

Gold comet platies, male below

Gold comet platy male

Gold platy female

Gold hifin platy female

Gold platy male

Gold platy

Gold "Mickey Mouse" platies

Gold "Mickey Mouse" hifin platy

Plate #180

Red comet or twinbar platy

Blue hifin platy female

Sunset hifin platy male

Black variatus platy male

Red tuxedo hifin platy male

Black hifin variatus platy male

Red salt and pepper platy male

Blue platies, male above

Plate #181

299

Gold wagtail platies, males

Red varigated platies

Bleeding heart platy male

Gold "Mickey Mouse" hifin platy male

Gold variatus platy

Gold platies, male right

Gold "Mickey Mouse" platy male

Plate #182

Gold "Mickey Mouse" platy female

300

Red wagtail platies

Red wagtail platy female

Red hifin wagtail platy male

Red tuxedo wagtail platy female

Red platy female

Gold wagtail platies

Red tuxedo comet platy

Plate #183

301

Sunset variatus platy male

Sunset variatus platy male

Sunset variatus var. male

Marigold variatus

Blue variatus platy male

Red-tailed gold variatus platy male

Albino variatus platy

Gold platies

Plate #184

Gold variatus platy female

Marigold variatus platy female

Red variatus male

Blue hifin variatus platy male

Red-tailed black-spotted variatus

Red-tailed black-spotted variatus

Marigold variatus platy male

Blue hifin variatus

Plate #185

303

Blue hifin variatus platy male

Red variatus hifin platy male

Sunburst platies, male right

Black variatus platies, male below

Red hifin variatus platy male

Red variatus platy male

Gold hifin variatus platy male

Marigold variatus platy male

Plate #186

304

SWORDTAILS (*XIPHOPHORUS* SPECIES)

Since their introduction as aquarium fishes in 1909, swordtails have been consistent favorites in the hobby. All the known species occur in the Atlantic coastal waters from Mexico to Honduras. The various species are often not easy to obtain in pure form since nearly every swordtail available in a petshop is the product of a cross with a platy. Pure strains from the original wild stock (*Xiphophorus helleri*) just do not exist in the commercial aquarium trade.

The roster of swordtail and platy species, now numbering 18 nominal species, includes: *Xiphophorus alvarezi, X. andersi, X. clemenciae, X. cortezi, X. couchianus, X. evelynae, X. gordoni, X. helleri, X. kosszanderi, X. maculatus, X. milleri, X. montezumae, X. nigrensis, X. pygmaeus, X. roseni, X. signum, X. variatus,* and *X. xiphidium.* Of these 18, 7 are usually called platies: *X. couchianus, X. gordoni, X. variatus, X. evelynae, X. milleri, X. roseni,* and *X. maculatus.* The other 11 are swordtails, though several look more like platies with short swords than like typical aquarium swordtails.

How the Swordtail Got its Name

In the early 1840's, the government of the old Austro-Hungarian Empire dispatched Karl Heller to Mexico to collect plants for the City of Vienna's Botanical Gardens. In his travels through the state of Veracruz, Heller reached Mount Orizaba, Mexico's mightiest peak, one that rises 18,696 feet above the sea. In the vicinity of the village of Orizaba, at an elevation of about 4,000 feet, Heller stood amid an amazing natural display of tropical plants. With just a glance above, he could see, in the far distance, the gleaming snow-white contours of the glacial mountain peak. An abundance of moisture, both from torrential mountain brooks and from the mist-laden clouds that hover about the icy peak, in combination with the rich volcanic soil, has made the Orizaba region a natural botanic garden.

Karl Heller gathered not only plants but many small terrestrial and aquatic animals characteristic of the country. In a stream near Orizaba, Heller discovered one of the most unusual fishes in Mexico. When Herr Doktor Jacob Heckel, the famous European ichthyologist, saw the fish that Heller brought to him for identification—dead and pickled in preserving fluid though it was—he exclaimed enthusiastically that it "was so indescribably beautiful that it must appear as something extraordinary even to the layman." Heckel said, in 1848, "This species I name in honor of Karl Heller, its discoverer: *Xiphophorus hellerii.*" Nothing could have been more appropriate, for the scientific name means "Heller's swordbearer."

Blood red swordtail female.

Gold tuxedo swordtails.

Brick red wag swordtail.

Brick red swordtail

Red Mexican swordtails.

Velvet red swordtail.

Black Berlin swordtails.

Red tuxedo swordtail platy hybrid.

Plate #187

Xiphophorus montezumae.

Green variegated swordtails, *X. helleri.*

Green swordtails.

Green swordtail male.

Green swordtail variation, male.

Green swordtail mickey mouse hybrid male.

Green swordtail male.

Golden swordtail male.

Plate #188

Brick red jet hifin swordtail male.

Brick red hifin wagtail swordtail female.

Brick red hifin wagtail swordtails.

Gold tuxedo hifin swordtail female.

Blood red wagtail lyretail swordtails.

Brick red swordtail male.

Blood red tuxedo hifin swordtails.

Albino hifin swordtail male.

Plate #189

Albino swordtail male.

Piebald swordtail male.

Marigold swordtail hybrids.

Red variegated swordtail female.

Marigold swordtails.

Red variegated swordtails, cancerous strain.

Gold variegated swordtails.

Red jet swordtail female, cancerous strain.

Plate #190

Gold tuxedo lyretail swordtail female.

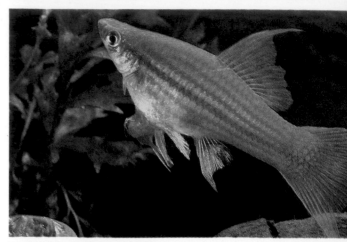

Brick red lyretail swordtail Siamese female.

Albino swordtail male.

Albino lyretail swordtail male.

Brick red lyretail swordtails, male on right.

Green hifin lyretail swordtail male.

Albino golden hifin swordtail male.

Blood red hifin swordtail female.

Plate #191

Blood red hifin or "highfin" wagtail swordtail females.

Velvet red hifin wagtail swordtail female.

Brick red hifin wag-pintails.

Blood red hifin comet swordtails, male below.

Plate #192

Blood red lyretail swordtail male.

Brick red hifin swordtail male.

Blood red Berlin lyretail swordtail male.

Blood red hifin swordtail pair.

Brick red tuxedo swordtail male.

Brick red lyretail swordtail female.

Xiphophorus cortezi male

Red hifin swordtail male.

Plate #193

Poecilia latipinna

Poecilia velifera

Poecilia latipinna (Black)

Poecilia latipinna (Albino)

Poecilia latipinna (Marbled)

Poecilia latipinna (Marbled)

Poecilia latipinna (Balloon Molly)

Poecilia latipinna (Starburst)

Plate #194

Poecilia latipinna (Le Sueur) • Sailfin Molly

RANGE: Southeastern coastal United States south to Yucatan.
HABITS: Peaceful toward other fishes, but best kept by themselves.
WATER CONDITIONS: Slightly alkaline water with a light addition of salt, a quarter teaspoon to the liter. Temperature 25 to 29°C.
SIZE: Males to 10 cm; females to 13 cm.
FOOD REQUIREMENTS: A hearty eater which should be fed frequently with a preponderance of foods which have a vegetable content.

Poecilia velifera (Regan) • Yucatan Sail fin Molly

RANGE: Yucatan.
HABITS: Individuals vary; some are peaceful and some, especially large males, are bullies.
WATER CONDITIONS: Hard, alkaline water with salt added is best. Temperature 23 to 26°C.
SIZE: Up to 13 cm.
FOOD REQUIREMENTS: Needs plenty of vegetable matter, especially algae, in diet, but also takes meat foods.

MOLLY VARIETIES

The mollies, like the platies and the swordtails and the guppy, are livebearers that can be depended upon to produce living young at regular intervals; since the newborn young of the livebearing species are in general far easier to feed and care for than the young of egg-laying species, the swordtails and other livebearers are among the most fecund of all aquarium species. Additionally, the relatively short gestation period (around 30 days in the popular livebearing species, provided they're maintained at a temperature of about 25 degrees C.) allows numerous generations of progeny to be reproduced within a relatively short time—a feature that is very useful in fixing genetic traits and establishing true-breeding new varieties.

The young produced by *Poecilia latipinna* and *Poecilia velifera* are larger than the young of the other popular livebearing species; also, the parents are less cannibalistic.

Poecilia caucana (Steindachner) • Cauca Molly

RANGE: Southern Panama to eastern Colombia.
HABITS: Peaceful.
WATER CONDITIONS: Neutral to slightly alkaline. Temperature about 25 to 28°C.
SIZE: Males about 3 cm; females about 6 cm.
FOOD REQUIREMENTS: Will take prepared foods, but should get occasional feedings of live or frozen foods.
COLOR VARIATIONS: Body blue and belly silver; dorsal fin yellow to orange with a black edge; males have about a dozen light vertical bars.

Carlhubbsia stuarti Rosen & Bailey • Banded Widow

RANGE: Rio Polochic and Laguna Izabal, Guatemala. The fishes of this genus are seldom seen, and it is possible that the photo represents an undescribed species.
HABITS: Virtually unknown in the aquarium, but probably not very different from *Phallichthys amates,* which it resembles.
WATER CONDITIONS: In nature it is found in warm, muddy water with a weak current. Probably not choosy in the aquarium as long as the water is warm, alkaline, and not polluted.
SIZE: Males about 45 mm, females 60 mm.
FOOD REQUIREMENTS: Unknown, but probably would take small crustaceans, worms, and other live foods.

Poecilia nigrofasciata (Regan) • Humpbacked Limia

RANGE: Haiti and Dominican Republic.
HABITS: Peaceful toward other fishes, but is very much apt to eat its own young.
WATER CONDITIONS: Slightly alkaline water required. Temperature should not be lower than 25°C.
SIZE: Males up to 5 cm; females slightly larger.
FOOD REQUIREMENTS: Not critical; will take dried foods as well as live or frozen foods.

Poecilia sphenops Cuvier & Valenciennes • Sphenops Molly

RANGE: Mexico and Central America, also parts of northern South America.
HABITS: Individual specimens show marked differences in behavior; some are completely peaceful and others are nasty.
WATER CONDITIONS: Hard, alkaline water best; tank should have plenty of plants and be well lighted. Temperature 23 to 26°C.
SIZE: Up to 10 cm; usually seen about half this size.
FOOD REQUIREMENTS: Doesn't like dry food unless it contains a high percentage of vegetable matter; small crustaceans form a good meaty portion of the diet.

Poecilia latipunctata Meek • Plain Molly

RANGE: Rios Tamesi and Panuco, eastern Mexico.
HABITS: Peaceful and rather delicate.
WATER CONDITIONS: Ranges into brackish water, so requires the addition of salt to its already alkaline water. Water should be warm (24-26°C) and clean.
SIZE: Males to about 50 mm, females considerably larger (at least 65 mm).
FOOD REQUIREMENTS: Like other livebearers, it prefers small live foods and vegetable matter but adapts readily to flakes and other aquarium foods.

Poecilia melanogaster Guenther • Black-bellied Limia; Blue Limia

RANGE: Jamaica and Haiti.
HABITS: Peaceful toward all but newly born young (including its own).
WATER CONDITIONS: Neutral to slightly alkaline. Temperature 22 to 25°C, slightly higher for breeding.
SIZE: Reaches a length of 6.5 cm for females; 4 cm for males.
FOOD REQUIREMENTS: Needs a varied diet and frequent changes of food.

Quintana atrizona Hubbs • Black-barred Livebearer

RANGE: Cuba.
HABITS: Because of their size, they should be kept only with small fishes; otherwise they may tend to be shy.
WATER CONDITIONS: Not critical. Prefers a sunny tank which is well heated, 24 to 26°C.
SIZE: Males about 2 cm; females about 3 cm.
FOOD REQUIREMENTS: Not choosy.

Poecilia caucana

Poecilia latipunctata

Carlhubbsia stuarti

Poecilia melanogaster

Poecilia nigrofasciata

Poecilia nigrofasciata

Poecilia sphenops

Quintana atrizona

Plate #195

Brachyrhaphis rhabdophora

Brachyrhaphis rhabdophora

Poecilia ornata

Poecilia ornata

Gambusia species

Gambusia species

Gambusia species

Gambusia species

Plate #196

317

Brachyrhaphis rhabdophora (Regan) • Regan's Bishop

RANGE: Both slopes of Costa Rica.
HABITS: An aggressive, active fish that will nip tails and challenge almost any other fish near its size. A bad fry-eater.
WATER CONDITIONS: Will live in almost any type of warm, clean water; salt may be added if desired. Frequent large water changes are necessary to ensure breeding as it is very sensitive to pollution.
SIZE: Females about 50 mm, males smaller (to 30 mm or so).
FOOD REQUIREMENTS: In nature this species is an insectivore, feeding on small insects that fall or wash into its streams. Will take most types of food in the aquarium though always prefers live foods.

Poecilia ornata (Regan) • Ornate Limia

RANGE: Haiti.
HABITS: Peaceful toward all but newly born young, including their own.
WATER CONDITIONS: Not critical, but the tank should be in a sunny location and not drop below 25°C.
SIZE: Males a little under 4 cm; females just under 6 cm.
FOOD REQUIREMENTS: Besides live, frozen and dried foods, they should get some vegetable nourishment.

Gambusia species • Mosquitofishes

RANGE: The three dozen or more species of *Gambusia* range from the coastal region of eastern North America south through the Atlantic slope of Mexico and Central America to northwestern South America; many of the species are found on the islands of the West Indies. The species are virtually all small grayish fishes with variable patterns of weak to distinct black spots; there are seldom any distinct patterns. Identification of *Gam-* *busia* species from photos (and even from specimens) is virtually impossible as the specific characters are mostly in the gonopodium of the male and the arrangement of the pores on the head.
HABITS: *Gambusia* are hardy fishes that can live in almost any type of warm water, though many of them prefer hard, alkaline water or water with salt added. All are fin-nippers and not really suitable for aquaria.
WATER CONDITIONS: Warm, hard water; additions of salt are usually helpful.
SIZE: Few species exceed 30-40 mm in the males and 50-75 mm in the females.
FOOD REQUIREMENTS: Notorious eaters of mosquito larvae and other surface-dwelling insects, these fishes will usually adapt to almost any type of food in the aquarium.

Priapichthys chocoensis (Henn) • Colombian Diamond-scale

RANGE: Rios Calima and San Juan, Colombia.
HABITS: Almost unknown in the aquarium; probably peaceful but a fin-nipper.
WATER CONDITIONS: Clean, warm water (22-26°C), with salt added.
SIZE: 30-40 mm long.
FOOD REQUIREMENTS: Live foods preferred as always, but should adapt to prepared foods.

Priapella intermedia Alvarez • Blue-eyed Livebearer

RANGE: Eastern Mexico north of the Yucatan Peninsula to Vera Crua.
HABITS: Peaceful.
WATER CONDITIONS: Hardness and acidity factors are of no great importance as long as extremes are avoided. Temperatures in the mid 20's (°C) are best. This species is especially susceptible to abrupt chills.
SIZE: Up to 5 cm; usually seen a bit smaller; males and females both reach the same approximate size.
FOOD REQUIREMENTS: Not at all choosy as to types of food accepted, taking all standard live, prepared and frozen foods eagerly. The method of feeding, however, is important, as this species has a tendency to ignore all foods that are not available to it at the top levels of the water; once they hit the bottom, the fish lose interest unless they are very hungry.

Phallichthys pittieri (Meek) • Iridescent Widow

RANGE: Atlantic slope of Panama and Costa Rica. Often considered a subspecies of *P. amates.*
HABITS: Peaceful. These fish do best in a large tank.
WATER CONDITIONS: Like most coastal livebearers, it lives well in any type of warm (24-26°C), hard, clean water; salt may be added.
SIZE: A large species, the females reaching 100 mm in length, although males seldom exceed 50 mm.
FOOD REQUIREMENTS: Will take most types of small live foods, vegetable matter, molly flakes, and typical aquarium fare.

Phallichthys amates (Miller) • Merry Widow

RANGE: Atlantic coastal regions from Guatemala to northern Panama.
HABITS: Peaceful toward other fishes, but very fond of eating its own young.
WATER CONDITIONS: Slightly alkaline water is best. Temperature 22 to 24°C.
SIZE: Males 3 cm; females 7 cm.
FOOD REQUIREMENTS: Should have some algae on which to nibble, as well as prepared, frozen and live foods.

Phalloceros caudomaculatus (Hensel) • Caudo

RANGE: From Rio de Janeiro to Paraguay and Uruguay.
HABITS: Peaceful at all times; not greatly inclined to eat their young if well fed.
WATER CONDITIONS: Slightly alkaline water that is well filtered and clean; the tank should stand in a sunny location. Temperature 23 to 26°C.
SIZE: Males up to 3 cm; females to 6 cm.
FOOD REQUIREMENTS: Small sizes of live and prepared foods, supplemented with algae which is nibbled from plants and glass sides.
COLOR VARIATIONS: Yellowish to golden with black irregular markings.

Priapichthys chocoensis

Priapella intermedia

Priapella intermedia

Priapella intermedia

Phallichthys pittieri

Phallichthys amates

Phalloceros caudomaculatus

Phalloceros caudomaculatus

Plate #197

Jenynsia lineata

Alfaro cultratus

Belonesox belizanus

Belonesox belizanus

Girardinus metallicus

Girardinus metallicus

Heterandria bimaculata

Heterandria bimaculata

Plate #198

321

Jenynsia lineata (Jenyns) • Broken-striped Livebearer

RANGE: Southern Brazil, northern Argentina and vicinity in the La Plata area.

HABITS: Found in slow rivers and streams in nature. A very unusual livebearer not only in color pattern but in the shape and functioning of the gonopodium; it is often put in its own family, Jenynsiidae. Additionally, both the gonopodium and the female genital opening are either left- or right-sided in every individual, and only pairs with corresponding organs can mate. A very quarrelsome species; will bother other fishes.

WATER CONDITIONS: Prefers a densely planted, heavily aerated aquarium with moderately cool (18-25°C) water.

SIZE: Males are only 30-40 mm long, but females may exceed 100 mm in length.

FOOD REQUIREMENTS: Omnivorous. Prefers live foods with some vegetable matter, but adapts to prepared foods.

Belonesox belizanus Kner • Pike Top Minnow, Pike Livebearer

RANGE: Southern Mexico, Honduras to Costa Rica, Nicaragua and Guatemala.

HABITS: Very vicious; cannot even be trusted with smaller members of their own family.

WATER CONDITIONS: Roomy tank which has been heavily planted is ideal. Water should have an addition of salt, 1 tablespoonful for every 4 liters.

SIZE: Males about 15 cm; females about 20 cm.

COLOR VARIATIONS: Sides are grayish to olive-green, with numerous tiny black dots on the sides.

Girardinus metallicus Poey • The Girardinus

RANGE: Cuba.

HABITS: A livebearing fish which greedily gobbles its young if they are not protected with a heavy planting of fine-leaved plants.

WATER CONDITIONS: Does best in hard water with a slightly alkaline pH of 7.4.

SIZE: Females reach 7.5 cm; males about 5 cm.

FOOD REQUIREMENTS: They eat everything, but they should have some frozen brine shrimp or live foods in their diet from time to time.

Heterandria bimaculata (Heckel) • Long-finned Spot-tail

RANGE: Tropical eastern Mexico south to Guatemala and Honduras. .

HABITS: A voracious, aggressive livebearer that cannot be kept with other fishes.

WATER CONDITIONS: The water should be well aerated and densely planted. A very adaptable fish that does well if kept warm (22-25°C) and clean.

SIZE: Males under 50 mm long, the females twice as large.

FOOD REQUIREMENTS: Will take almost any type of food small enough to grab and swallow.

Alfaro cultratus (Regan) • Knife-edged Livebearer

RANGE: Central America on the Atlantic slopes from Costa Rica to Panama; also from the northern Amazon basin (possibly a different species).

HABITS: In nature occupies clear, stony streams with rather deep water. Shy and not suitable for a community tank. The tank should be densely planted to help avoid disputes. The knife-edge is on the underside of the caudal peduncle.

WATER CONDITIONS: Clear, clean water of about 25-28°C. Salt may be added.

SIZE: 90-100 mm, the females larger than males but not markedly so; the supposed Amazonian form is about half this size.

FOOD REQUIREMENTS: Takes the usual live foods but probably becomes adapted to prepared foods.

Ameca splendens Miller & Fitzsimmons • Butterfly Goodeid

RANGE: Rio Ameca and its tributaries, State of Jalisco in western Mexico.

HABITS: Peaceful; good for a community tank. Males aggressive toward females.

WATER CONDITIONS: Does well with a bit of salt (up to 10%) added to the water; pH about 6.7-7.4. The temperature range is 23 to 29°C, with an optimum of 25°C.

SIZE: Attains a length of 9 cm (standard length) in nature.

FOOD REQUIREMENTS: Will take a wide variety of aquarium foods, but prefers algae, daphnia, live brine shrimp and mosquito larvae.

Xenoophorus captivus (Hubbs) • Green Goodeid

RANGE: Rio Panuco near Jesus Maria, Mexico.

HABITS: Peaceful. Can be kept in a community tank with other peaceful fishes.

WATER CONDITIONS: Not critical, but be sure not to let it get too acid or too soft. Temperature range about 20 to 25°C.

SIZE: Attains a length of about 4.5 cm.

FOOD REQUIREMENTS: Will accept a wide variety of aquarium foods. A supplement of spinach or other greens is recommended.

Ilyodon "Black Band" • Black-banded Goodeid

RANGE: Like all goodeids, restricted to an interior drainage somewhere in western central Mexico. This seems to be an undescribed species or perhaps a color variety of a described species.

HABITS: Peaceful and can be kept with other fishes. A livebearer like other goodeids.

WATER CONDITIONS: Warm, hard water is required.

SIZE: About 50 mm in length.

FOOD REQUIREMENTS: An omnivore that will take insects and other live foods, including a good bit of vegetable matter.

Xenotoca eiseni (Rutter) • Red-tailed Goodeid

RANGE: Mexico, Rios Tepic and Compostela south into Jalisco at least to Magdalena; Rios Tamazula and Tuxpan in southern Jalisco south to Atenquique.

HABITS: Peaceful; does well with others of the same species of all sizes, except possibly for equal sized males which may tend to be scrappy over females.

WATER CONDITIONS: Not critical as far as pH is concerned (pH 6-8 presents no problems), but hard water (DH 8-10 is sufficient) is necessary. Temperature 20 to 29°C.

SIZE: Reaches a length of 8 cm.

FOOD REQUIREMENTS: Omnivorous; accepts a wide variety of live or prepared fish foods, and vegetable-based flake food is recommended to balance the diet.

Anableps anableps Linnaeus • Four-Eyes

RANGE: Northern South America from the Guianas and Venezuela to the Amazon in Brazil.

HABITS: Surface fish spending most of their time on the surface of the water with their bulging eyes exposed to the air. In nature they move quickly over the surface of the water.

WATER CONDITIONS: They prefer very hard, warm water. Their natural habitat is usually brackish water canals. They are not found in large rivers or fast moving streams. Temperature 22-26°C.

SIZE: To about 30 cm in length.

FOOD REQUIREMENTS: They prefer live food such as small fishes, worms and insects, but they can be tempted to take frozen brine shrimp and bits of beef heart on occasion.

Ameca splendens

Ilyodon "Black Band" (male)

1

2

Xenoophorus captivus

Xenotoca eiseni

3

4

Xenotoca eiseni

Xenotoca eiseni

5

6

Anableps anableps

Anableps anableps

7

8

Plate #199

Cichla ocellaris

Cichla ocellaris

Cichla temensis

Cichla temensis

Uaru amphiacanthoides (juv.)

Uaru amphiacanthoides (juv.)

Uaru amphiacanthoides

Uaru amphiacanthoides

Plate #200

325

FAMILY CICHLIDAE

Though many families of fishes are unique to a specific continent, cichlids, as fishes of the family Cichlidae are called, are found in just about every tropical to temperate area of the world, having been introduced for food purposes.

In their natural distribution, cichlids occur throughout South and Central America, except where it gets very cold or very high, with one species even making its way into Texas; over almost all of Africa, especially the Great Lakes of Africa, which probably contain more than 1,000 different cichlids; and odd places such as Madagascar, Israel, and Sri Lanka.

This section will only deal with the cichlids found in Central and South America except for the additional single species from Texas that has been variously known as *Herichthys* or *Cichlasoma cyanoguttatum*. These fishes are very popular with aquarists because they are hardy, easy to sex and breed, very colorful, interesting, and friendly, with many of them becoming tame enough to take food from their owner's fingers.

The tribe Cichlasomini contains most of the cichlids that are *not* referred to as "dwarf cichlids;" nor does it include the large game cichlids of the genus *Cichla*. This tribe contains the genera *Cichlasoma, Petenia, Paraneetroplus, Neetroplus, Herotilapia, Uaru, Symphysodon,* and *Pterophyllum*. Another tribe, the Astronotini, contains the genera *Astronotus, Aequidens, Geophagus,* and *Acaronia* plus the dwarf cichlid genera including *Apistogramma* and *Nannacara*. The Astronotini is differentiated from the Cichlasomini by the simple character of the number of spines in the anal fin. The Astronotini have three or fewer, while the Cichlasomini have four or more. A few other very small tribes are also recognized.

Recently several ichthyologists have begun to doubt that these tribes truly reflect relationships in the American cichlids. For instance, certain forms of *Cichlasoma* are seemingly more closely related to *Aequidens* species than to other *Cichlasoma* species. The number of anal spines does allow a convenient way to group the genera, however, although it must be remembered that the resulting tribes are probably artificial and may not reflect true relationships.

THE GENUS *ASTRONOTUS*

Basically, *Astronotus* is a genus with only one species, *ocellatus*. However, the author (HRA) has collected series of *Astronotus* that are easily separable, one group from the other. One group found in central Brazil near Manaus all have several ocelli (eye spots) on their dorsal fin base. In most cases these ocelli are not bilaterally symmetrical on the fish; that is, one side of the fish may have four ocelli while the other side may have five or three. Another group found to the south around the Rio Paraguay have no ocelli in the dorsal fin but do have an ocellus on the top half of their caudal peduncle. *Astronotus* are excellent food fish and are fished for by the local people over their entire range.

The Oscar, as this fish is called, is very popular with aquarists lucky enough to have a large aquarium. A large aquarium is necessary since these fish grow to at least 350 mm in total length. They are easily spawned if given the correct conditions. The author (HRA) spawned them in shallow dirt pools in Florida. A group of Oscars, say about 20, were kept in a pool with about 200 square meters of surface and about one meter deep. The edges of the pool under the water were covered with pieces of slate laid at an angle. Daily feedings of live crayfish were given to the Oscars. Spawnings were very regular, with about one spawning per day minimum from the group. The eggs were removed and hatched artificially. Many color varieties have been developed, with the bronze, red, tiger, veiltail, ocellated, and normal varieties being the most common.

In their native habitat Oscars are found in slow-moving rivers close to the banks where there is very heavy aquatic vegetation as well as overhanging plants. They do not school but stay close to each other in their own territories. Except for the heaviness of the females, there are no apparent sexual differences.

THE GENUS *AEQUIDENS*

This is a large genus that is well distributed over tropical America from Panama to Argentina to Guyana. These fishes are small, mostly staying under 100 mm, and they are basically very timid, usually not attacking any other fish unless it is small enough to swallow in one gulp. They are very colorful, as the accompanying photographs show. For some reason they have not developed into many color varieties as have, for example, the fishes of the genera *Pterophyllum*, *Symphysodon* and *Astronotus*. One of the many species, *Aequidens portalegrensis*, was among the first tropical aquarium fishes kept as pets. This is evidenced by their appearance in old aquarium books. It was also the first cichlid spawned by the author (HRA).

The fish in this genus should be kept in as large an aquarium as possible as they are territorial when they spawn. A 40-liter aquarium is suitable for only a single pair. They usually find a smooth rock, clean it thoroughly with their mouths, then lay their eggs on the rock. At times they lay their eggs on plant leaves, sticks or even the aquarium glass. The pair usually guards the eggs, but sometimes only the male has this responsibility. Usually between 100-400 eggs are laid, and they hatch in about four days depending upon the temperature of the water. The eggs are easily hatched artificially, but in most cases the parents are to be trusted with the eggs, especially if they are well fed and left undisturbed. These fishes spawn all year long in the aquarium.

Feeding *Aequidens* is no problem as they eat everything from frozen and freeze-dried foods to live foods and such prepared foods as beef heart and Gordon's formula. They do best in temperatures ranging from 23-28°C in slightly acid water from pH 6.4-7.0.

THE GENUS *APISTOGRAMMA*

This is a large genus of small cichlids that are rather localized in their distribution. Because the genus is so large, perhaps having 65 described species by this time, some scientists have started chopping the genus into

Cichlasoma synspilum

Cichlasom synspilum

Cichlasoma maculicauda

Cichlasoma nicaraguense (juv.)

Cichlasoma nicaraguense

Cichlasoma nicaraguense

Cichlasoma spilurum

Cichlasoma spilurum

Plate #201

Cichlasoma salvinii

Cichlasoma motaguense (juv.)

Cichlasoma motaguense

Cichlasoma friedrichsthali

Cichlasoma managuense

Cichlasoma managuense

Cichlasoma dovii

Cichlasoma dovii

Plate #202

329

smaller units based upon very minor differences. The familiar *Apistogramma ramirezi* is now in the genus *Microgeophagus*, for example.

These small cichlids, called "dwarf cichlids" by aquarists, are extremely popular. They spawn in generally the same way that their larger brethren spawn, with the exception that many of them prefer to lay their eggs in a "secret" place rather than out in the open. Their eggs are laid on a solid base, whether it be a rock or a plant. Sexual differences in this genus are generally very apparent, with the male being much more colorful and usually with more pointed dorsal and anal fins, and with the first spines of the dorsal fin extended. Females and young males of many of these species look so much alike that they are often sold as "mixed dwarf cichlids" by fish collectors since they cannot ascertain to which species a particular female belongs. This makes it "fun" for the petshop that is trying to sell them, so beware. If you buy a "pair" and they don't seem to be interested in each other, then you probably have two different species. This has led to some interesting hybrids. The eggs of many of these species are ovoid (see the illustration of the *Apistogramma trifasciatum* female), especially those that are laid on the sides of objects rather than on the top of them. Most of their eggs are rust-brown in color, but some are white or clear. They hatch in two to five days depending upon the species and water temperature. They do best in water 22-28°C at a pH of 6.2-7.0. They do not like too much aeration or noise in their tanks. I have seen many dwarf cichlids live very short lives and never attain their beautiful color because their tank was connected to a very noisy pump or filter or because they were in an aquarium situation with very aggressive fishes.

They eat everything, but to bring them into good condition you must offer them live foods, especially small crustaceans such as brine shrimp and daphnia. A few worms now and then are also appreciated.

THE GENUS *CICHLASOMA*

This large genus ranges from Texas to Argentina, its species being found in small, slow-moving creeks and natural springs. Some of them are even found in brackish water. Including all their subgenera, there are at least 100 different fishes in this genus, and perhaps a lot more depending upon how you look at subspecies.

All of them make interesting aquarium specimens, though some are a bit large. Usually their sizes range from 100 to 300 mm, but they are friendly, interesting fishes and do well in very large tanks. Since they dig up plants and tear up the gravel beds, they are usually kept in unplanted tanks filled with rocks, driftwood and perhaps some plastic plants or aquarium gadgets that form caves and hiding places. Their spawns are usually large and are well protected by the male. Spawning usually takes place in an open area on top of a flat rock. If plants are near the chosen site the male usually tears them out. He wants lots of room around his nest to protect his fry and eggs. After hatching the fry are usually moved to previously dug pits in the sand.

The fishes of the genus *Cichlasoma*, with some exceptions, are usually easy to sex, with the males having longer and more pointed anal and dorsal fin rays and being much more colorful, especially during spawning.

These fishes are very hardy and can withstand water temperatures of 21-30°C with a pH of 6.0 to 7.5 with little difficulty. As a matter of fact, they may even be said to do better with a little salt added to their tank water to make it harder and raise the pH, but this is not advised for the beginner.

A single pair should be given lots of tank space, with at least 10 liters for each 3 cm of fish length per pair (that is, a pair 21 cm long should have a tank of 70 liters). All aquarium fish tanks should be covered; this is especially true of tanks containing cichlids that jump.

THE TRIBE CRENICARINI

The tribe Crenicarini contains three genera of interest to aquarists: *Crenicara, Batrachops,* and *Crenicichla*. The fishes of the genus *Crenicichla* are called "pike cichlids" because they are long and slender. They attack and devour other fishes, and in their natural range and habitats they travel in packs of a few dozen to attack schools of characins that occur in the same areas. They are very fast open-water fishes usually found in the clear, fast-moving waters of small creeks. They are extremely difficult to catch with a seine as they sneak under, jump over or find small holes to wriggle their slippery bodies through. They are not easy to keep successfully in an aquarium since they require lots of room and copious amounts of live fishes for food. Few have spawned in an aquarium to date, but as tanks in homes get larger and larger, more spawnings may soon be expected.

Batrachops species more or less follow the same description as the pike cichlids, but they are more rounded and have a deeper body. They are just as slime-covered, however. They are extremely difficult to catch alive except for hook and line fishing, thus they are rare.

These fishes, *Batrachops* and *Crenicichla*, often get to 300 mm or more in length. Smaller specimens are often kept in the aquarium, but they seldom live to maturity because they begin eating their tankmates.

Crenicara species, on the other hand, are the opposite of their relatives *Batrachops* and *Crenicichla*. They are small, peaceful, relatively easy to breed, and eat a normal aquarium diet. They are usually considered with the dwarf cichlids as they have all the qualities of *Apistogramma*. They rarely get larger than 125 mm.

THE *GEOPHAGUS* OR EARTHEATERS

In *Breeding Aquarium Fishes* (Book 5 in the series) is a report made by the author (HRA) on the spawning of three *Geophagus* (*balzani, jurupari, surinamensis*) with lots of nice color photographs. These fishes breed like few (if any) other fishes in the world. They lay their eggs, like a typical cichlid, on a flat rock that they have cleaned. Then the pair cover the rock with sand and keep it buried for two days. At that point they take the eggs into their mouths until they hatch. After hatching the young still take refuge in their mother's mouth. The mother takes care of them for three weeks, spitting them out only when she feeds.

In the aquarium these fishes are constantly digging up the bottom, chewing on the sand and taking from it whatever they are searching for. They are found throughout South America and are especially plentiful in the Rio Negro of Brazil.

Cichlasoma sajica

Cichlasoma sajica

Cichlasoma hellebruni

Cichlasoma hellebruni

Cichlasoma hellebruni

Cichlasoma festae ?

Cichlasoma coryphaenoides

Cichlasoma axelrodi

Plate #203

Cichlasoma popenoi

Cichlasoma citrinellum

Cichlasoma labiatum

Cichlasoma labiatum

Cichlasoma alfari

Cichlasoma urophtalmum

Cichlasoma trimaculatum

Cichlasoma festae

Plate #204

333

Other species of *Geophagus* have different habits. Some have been reported as spawning like a *Cichlasoma*, never taking the eggs into their mouths, while still other species take the eggs into their mouths as soon as they are laid.

These eartheaters have a great range—from Panama to Argentina. There are many species, most of which are unknown to aquarists; many are also unknown to science. With so many other species available, this is not a genus recommended for the average aquarist. They do best in acid waters with a pH of 6.0-6.8 at a temperature of 24-28°C. They take a normal aquarium diet.

THE GENUS *UARU*

There are one or two species of *Uaru* depending upon which book you read, but if you buy the "two species" theory, then you have to add a third species since there are three different color varieties. The juveniles all look different, too. An article in *Breeding Aquarium Fishes* by the author (HRA) starting on page 171 in Book 4 covers this interesting fish nicely. It is a gentle fish, very shy and very rare. It takes an expert to breed them and to make them thrive. They require the same diet as *Symphysodon*, with beef heart and white worms in quantity.

Key to the Guiana Genera of Cichlidae (After Eigenmann, 1912)

    a. First dorsal and anal rays not especially prolonged.
      b. Gill-rakers numerous, more than fifty on the lower arch, setiform; mouth moderate; anal spines three, alternating . . . .*Chaetobranchus.*
    bb. Gill-rakers not setiform.
      c. Preopercle entire.
        d. Gill-rakers minute; scales of the lateral line of the same size as those above or below it.
        e. Upper gill-arch without a downward projecting lobe.
          f. Mouth large, freely protractile; end of maxillary exposed . . . .*Acaropsis.**
        ff. Mouth small, not greatly protractile; end of maxillary concealed.
          g. Lateral line running close to the dorsal; head densely scaled . . . .*Nannacara.*
        gg. Lateral line well separated from the dorsal.
          h. Anal spines three; soft fins naked, or with scales at the bases only . . . .*Aequidens.*
        hh. Anal spines more than three.
          i. Ventrals inserted behind the origin of the dorsal . . . .*Cichlasoma.*
          ii. Ventrals inserted in front of the origin of the dorsal . . . .*Mesonauta.*
        ee. Upper gill-arch with a downward projecting lobe.
          j. Lateral line well separated from the dorsal for most of its length.

k. Gill-rakers at the base of the lobe; mouth small, not greatly protractile; caudal emarginate ....*Acarichthys.*

kk. Gill-rakers running at the edge of the lobe of the first gill-arch; mouth small; premaxillary not greatly protractile.

l. Preorbital little if any wider than the eye; eye a little nearer to gill-opening than to snout; lateral line not continued on the caudal ....*Biotodoma.*

ll. Preorbital twice as wide as the eye in the adult. Eye three times as far from the snout as from the gill-opening; lateral line forked at the caudal peduncle. Lower lip with a frenum . *Geophagus.*

jj. Lateral line running within a scale, or a scale and a half, from the dorsal...................*Heterogramma.**

dd. Gill-rakers large, stiff; perciform, mouth large; scales of the lateral line larger than the rest ....*Cichla.*

cc. Preopercle finely serrate.

m. Jaws equal; mouth small; scales 26-29, those of the lateral line of the same size as those above or below it ....*Crenicara.*

mm. Lower jaw projecting; scales of the lateral line larger than those above or below it.

n. None of the teeth depressible; scales 55-70 ...*Batrachops.*

nn. Inner teeth depressible; scales 38-130........*Crenicichla.*

aa. First dorsal and anal rays prolonged; body much compressed, deep; gill-rakers moderate ....*Pterophyllum.*

*f. *Acaropsis* is now *Acaronia.*

*jj. *Heterogramma* is now *Apistogramma.*

Cichlasoma nigrofasciatum

Cichlasoma nigrofasciatum (var.)

Cichlasoma nigrofasciatum (var.)

Cichlasoma centrarchus

Cichlasoma octofasciatum

Cichlasoma octofasciatum

Cichlasoma longimanus

Cichlasoma longimanus

Plate #205

Cichlasoma bimaculatum

Cichlasoma bimaculatum

Cichlasoma severum

Cichlasoma severum

Cichlasoma severum

Cichlasoma severum (Gold)

Cichlasoma severum (juveniles)

Cichlasoma festivum

Plate #206

Cichlasoma festae

Cichlasoma tetracanthum

Cichlasoma carpintis

Cichlasoma carpintis

Cichlasoma cyanoguttatum

Cichlasoma atromaculatum

Cichlasoma atromaculatum

Cichlasoma atromaculatum

Plate #207

Cichlasoma meeki

Cichlasoma meeki

Cichlasoma aureum

Cichlasoma aureum

Cichlasoma bartoni

Cichlasoma bartoni

Cichlasoma psittacum

Cichlasoma psittacum

Plate #208

339

Petenia splendida

Petenia kraussi

Petenia splendida

Cichlasoma umbriferum

Neetroplus nematopus

Herotilapia multispinosa

Herotilapia multispinosa

Herotilapia multispinosa

Plate #209

Aquidens curviceps

Aquidens curviceps

Aquidens dorsigerus

Aquidens dorsigerus

Aequidens portalegrensis

Aequidens portalegrensis

Aequidens portalegrensis

Aequidens portalegrensis

Plate #210

341

Aequidens pulcher

Aequidens pulcher

Aequidens itanyi

Aequidens caeruleopunctatus

Aequidens rivulatus

Aequidens rivulatus

Aequidens "gold saum"

Aequidens "gold saum"

Plate #211

342

Aequidens species

Aequidens species

Aequidens

Aequidens dorsigerus

Aequidens maroni

Aequidens awani

Aequidens thayeri

Aequidens itanyi

Plate #212

343

Aequidens vittata

Aequidens tetramerus

Aequidens duopunctatus

Aequidens tetramerus

Aequidens sapayensis?

Aequidens

Aequidens mariae

Aequidens awani

Plate #213

344

Crenicichla strigata

Crenicichla lenticulata

Crenicichla lepidota

Crenicichla saxatilis

Crenicichla species

Batrachops species

Acaronia nassa

Acaronia nassa

Plate #214

345

Crenicara filamentosa (female)

Crenicara filamentosa (male)

Crenicara punctulata

Crenicara maculata (female)?

Crenicichla sp.

Crenicichla wallacei

Crenicichla geayi

Crenicichla johanna

Plate #215

Chaetobranchus bitaeniatus

Chaetobranchus bitaeniatus

Chaetobranchus flavescens

Nannacara anomala (male)

Nannacara anomala (female w/young)

Nannacara anomala (female w/eggs)

Apistogrammoides pucallpaensis (male)

Apistogrammoides pucallpaensis (female)

Plate #216

Taeniacara candidi

Apistogramma agassizi (var.)

Apistogramma agassizi (var.)

Apistogramma agassizi (var.)

Apistogramma agassizi (var.)

Apistogramma agassizi (var.)

Apistogramma agassizi (female)

Apistogramma agassizi (pair)

Plate #217

Apistogramma agassizi (wild male)

Apistogramma agassizi (domestic male)

Apistogramma borelli? (var.)

Apistogramma borelli (female)

Apistogramma bitaeniata

Apistogramma bitaeniata (var.-yellow)

Apistogramma bitaeniata (female)

Apistogramma bitaeniata (pair)

Plate #218

349

Apistogramma gossei (male)

Apistogramma caetei (male)

Apistogramma eunotus?

Apistogramma caetei (female)

Apistogramma macmasteri (male)

Apistogramma macmasteri (female)

Apistogramma luelingi

Apistogramma sp. cf. macmasteri

Plate #219

Apistogramma cacatuoides (female)

Apistogramma cacatuoides (male)

Apistogramma cacatuoides? (male)

Apistogramma cacatuoides (male)

Apistogramma gibbiceps

Apistogramma sp.

Apistogramma pertensis (male)

Apistogramma sp.

Plate #220

Apistogramma steindachneri

Apistogramma steindachneri (male)

Apistogramma steindachneri (female)

Apistogramma steindachneri (female)

Apistogramma hippolytae

Apistogramma inconspicua

Apistogramma hippolytae (female)

Apistogramma inconspicua (female)

Plate #221

Apistogramma trifasciatum

Apistogramma trifasciatum

Apistogramma trifasciatum (female)

Apistogramma trifasciatum

Apistogramma trifasciatum heraldi

Apistogramma sp.

Apistogramma gossei

Apistogramma gephyra

Plate #222

353

Microgeophagus ramirezi (blond)

Microgeophagus ramirezi (normal)

Biotodoma cupido

Acarichthys heckelii

Geophagus gymnogenys

Geophagus australis

Geophagus rhabdotus

Acarichthys geayi

Plate #223

Geophagus steindachneri

Geophagus steindachneri

Geophagus balzanii (male)

Geophagus balzanii (female)

Geophagus surinamensis

Geophagus surinamensis

Geophagus jurupari

Geophagus surinamensis

Plate #224

Geophagus surinamensis (var.)

Geophagus surinamensis (var.)

Geophagus brasiliensis

Geophagus brasiliensis

Geophagus acuticeps

Geophagus jurupari

Geophagus daemon

Geophagus sp. cf. daemon

Plate #225

356

Astronotus ocellatus

Astronotus ocellatus (red)

Astronotus ocellatus (tiger)

Astronotus ocellatus (w/ocelli)

Astronotus ocellatus (normal)

Astronotus ocellatus (juvenile)

Biotoecus opercularis

Biotoecus opercularis

Plate #226

357

THE "REAL" OSCAR

Dr. Axelrod has often brought back specimens of the Oscar, *Astronotus ocellatus*, from his trips to South America. Normally, such large, well known fishes are ignored and the valuable shipping space is allotted to more unusual species of fishes. But Dr. Axelrod noted some oscars from Brazil were different. Along their back and dorsal fin they had red-rimmed black spots. Some Oscars available in the aquarium trade also have such spots, but these fish are not as distinctively decorated as the ones obtained by Dr. Axelrod. In any event, the specimens found their way to my desk so I (WEB) could try to interpret the discrepancy.

A little basic research turned up the answer. The original description of the Oscar left little doubt that the Brazilian Oscar specimens with the spots were identical to the one in the original description of the species.

The number and placement of the spots varied (within limits) from fish to fish and even differed from one side of the fish to the other. The spots were also of varying shapes and sizes, some even coalescing with others to form short rows of spots. In one specimen the spot at the base of the caudal fin was missing (but only on one side). These spots were once even considered as a possible means of identifying sexes. In fishes like the Oscar, where sexes are very difficult to tell apart, every little difference is used at one time or another in an attempt to obtain breeding pairs. Unfortunately the spots are of no help in this area.

I was able to check specimens of Oscars from other areas and found that they also differed in color pattern. Not only were the spots different, but even the pattern on each individual scale and a dark marking on the base of the pectoral fin varied. In one group the pectoral marking was a distinct spot, in another it was a dark but indistinct spot, and in still others there was a general blackish area covering the entire base of the fin. Not enough specimens were available to indicate whether or not there was a geographic pattern to these color varieties or how much blending occurred from one area to the next. For example, specimens from Manaus had spots similar to those from Tefe but generally fewer of them (one specimen had only the caudal spot).

The Oscar is therefore a variable species that shows individualities from population to population. The question arises as to whether there is more than one species involved (that is, exclusive of *Astronotus orbicularis*, a virtually unknown fish that may turn out to be a valid species). Looking at the specimens and comparing them to the common aquarium Oscars, one might think that there is a good basis in considering them distinct. There are certainly enough names in the synonymy so that one is probably available for the non-spotted form if it should be a true species. Some of the names given to the Oscar over the years are *Acara crassispinis*, *Cychla rubroocellata*, *Acara compressus*, *Acara hyposticta*, and *Astronotus ocellatus* var. *zebra*.

In this specimen the large ocellus on the base of the tail is missing. Photo by Dr. Herbert R. Axelrod.

The ocelli on the dorsal and the caudal peduncle on this individual are very vividly outlined in red.

This closeup photo shows some of the spots and the orange-red color on many of the scales. Photo by Dr. Herbert R. Axelrod.

Plate #227

THE ANGELFISHES, *PTEROPHYLLUM*

People who have been in the aquarium hobby for enough years (more than 50 years anyway) can well remember how difficult it was to successfully spawn and raise South American angelfishes of the genus *Pterophyllum*. In the 1930's and 1940's it was the rare aquarist who could spawn these fishes, and EVEN TODAY no one successfully spawns ANY of the angelfishes imported directly from South America on a regular basis. The only successful breeding is now accomplished from parents that were previously spawned in the aquarium. The initial spawnings of "wild" fish, that is fish from the wild and not aquarium-raised, were small and erratic, but they formed the base from which 25 million angelfish are produced every year from Singapore and Hong Kong to Europe and the Americas. I have not heard of anyone spawning wild angelfish since 1949. . .correct me if I am wrong. . .and many famous fish breeders have tried.

How Many Species of Angelfish are There?
When we talk about "species" we are making a scientific statement that has special significance. Basically, all the fish in a population that look alike and have certain physical characteristics in common belong to the same species (allowing, of course, for normal variation and cases of sexual dimorphism where the females and males look different). Groups of these similar populations comprise the species. Species that are closely related belong to the same genus. It is rare that every scientist who studies a given genus of fishes agrees completely with previous studies of the same genus, thus fishes' names are never stable and keep changing. The scientist sometimes changes a few names either to show that fishes previously thought to be different species are actually the same (these scientists are commonly referred to as "lumpers") or that fishes that were thought to be the same species are actually different (these are the "splitters"). With the angelfishes of the genus *Pterophyllum*, however, there aren't any other fishes that look like them, thus even a beginner can tell which fishes belong to the genus *Pterophyllum*. When it comes to the number of species, however, this has long been a scientific mystery that has only lately been solved by Dr. Warren E. Burgess, one of the world's leading ichthyologists. (His huge work *Butterfly Fishes of the World* has been hailed as a masterpiece. Each of the 114 species known at that time is illustrated in color in this book.) Dr. Burgess concluded that there are only two valid species plus a subspecies in the genus *Pterophyllum*. These are *Pterophyllum dumerilii, P. scalare scalare,* and *P. s. altum.* For those of you who are interested, you should read his chapter entitled "The Species of Angelfishes (*Pterophyllum*)" in the book *Freshwater Angelfishes* by Dr. Burgess and myself (T.F.H. Publications, Inc.).

What Varieties of Angelfish are Available?
There are two general groups of varieties. One group comprises the

varieties with different fin shapes. There are normal-finned varieties and there are long-finned varieties. Some people use their imagination and differentiate between different types of long fins.

Then there are the color varieties. There are a lot more color varieties than finnage varieties. We can expect many more color varieties in angelfishes than we already have, but the varieties will be limited by the genetic material already available within the genes and chromosomes of the original wild angels from which our current breeding stocks are derived. It is quite possible (though no one has studied it to date) that some of the newly imported angels contain genetic material that might enable mutants or sports to appear with such desirable colors as reds, blues, oranges, and derivatives or combinations of these colors. Basically, angels are black and silver, and all varieties produced to date are derivatives of silver and black . . .or lack these colors, which produce albinos or lutinos (albino yellow body with black eyes). . .or are all silver with little black coloration (produced by melanophores in the skin of the angelfish).

The All-Black Angelfish

It is only natural that animals that have been "domesticated" and inbred for generations start to produce sports or mutants that differ significantly from their parents. This happens in nature, too, but usually any major departures from the norm are unable to compete with their natural brethren and the hazards occupying the same ecological niche. Thus they succumb to disease or predators or simply starve to death. In domesticated animals, like the angelfish we are discussing now, the domesticator (that's you and me) isolates the odd fish from the flock and gives them special attention so they thrive and may form the basis for a new variety.

This is essentially what happened with the all-black angelfish. A melanistic (black) individual appeared quite suddenly among a spawn of normal fish. The breeder isolated the black individual and raised it to sexual maturity. It was then crossed with one of its brethren and the offspring crossed back to the black fish until more and more black fish began to appear in the spawns. It wasn't until after several years of inbreeding that one could expect a majority of the fish produced in this manner to be black. In the first spawnings—that is, the first all-black fish crossed with a fish from the same parents— there were no black fish at all, but after one of these babies was crossed back to its black father, then some black fish began to appear. By crossing these black fish with their father again and again, more and more black fish appeared until now there are pure strains available in which all the offspring are black. This is not true, however, of all strains. Some strains, especially those strains that seem to produce the blackest of the black angels, never produce 100% all-black angelfish. Some are normal and some are darker than normal but could not be considered to be all-black.

The same technique was used to add the long fins to the black angelfish. An all-black male was crossed with a long-finned normal female. The offspring from this crossing were then crossed back to their parents, with the blackest of the young black males crossed with their normally colored long-finned mother and the young black females crossed with their father.

In both cases only those offspring that showed longer than normal fins were used for breeding purposes. It took about ten inbreedings like this, always breeding brother to sister, always selecting the blackest and most long-finned specimens, before a commercially successful strain evolved.

The Golden Angelfish
There are, basically, two strains of golden angelfish. One is a lutino strain and the other is a weird kind of albino strain. The lutino strain is one in which all of the black pigment cells (the melanophores) in the fish have been lost, thus what was once black is now yellow. This is true for the whole body of the fish except for the eyes, which retain their black coloration.

The albino angelfish is quite another story. This is a true genetic mystery at this time. Certain strains of normally colored angelfish begin to lose their black coloration on reaching a certain age and become true yellow angelfish, even with red eyes. They have been developed with both normal fins and long fins, but not the really lengthy fins of some of the normally colored individuals. I brought some of these fish to Hans-Joachim Richter in Leipzig, East Germany, and he spawned them and photographed them as they matured.

The Gray, Ghost, or Blushing Angelfish
Many breeders have produced an angelfish in which the black has been reduced and the fish is basically a silver fish. Because of the disappearance of the large melanophores from the skin and a lack of the yellow chromatophores (a melanophore is a black chromatophore), this fish is whitish, grayish, or silvery. Since the skin is so transparent, the vital organs and blood vessels can be seen through the skin, giving the fish a "blushing" appearance, thus the name "blushing angel".

The Zebra Angelfish
This is a very dark strain in which the stripes are thin and close together.

Photoperiod and Genetics
Adding to the complexities of obtaining true-breeding angelfish of some color varieties is the recently discovered fact that the amount of light received by the developing fry (photoperiod or length of day) can have a strong and sometimes permanent influence on the final adult pattern. Researches by Dr. Joanne Norton have shown that length of day can over-ride some genetic factors to produce a different pattern in an adult fish. For instance, the variety "cobra" can be produced by raising normally three-striped zebra lace angels in a 24-hour day (light all the time) —the stripes break into large black spots. The variety "leopard" has small black spots over the body and is the result of exposing selected individuals (with zebra lace and smokey genetic backgrounds) to either 4-hour or 8-hour days. It is not uncommon for light-induced patterns in small angels to change after the fish matures, but with at least some varieties the pattern developed in the fry may be constant through adulthood—though not directly inherited. This discovery offers many possibilities for research by aquarists.

Wild *Pterophyllum scalare altum*.

P. scalare altum, showing long dorsal and anal fins.

The long-nosed angelfish, *P. dumerili*.

P. dumerili

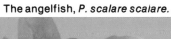

The angelfish, *P. scalare scalare*.

P. s. scalare

Plate #228

363

Silver veiltail angelfish.

Silver veiltail angelfish.

Black veiltail angelfish.

Black angelfish.

Silver angelfish.

Blushing, or gray angelfish.

Zebra angelfish

Zebra lace angelfish

Plate #229

364

Marble angelfish.

Half-black angel var.

Marble veiltail angelfish.

Half-black angel veiltail var.

Plate #230

365

Juvenile gold angelfish

Juvenile gold angelfish

White or "ghost" angelfish.

Gold or Lutino angelfish.

Blushing or gray veiltail angelfish.

Blushing angelfish

White or ghost-type angelfish.

Variety of the spotted angelfish.

Partial half-black veiltail angelfish.

Half-black angelfish.

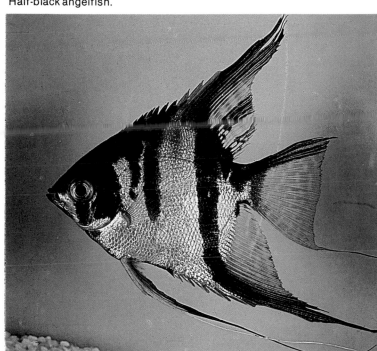

Half-striped angelfish

Blushing or gray angelfish.

Plate #232

367

DISCUS: KING OF THE AQUARIUM FISHES

Although the cichlids may comprise a thousand or more species, there is no doubt that one cichlid—and one cichlid only—is *the* most respected and desirable of all the aquarium fishes. The discus (actually two species), *Symphysodon*, has been treated with near reverence since it was first brought to the attention of aquarists in the early 1930's. Even after over 50 years in the hobby, the discus is still an expensive fish, and breeding it is considered to be the acme of successful aquarium keeping.

Both species of discus (the Common discus is *Symphysodon aequifasciata,* and the Heckel or Red discus is *Symphysodon discus)* are virtually restricted to the Amazon River and its primary tributaries. Discus can be found in all types of waters from the very acid black waters of the Rio Negro to the silty whitish waters of some of the major tributaries and from streams to lakes; few discus are taken from the Amazon itself except perhaps in the far upstream areas. The round bodies of discus are associated with their habit of staying mostly in protected areas that are heavily vegetated or have an abundance of exposed tree roots, the round bodies allowing them to slip between the plants with ease. They are also very shy and are active mainly at night, facts that do not make their collection any easier.

The two species of discus are divided into a total of five subspecies that are useful at least in a general way when discussing variation within the species. Thus *S. aequifasciata* (distinguished by having 9 equally dark bands on the body) has three recognized subspecies: *S. aequifasciata aequifasciata* Pellegrin—the Green discus from the central Amazon; *S. a. axelrodi* Schultz—the Brown discus from the lower Amazon; and *S. a. haraldi* Schultz—the Blue discus from the upper Amazon. *S. discus* (which has only 3 distinct dark bands on the body) has two recognized subspecies: *S. discus discus* (Heckel)—the Heckel or Red discus, known in modern times only from the Rio Negro and Rio Trombetas, north of the Amazon; and *S. discus willischwartzi* Burgess—the Pineapple discus, known so far only from the Rio Abacaxis (Portuguese for pineapple) south of the Amazon. There are numerous local color varieties and sports, plus a multitude of aquarium-produced stable color varieties, some of which probably originated by hybridizing the natural subspecies and species. It is virtually impossible to put a meaningful scientific name on aquarium specimens of discus, so it is perhaps most accurate to call them all just discus, *Symphysodon.*

Discussions about keeping and spawning discus usually result in heated arguments, as there are probably as many different methods to successfully keep and breed discus as there are successful discus keepers and breeders. There are many articles and books on discus, many controversial, but the subject is covered very well in two books from T.F.H.: *All About Discus,* by Dr. Herbert R. Axelrod, and Jack Wattley's *Handbook of Discus.* Both are required reading for anyone even contemplating purchasing a discus.

Color varieties of discus being bred now have little resemblance to the wild fishes found in South America. The Turquoise discus shown above also features a very high body while the Turquoise discus shown below shows a moderately high body with a deeper green. Photos by Mitsuyoshi Tatematsu courtesy of Midori Shobo Magazine.

Plate #233

369

1

4

The Japanese people are very fond of discus. They started with *Symphysodon aequifasciata haraldi* (1) which they crossed with the Tefe discus, *Symphysodon aequifasciata aequifasciata* (2). This cross resulted in a highly colorful "Royal Blue" strain (3). "Royal Blue" has been a term applied to many strains. Then inbreeding of the *Symphysodon discus discus* resulted in this pale discus (4). The ultimate discus is the Turquoise fish shown below (5) which is being worked to produce a fish of solid turquoise, without body markings. Photos courtesy of Midori Shobo, Tokyo, Japan.

2

3

5

Plate #234

This is a new Japanese strain of Electric Blue discus which was derived from fishes found in the western extremes of the discus range.

The common Brown discus, *Symphysodon aequifasciata axelrodi* is being enhanced colorwise with brighter reds, yellows and greens. Photo courtesy of Midori Shobo.

The Lutino discus derived from *Symphysodon discus discus*. It is not a popular strain but is being used for the basis of many breeding experiments. Photo courtesy of Midori Shobo.

Dr. Eduard Schmidt-Focke produced this strain of almost perfect "Tomato-red-eyed Turquoise" with just a few light body markings. Photo by Heiko Bleher.

Plate #235

The original Green discus collected by the author in Lago Jurity.

Symphysodon d. discus found in Trombetas by the author (HRA).

Symphysodon d. discus collected by the author (HRA) in the Rio Trombetas.

Symphysodon a. haraldi collected by the author (HRA) in the Rio Ipixuna (near Humaita).

1

2

3

(1) A new discus color variety of *S. a. aequifasciata* discovered by HRA at Tefe. (2) A Pineapple discus, *S. d. willischwartzi* discovered by the author (HRA) at Rio Abacaxis. This is the holotype. (3) Another new color variety discovered by the author (HRA) in Tefe. (4) A typical Tefe Blue discus, *S. a. aequifasciata* (5) Another Tefe discus found by the author (HRA).

5

4

Plate #237

S. a. haraldi discovered by the author (HRA) in Rio Purus.

S. a. aequifasciata collected by the author in Tefe.

Constant inbreeding selectively of the *S. a. aequifasciata* from Tefe resulted in this magnificent fish. Photo courtesy of Midori Shobo.

Plate #238

Young Turquoise discus.
Brown discus, *S. a. axelrodi*.

S. a. haraldi, the Blue discus.
Hybrid Red discus derived from Tefe discus.

Plate #239   375

The world's most famous discus breeder is Jack Wattley who produced the Turquoise discus. He is now working on a Metallic Turquoise strain, specimens of which are shown on this and the facing page.

Plate #240

Plate #241

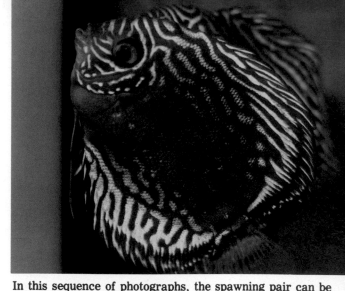

In this sequence of photographs, the spawning pair can be seen approaching the spawning surface; the female is above. In the top left photo, the eggs are clearly visible as the attending male completes fertilization.

Plate #242

Top, left and right: In the two upper photos, the spawning pair approaches the spawning surface. Discus are shy and sensitive fishes at all times and especially so during spawning. Breeders should be given as much privacy as possible.
Lower four photos: A pair of royal blue discus depositing and fertilizing their eggs. In the bottom right photo, one of the parent fish can be seen carefully removing the whitish, fungused eggs from the spawning site.

Plate #243 379

Top, left and right: As hatching nears, both parents hover in close attendance of the eggs. **Center, left and right:** The newly-hatched fry appear as minute specks on the PVC pipe. The adults are especially sensitive to disturbance at this point and may eat their fry if distracted. **Bottom, left and right:** The growing fry have left the hatching site and taken up positions on the parents' bodies. Here they receive both protection and nourishment, feeding on the mucus secreted by the adult fish.

Plate #244

Top, left and right: The discus method of child-rearing is surely one of the more unique in the animal kingdom. Here the still-small young cling closely to the parent fish. **Center, left and right:** As the fry grow progressively larger, the parents alternate babysitting duties with greater frequency. In the photo to the right, the parents can be seen literally shifting responsibility from one to the other. **Bottom, left:** The same pair during the course of the exchange of the fry. **Bottom, right:** The fry cling so closely to the parent as to virtually disappear from sight.

Plate #245

381

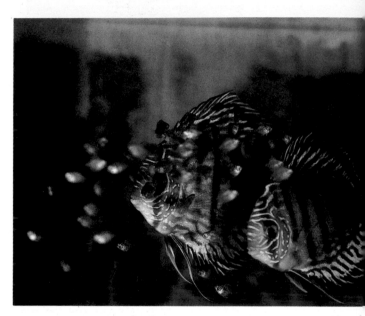

Top, left: This patient discus parent, almost hidden from view by a swarm of oversized youngsters, appears to show definite signs of tiring of its parenting duties. Top, right: This fish is shepherding a relatively small brood; discus may produce as many as 300 fry in a single spawn, but the average is between 100 and 150. Lower three photos: Although discus fry feed off the mucus secretions of the adults for only a week or ten days, growth is extremely rapid. In the photo to the extreme lower right, the fry are now on their own and measure about half an inch in length.

Plate #246

Europe's most famous discus breeder is Dr. Eduard Schmidt-Focke shown above. The fishes shown on this page are some of his many discus varieties.

Plate #247

Colomesus asellus (Mueller & Troschel) • Brazilian Freshwater Puffer

RANGE: Throughout tropical South America, mainly in fresh water but occasionally in brackish waters.
HABITS: This is a river fish that is sometimes found in creeks or streams but always found when seining directly in the Amazon River itself. Young fish are golden when taken in the muddy waters of the Amazon. The older fish are camouflaged for life in streams. The familiar name *C. psittacus* is now applied to a much larger species found in marine to brackish waters.
WATER CONDITIONS: They thrive in most neutral to slightly alkaline waters with a pH of 6.9-7.9 at 20-30°C.
SIZE: Reaches a maximum length of 150 mm; usually smaller.
FOOD REQUIREMENTS: They eat everything but prefer live snails and small fishes.

Potamorrhaphis guianensis (Schomburgk) • Freshwater Needlefish

RANGE: Guianas to Paraguay.
HABITS: Must be kept away from other fishes; likely to become very nasty.
WATER CONDITIONS: Soft, slightly alkaline water. Temperature 23 to 26°C.
SIZE: Said to attain a length of 80 cm in native waters.
FOOD REQUIREMENTS: Must be fed small living fishes.

Achirus lineatus (Linnaeus) • Freshwater Flounder, Lined Sole

RANGE: Throughout much of Brazil and northern South America, with the same or a very similar species north to the eastern United States.
HABITS: These little flounders stay in fresh water and most do not migrate to the sea. Flounders all over the Americas are normally freshwater to brackish water to sea water depending upon their growth. These small flounders, being found thousands of miles from the sea, probably don't migrate.
WATER CONDITIONS: They survive in any aquarium conditions, but they thrive in brackish water. Their pH range is 6.8-7.8; temperature 23-28°C.
SIZE: They hardly reach 125 mm; mostly smaller.
FOOD REQUIREMENTS: They are bottom feeders but they lunge at small fishes that pass by them as they lie on the bottom; they learn to eat small chunks of food that fall to the bottom, but most of them starve to death in the hands of inexperienced aquarists. They are not recommended for most aquarium situations.

Pristigaster cayana Cuvier • Amazonian Hatchet Herring

RANGE: Throughout the coasts of northern South America, including Brazil. Very common in the Amazon River itself.
HABITS: A freshwater herring that cannot live in captivity.
WATER CONDITIONS: Large open waters where it can feed upon plankton. Survives under brackish to freshwater conditions. In the Amazon the waters in which it was found by the author (HRA) were pH 6.5 at 25°C.
SIZE: Reaches over 140 mm.
FOOD REQUIREMENTS: Plankton.

Arius jordani (Eigenmann & Eigenmann) • Jordan's Catfish

RANGE: Panama Bay to Peru, eastern Pacific Ocean.
HABITS: A peaceful bottom-feeder that normally will not bother other fishes.
WATER CONDITIONS: Not critical. Can be kept in both fresh or salt water. The temperature range should be 20 to 25°C.
SIZE: Attains a length of at least 33 cm.
FOOD REQUIREMENTS: Eats a wide variety of foods.

Synbranchus marmoratus Bloch • Marbled Eel

RANGE: From Mexico to Brazil.
HABITS: This is a nasty fish that will eat anything small enough to ingest. They are also very hardy. There is a story going around that some climbed out of a holding tank at Willi Schwartz' holding facility in Brazil, snaked their way across 300 m of lawn and ended up in the swimming pool, scaring everyone because they look like snakes.
WATER CONDITIONS: These eels thrive under most aquarium conditions at temperatures of from 23-30°C with a pH of 6.0-7.6.
SIZE: They grow large, easily reaching 1500 mm (1½ m). Only the large ones are nicely mottled; small ones are uncolored.
FOOD REQUIREMENTS: They like live worms and small fishes. Sometimes they can be acclimated to chunks of fish or meat.

Pellona castelneana Cuvier & Valenciennes • Golden Herring

RANGE: Probably throughout South American rivers and the coast. This specimen was collected by the author (HRA) in the Amazon.
HABITS: A typical herring. Not really suitable for the home aquarium. Lives a very short time (only minutes) when captured.
WATER CONDITIONS: This specimen was collected by the author in the Amazon River where the water had a pH of 6.5 at 25°C.
SIZE: The typical size is 29 cm, but it does grow larger.
FOOD REQUIREMENTS: A plankton-feeder that cannot be properly maintained in a home aquarium.

Colomesus asellus (juv.)

Colomesus asellus (adult)

Potamorrhaphis guineensis

Arius jordani

Achirus lineatus

Synbranchus marmoratus

Pristigaster cayana

Pellona castelneana

Plate #248

African Region

Protopterus dolloi Boulenger • Spotted African
Lungfish

RANGE: Congo and Gabon.
HABITS: A large swamp fish that is sold in its cocoon in native
fish markets and is considered a delicacy. Dangerous
with small fishes.
WATER CONDITIONS: Thrives under most aquarium conditions but prefers soft water with a neutral to alkaline pH
between 6.8-8.8 at warm temperatures between 26-30°C.
SIZE: A large aquarium fish reaching 830 mm.
FOOD REQUIREMENTS: Prefers live fishes but soon takes
chunks of meat and fish.

Protopterus aethiopicus Heckel • Speckle-bellied
Lungfish

RANGE: Eastern Sudan to the borders of Lake Tanganyika.
HABITS: A very ancient fish, one of Africa's oldest forms.
Small specimens are interesting when kept alone in a
large aquarium. Not very mobile.
WATER CONDITIONS: Does well under most aquarium con-
ditions.
SIZE: Reaches a size of over 1400 mm.
FOOD REQUIREMENTS: Does not eat much for its size since
it moves so rarely, but it takes live fishes that swim by.
Can be trained to take chunks of meat and fish. A favorite
public aquarium fish.

Calamoichthys calabaricus Smith • Rope Fish

RANGE: Niger Delta, Cameroon.
HABITS: Largely nocturnal; spends most of its time on the
bottom. Best kept only with its own kind.
WATER CONDITIONS: Not critical; is not dependent upon the
oxygen content of the water for breathing.
SIZE: Up to 40 cm; tank-raised specimens do not attain this
size.
FOOD REQUIREMENTS: All living foods which are not too
large to be swallowed are accepted; also strips of lean
beef, beef heart or earthworms.

Polypterus congicus Poll • Tanganyikan Fossilfish

RANGE: Congo and Lake Tanganyika.
HABITS: This specimen was collected by the author (HRA) in
Lake Tanganyika near Burundi. It was brought back
alive under the worst of conditions but lived even after
the plastic bag in which it was transported leaked almost
all of the water. The fish lived for two days by only being
kept damp.
WATER CONDITIONS: pH 9.0 at 25°C.
SIZE: Over 700 mm.
FOOD REQUIREMENTS: Eats smaller fishes but can be
trained to take chunks of fish and meat.

Protopterus annectens Owen • African Lungfish

RANGE: Widespread from central to southeastern Africa,
mostly in low-lying swampy areas.
HABITS: Strictly a predator; will ignore small fast-moving
fishes but will eat anything slow enough to be caught.
WATER CONDITIONS: Not critical.
SIZE: To well over 60 cm.
FOOD REQUIREMENTS: Younger specimens will accept most
standard aquarium foods.

Protopterus dolloi

Protopterus annectens

Protopterus aethiopicus

Protopterus annectens

Erpetoichthys calabaricus

Erpetoichthys calabaricus

Polypterus congicus

Polypterus congicus

Plate #249

388

Polypterus ornatipinnis

Polypterus senegalus

Polypterus palmas

Polypterus palmas

Polypterus congicus

Polypterus congicus

Polypterus palmas

Polypterus delhezi

Plate #250

389

THE GENUS *POLYPTERUS*

The fishes of the genera *Polypterus* and *Erpetoichthys* have been around for a very long time. Their ancestry has been traced back almost 200 million years based upon a scale found in Egypt, and skeletal fossils are known since the Triassic period.

The scales of these fishes are rather unique. They are diamond-shaped and protected with a glazed coating. They also have very fine tooth-like projections. The fishes of the genus *Polypterus* have ventral fins, while the single species of *Erpetoichthys* has none.

Polypterids are superficially similar, though probably not closely related, to the lungfishes of the genus *Protopterus* and are able to take air into their swim bladders and use it for breathing. They can remain alive for days out of water since their scales are not porous. They also have a very characteristic spiral end to their intestine that is not exhibited by other modern fishes.

There have been several reports of preserved fishes having contained developing eggs, which would indicate that internal fertilization takes place. This type of reproduction is not unknown among similarly primitive fishes, so it might not be long before a "spawning" of one of these fishes takes place since more and more polypterids are being imported. Unfortunately for aquarists, most of these polypterids grow rather large. The best known species are:

P. bichir Geoffrey, which is found in the Nile, Lake Rudolf and the Chad basin. It grows to 720 mm;

P. lapradii Steindachner, which ranges in Senegal, Gambia and Niger waters and reaches 740 mm in length;

P. congicus Boulenger, from the Congo and Lake Tanganyika. This fish reaches a total length of over 700 mm;

P. endlicheri Heckel, which is found in the White Nile, Bahr-el-Gebel, Lake Chad and the Niger River. It reaches 630 mm;

P. weeksii Boulenger is found in the upper Congo and Katanga. It is one of the smaller species, growing to 380 mm;

P. ornatipinnis Boulenger, from the Monsembe and Kassai Rivers in the upper Congo, reaches 370 mm in length;

P. delhezi Boulenger, from the upper Congo, reaches 340 mm;

P. senegalus Cuvier is a very widespread species found in Lakes Albert, Chad, and Rudolf as well as in Senegal, Gambia and Niger. It reaches 420 mm in length;

P. palmas Ayres is found in Sierra Leone, Liberia and the Congo and reaches 320 mm in length;

P. retropinnis Vaillant may very well be the smallest species, reaching only 230 mm. It has a restricted range in the Alima River, upper Congo.

All species are very hardy and thrive under most aquarium conditions. They prefer small fishes as their diet, but they learn to take chunks of fish and meat. Because of their ability to live under abnormally poor aquarium conditions, aquarists rarely see them in full color.

Xenomystus nigri Guenther • African Knife Fish

RANGE: Broad east-to-west range in tropical Africa.
WATER CONDITIONS: Soft, acid water is best. Temperature range 24 to 28°C.
HABITS: A nocturnal prowler; should be provided with good cover within the tank. Young, small fish are peaceful, but older fish are quarrelsome among themselves and definitely predatory upon small tankmates.
SIZE: Up to 20 cm; usually seen much smaller.
FOOD REQUIREMENTS: Accepts all standard aquarium foods, but especially prefers live foods and frozen foods; floating dry foods are usually not accepted.

Papyrocranus afer Guenther • African Featherfin

RANGE: Widely distributed from Gambia to the Congos.
HABITS: Swims with a wave-like movement that enables it to move forward and backward. The anal fin joins the caudal fin and the dorsal fin is rather small. Sometimes called the "African knifefish."
WATER CONDITIONS: Found in stagnant, heavily vegetated waters. Prefers warmth from 25-30°C with a pH from 4.8-7.8.
SIZE: May reach 600 mm, but only small specimens are imported.
FOOD REQUIREMENTS: Usually only takes live foods such as small fishes, worms, daphnia, brine shrimp and the like. Eats mostly under very subdued light.

Phractolaemus ansorgei Boulenger • African Mudfish

RANGE: Mouth of the Ethiope river, Niger Delta and the Upper Congo.
HABITS: Apparently not very aggressive. Can be kept with smaller fishes.
WATER CONDITIONS: Soft, slightly acid water best, with a temperature about 24 to 26°C.
SIZE: Attains a length of about 16 cm.
FOOD REQUIREMENTS: Bottom-feeder with a preference for worms.

Pantodon buchholzi Peters • Butterfly Fish

RANGE: Tropical West Africa.
HABITS: Harmless to other fishes, but better kept by themselves to prevent damage to their filamentous ventral fin extensions.
WATER CONDITIONS: Soft, slightly acid water is preferable. The tank should not be too heavily planted; it must have a large surface and be covered. Temperature 23 to 27°C.
SIZE: To 10 cm.
FOOD REQUIREMENTS: Prefers live insects but it can be trained to take bits of shrimp.

Petrocephalus catostoma Guenther • African Whale

RANGE: Rovuma River and Lake Malawi.
HABITS: Prefers dimly lit aquarium conditions where it can hide. This small fish is an aquarium favorite, but it doesn't live very long in captivity. Nothing is known about its spawning habits.
WATER CONDITIONS: Warm waters with high alkalinity, about pH 8.8 at 28-30°C.
SIZE: Barely reaches 60 mm; usually imported at about 45 mm.
FOOD REQUIREMENTS: Small worms and live daphnia and brine shrimp.

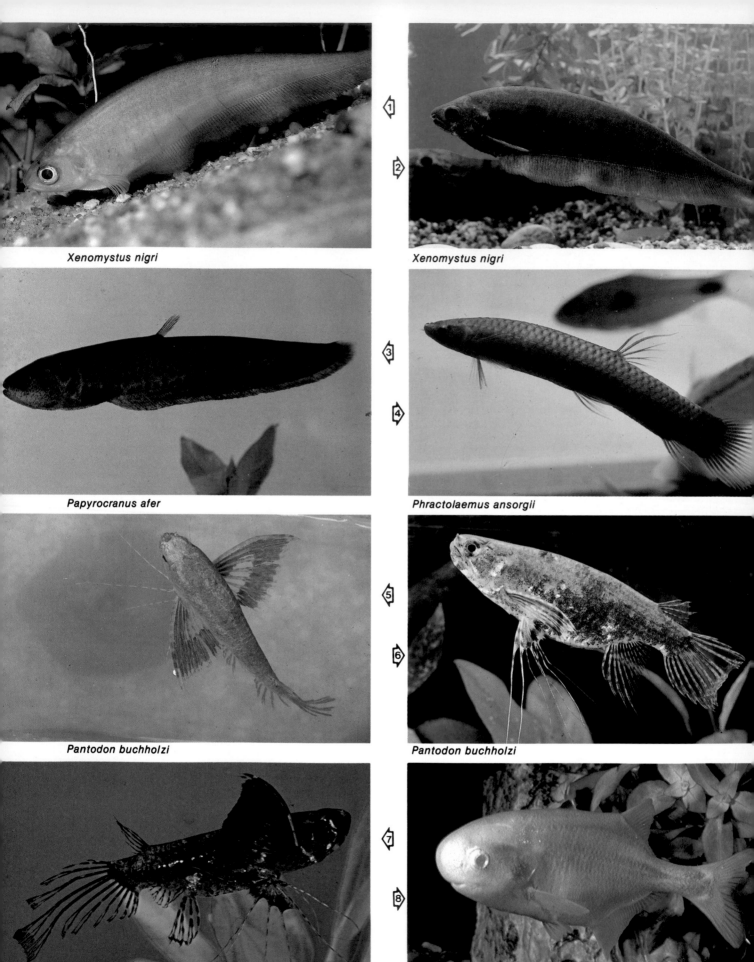

Xenomystus nigri

Xenomystus nigri

Papyrocranus afer

Phractolaemus ansorgii

Pantodon buchholzi

Pantodon buchholzi

Pantodon buchholzi

Petrocephalus catostoma

Plate #251

Petrocephalus simus

Petrocephalus simus

Pollimyrus nigripinnis

Pollimyrus castelnaui

Marcusenius angolensis

Campylomormyrus cassaicus

Gnathonemus elephas

Gnathonemus petersii

Plate #252

Petrocephalus simus Sauvage • Dorsal-band Whale

RANGE: Widespread from Liberia to the Congo.
HABITS: Likes dim light. Makes a fine aquarium fish but
   does not live long in captivity.
WATER CONDITIONS: Warm waters from 25-30°C. Never
   spawned, but it probably will be as soon as hormonal
   techniques are attempted on this species.
SIZE: Up to 120 mm; usually imported at 80 mm.
FOOD REQUIREMENTS: Prefers small living foods such as
   tubifex and daphnia.

Pollimyrus nigripinnis Boulenger • Dusky Whale

RANGE: Upper Congo.
HABITS: Prefers dimly lit aquarium situations. Nothing
   known about sex differences or spawning habits.
WATER CONDITIONS: Prefers quiet aquarium situations
   where the water is warm and clean. pH 7.2-9.0 at 25-28°C.
SIZE: A small fish barely reaching 110 mm.
FOOD REQUIREMENTS: Prefers small worms and live foods.

Pollimyrus castelnaui (Boulenger) • Silver Whale

RANGE: The Upper Zambesi River system, South Africa,
   from the Cunene and Kafue Rivers.
HABITS: This small species may be bred. The male has a
   curved anal fin while the female's is straight. They pre-
   fer dimly lit aquaria.
WATER CONDITIONS: Prefers clear water with a pH of 7.0-9.0
   at 20-25°C.
SIZE: A small species barely reaching 75 mm.
FOOD REQUIREMENTS: Small insects, worms and daphnia.
   Difficult to acclimate to dried foods.

Marcusenius angolensis Boulenger • Spotted Elephant

RANGE: Angola.
HABITS: Prefers dimly lit aquarium conditions. Has a wide
   tolerance to other fishes. Its pugnosed face once gave it
   the name "Jack Dempsey Elephant," but the name
   didn't stick.
WATER CONDITIONS: pH 7.0-9.0 at 25-30°C. Probably tolerates other conditions, too.
SIZE: A relatively small 135 mm is about the maximum size;
   imported specimens are much smaller.
FOOD REQUIREMENTS: Prefers live foods such as tubifex
   worms and daphnia.

Campylomormyrus cassaicus (Poll) • Angolan
Elephantnose, Luseya, Sosha

RANGE: Angola.
HABITS: A rapids fish that requires heavy aeration and very
   turbulent water or it quickly becomes infected with external parasites.
WATER CONDITIONS: pH 6.0-7.6 at 20-25°C. Turbulent water.
SIZE: Barely reaches 250 mm.
FOOD REQUIREMENTS: Its curved snout indicates it is best
   suited for poking between rocks and in the sandy bottom,
   grubbing for small worms or other tiny living things.

Gnathonemus elephas Boulenger • Black Elephant

RANGE: Upper Congo.
HABITS: The illustration shows a young specimen in which
   the black lateral bands are edged in yellow and the black
   rhomboidal marking between the anal and dorsal is
   remarkable. These juvenile colors are lost when the fish
   reaches about 200 mm.
WATER CONDITIONS: pH 7.0-8.4 at 25-29°C.
SIZE: Reaches 400 mm and is a food fish in its range.
FOOD REQUIREMENTS: Pokes about between stones searching for small fishes and other live foods. Takes worms
   and daphnia eagerly in the aquarium.

Gnathonemus petersi (Guenther) • Peter's Elephant-Nose

RANGE: Central Africa.
WATER CONDITIONS: Soft, slightly acid warm water pre-
   ferred. Temperature 24 to 27°C.
HABITS: Generally peaceful and shy.
SIZE: About 23 cm.
FOOD REQUIREMENTS: Small live foods, tubifex worms es-
   pecially; will not take coarse-ground dry foods.

Campylomormyrus rhynchophorus Boulenger •
Down-poker

RANGE: Very rare throughout its range from Ghana through
western central Africa.
HABITS: This species has been well studied for its electric
organs by Philippe Quinet (Musee Royal de l'Afrique
Centrale, Tervuren, Belgium, 1971). If you read French
and have an interest in these fish his book is very valuable.
WATER CONDITIONS: pH 6.4-7.0 at 25-30°C.
SIZE: Probably gets larger than the 100 mm specimens that
were available to the author (HRA).
FOOD REQUIREMENTS: Likes tubifex worms taken off the
bottom but probably does well on all foods since it
scavenges the bottom.

Mormyrops engystoma Boulenger • Torpedo Mormyrid

RANGE: Lower Congo River.
HABITS: Should not be kept with smaller fishes which it could
swallow; usually peaceful with the larger fishes.
WATER CONDITIONS: Neutral to slightly acid water. Temperature 24 to 26°C. Tank should be well planted and
partly shaded.
SIZE: To 35 cm.
FOOD REQUIREMENTS: Tubifex or small earthworms are
the preferred foods.

Mormyrops boulengeri Pellegrin • Slender-nosed Elephant

RANGE: Congo, but probably more dispersed.
HABITS: A very shy fish that pokes around the bottom of the
tank in search of food. They are very delicate fish and
rarely thrive in the hands of inexperienced aquarists.
They should really be kept by themselves.
WATER CONDITIONS: Slightly acid, pH 6.7-7.0 at 26-29°C.
SIZE: Reaches 350 mm, but only small specimens are suitable
for the home aquarium.
FOOD REQUIREMENTS: Takes tubificid worms and dead
brine shrimp that fall to the bottom. They truly thrive on
brine shrimp.

Mormyrus longirostris Peters • Short-faced Elephant-nose

RANGE: Kasenga.
HABITS: They poke about the bottom searching for food. They
never thrive unless fed dead brine shrimp that falls to the
bottom (frozen, thawed brine shrimp is best).
WATER CONDITIONS: Slightly acid, pH 6.7-7.2 at 26-30°C.
SIZE: Reaches at least 300 mm.
FOOD REQUIREMENTS: Picks "crumbs" from the bottom. It
is always grubbing in the sand looking for live worms,
but it does better on brine shrimp since tubificids may
contain too many dangerous bacteria.

Brienomyrus brachyistius (Gill) • Whale-faced
Marcusenius

RANGE: Sierra Leone.
HABITS: This is a small fish and it likes to move among small
stones on the bottom of the aquarium. It has electric
organs and has a rather large eye for the group. It does
very well in the aquarium.
WATER CONDITIONS: pH 6.4-7.2 at 26-30°C.
SIZE: The largest seen by the authors was 75 mm.
FOOD REQUIREMENTS: Likes tubifex worms but generally
settles into the normal aquarium fare.

Gymnarchus niloticus Cuvier • Aba Aba

RANGE: Upper Nile through Chad and Niger to Senegal.
HABITS: A predator with an electric potential but generally
shy; should be treated like the elephant-nose (Mormy-
ridae).
WATER CONDITIONS: Soft, slightly acid warm water is preferred. Temperature should be in the mid 20's (°C).
SIZE: Grows to a length of about 150 cm and a weight of more
than 12 kilos.
FOOD REQUIREMENTS: Small live foods including fishes.

Campylomormyrus rhynchophorus

Mormyrus longirostris

Mormyrops engystoma

Brienomyrus brachistius

Mormyrops boulengeri

Gymnarchus niloticus

Gymnarchus niloticus

Gymnarchus niloticus (albino)

Plate #253

Hepsetus odoe

Bryconaethiops microstoma

Bryconaethiops boulengeri

Brycinus macrolepidotus

Brycinus taeniurus

Brycinus lateralis

Brycinus nurse

Brycinus brevis

Plate #254

Hepsetus odoe (Bloch) • African Pike

RANGE: Widely distributed all over tropical Africa.
HABITS: Vicious, greedy and predatory; can only be kept with their own kind or larger fishes.
WATER CONDITIONS: Not critical, but soft, slightly acid water is best. Temperature 24 to 27°C.
SIZE: To 30 cm.
FOOD REQUIREMENTS: Living smaller fishes only; possibly they may be trained to eat strips of raw fish.
COLOR VARIATIONS: Body olive green, belly golden. Young specimens have dark spotted fins.

Bryconaethiops boulengeri Pellegrin • Black-barred Featherfin

RANGE: Congo basin.
HABITS: This is a female of the species. The male will turn almost pitch black and have elongated dorsal filaments.
WATER CONDITIONS: Slightly acid water, pH of 6.5-6.9 at 24-30°C.
SIZE: Reaches 230 mm.
FOOD REQUIREMENTS: This is a fish-eating species. They can be weaned over to chunks of meat or fish, but to thrive they need live guppies or their equivalent.

Brycinus taeniurus (Guenther) • Narrow-lined African Tetra

RANGE: Central Africa.
HABITS: Peaceful and active; may be a fin nipper due to its teeth. Relatively unknown.
WATER CONDITIONS: Soft, acid water with a pH close to 6.0 or even lower. Temperatures should be above 24°C.
SIZE: Up to 10 cm; may grow larger if properly cared for.
FOOD REQUIREMENTS: Accepts all live foods; better fed freeze-dried tubifex worms, especially those worms with added daphnia, chlorella algae, etc.

Brycinus nurse (Rueppel) • Nurse Tetra

RANGE: Widely distributed in tropical African waters, Nile to Senegal.
HABITS: Somewhat shy, very active. Prefer to swim in groups in the middle reaches of the aquarium.
WATER CONDITIONS: Water should be soft and slightly acid, preferably filtered through peat moss. Temperature 24 to 26°C.
SIZE: To 25 cm; usually offered for sale at 8 to 10 cm.
FOOD REQUIREMENTS: Large live foods such as cut-up earthworms or fully grown brine shrimp; can be accustomed to frozen foods.

Bryconaethiops microstoma Guenther • African Featherfin

RANGE: Congo basin, but very widespread.
HABITS: The fish changes drastically as it gets older. This particular species, one of three in the genus, will turn black when it reaches about 125-150 mm on its way to 250 mm, and the caudal filaments of the male will reach past the membrane of its tail. A very interesting aquarium fish.
WATER CONDITIONS: Prefers slightly acid water, pH of 6.5-6.9, but gets along under most aquarium situations where the temperature ranges between 24-30°C.
SIZE: Reaches 250 mm.
FOOD REQUIREMENTS: A fast-growing species that prefers small living foods, especially adult brine shrimp.

Brycinus macrolepidotus Valenciennes • Macrolepidotus Groupee

RANGE: Most of Africa from the Nile to the Congo.
HABITS: This group contains 5 or 6 different fishes, all of which look slightly different externally but are indistinguishable unless a series of fully grown specimens is at hand. They may well be one species that have been misidentified as juveniles or sub-adults.
WATER CONDITIONS: Thrive under most aquarium conditions but need lots of room.
SIZE: This species reaches over 300 mm in length.
FOOD REQUIREMENTS: Live fishes are their normal diet, but they can be acclimated to bits of raw fish and meat.

Brycinus lateralis (Boulenger) • False Alestes

RANGE: Katanga and Angola up to the Zambezi River.
HABITS: A small characin that looks very similar to a *Micralestes* and has often been misidentified as *Alestes* and *Micralestes*.
WATER CONDITIONS: Slightly acid, pH 6.4-7.0 at a temperature of 25-30°C.
SIZE: Probably reaches 150 mm.
FOOD REQUIREMENTS: Small live foods like brine shrimp and daphnia are preferred, but they soon acclimate to a normal aquarium diet.

Brycinus brevis (Boulenger) • Macrolepidotus Silver

RANGE: From Nigeria and the Gold Coast.
HABITS: This is probably *B. brevis*, as it never developed the black band characteristic of the adult *B. macrolepidotus* Identifications are almost impossible in this genus.
WATER CONDITIONS: Very hardy and thrives in most aquarium situations where the pH is 6.6-7.2 at a temperature between 25-30°C.
SIZE: Probably reaches over 225 mm, its "official" maximum size.
FOOD REQUIREMENTS: Small live fishes, insects, and crustaceans. Leaps for insects flying close to the surface of the water.

Brycinus longipinnis (Guenther) • Long-finned African Tetra

RANGE: Tropical West Africa, Sierra Leone to Zaire.
HABITS: Timid; an active swimmer which remains in the middle reaches of the aquarium.
WATER CONDITIONS: Water should be soft and slightly acid, preferably filtered through peat moss. Temperature 24 to 26°C.
SIZE: To 12.5 cm.
FOOD REQUIREMENTS: Larger sized live foods; can be accustomed to frozen foods or beef heart.

Micralestes acutidens (Peters) • Sharp-toothed Tetra

RANGE: Nigeria to Angola and the Zambezi basin.
HABITS: Peaceful and active fish which require adequate swimming room.
WATER CONDITIONS: Soft, slightly acid water which is clean and well aerated is best. Prefers warmth, about 26°C, but a drop to 23°C or so is tolerated.
SIZE: 6 cm maximum.
FOOD REQUIREMENTS: Not critical; may be maintained on dried foods with only occasional feedings of live foods.

Phenacogrammus huloti (Poll) • Black-banded Congo Tetra

RANGE: Congo Basin.
HABITS: A typical characoid. Very active in the aquarium as it flutters about. Never been spawned.
WATER CONDITIONS: Not very fussy about aquarium conditions as long as the water is clean and well aerated. It likes slightly acid warm water at a pH 6.0-6.8 with a temperature of 25-30°C.
SIZE: Under 100 mm; probably more like 80 mm.
FOOD REQUIREMENTS: Prefers live foods but does well on the normal aquarium diet with flake foods.

Brycinus chaperi (Sauvage) • Chaper's Characin

RANGE: West Africa, Upper Guinea, Gold Coast to the Niger River.
HABITS: Peaceful if kept with fishes of its own size.
WATER CONDITIONS: Water should be soft and slightly acid. Temperature 24 to 26°C.
SIZE: Attains a length of 9 cm.
FOOD REQUIREMENTS: Dried food is taken when hungry, but any kind of live food is preferable.

Micralestes stormsi Boulenger • Blue-barred Congo Tetra

RANGE: Congo Basin
HABITS: For the aquarist, this fish and M. humilis are identical in looks, care, etc. The species is sexually dimorphic with the male showing more intense red in the dorsal and caudal fins. They are very nice aquarium fish especially when they are mid-sized.
WATER CONDITIONS: pH 6.2-6.8 at a temperature of 25-30°C.
SIZE: Up to 110 mm.
FOOD REQUIREMENTS: They prefer living, swimming foods but they quickly acclimate to flake foods and a normal aquarium fare. Freeze-dried foods are appreciated.

Phenacogrammus interruptus (Boulenger) • Congo Tetra

RANGE: Congo River region.
HABITS: Peaceful toward fishes of comparable size; a school fish which prefers to swim in groups.
WATER CONDITIONS: Soft, slightly acid water which has been treated with the addition of an acid peat moss. Temperature about 24°C.
SIZE: Males to 8 cm; females to 6 cm.
FOOD REQUIREMENTS: Large live and frozen foods, supplemented by coarse prepared foods.
COLOR VARIATIONS: Large opalescent scales; fins grayish violet with white edges; indistinct yellowish horizontal stripe.

Phenacogrammus urotaenia (Boulenger) • Half-barred Congo Tetra

RANGE: Congo Basin.
HABITS: Males are more colorful than females and have the extended dorsal rays. They are lovely aquarium fish especially if you can find enough of them to have a school in a large tank with subtle lighting so their scales can dazzle.
WATER CONDITIONS: pH 6.4-6.9 at about 28°C.
SIZE: About 80 mm.
FOOD REQUIREMENTS: They eat everything normally fed to aquarium fishes but they do best with small live foods that swim about.

Brycinus longipinnis

Brycinus chaperi

Micralestes acutidens

Micralestes stormsi (female)

Micralestes stormsi (male)

Phenacogrammus interruptus

Phenacogrammus huloti

Phenacogrammus urotaenia

Plate #255

Phenacogrammus aurantiacus

Phenacogrammus caudomaculatus

① ②

Phenacogrammus deheyni

Hemigrammopetersius caudalis

③ ④

Hemigrammopetersius intermedius

Hemigrammopetersius rhodesiensis

⑤ ⑥

Arnoldichthys spilopterus

Ladigesia roloffi

⑦ ⑧

Plate #256

Phenacogrammus aurantiacus (Pellegrin) • Gold Congo Tetra

RANGE: Congo Basin.
HABITS: A wonderful aquarium fish that has many of the characteristics associated with Congo tetras, namely sexual dimorphism in which the male has longer fins with extended dorsal and caudal filaments, very shiny scales, and a peaceful aquarium disposition.
WATER CONDITIONS: pH 6.2-6.8 at a temperature of 25-30°C.
SIZE: Up to 100 mm.
FOOD REQUIREMENTS: Prefers live, swimming foods but adapts to flake foods and freeze-dried foods.

Phenacogrammus caudomaculatus (Pellegrin) • African Moon Tetra

RANGE: Congo River region.
HABITS: A shoaling fish which is happiest among its own kind; generally peaceful toward fishes of a comparable size.
WATER CONDITIONS: Soft, slightly acid water. Temperature 22 to 25°C.
SIZE: Males to 8 cm; females to 6 cm.
FOOD REQUIREMENTS: Its diet should consist primarily of live or frozen foods, but can be supplemented with flake foods.

Phenacogrammus deheyni Poll • Deheyni's Congo Tetra

RANGE: Congo Basin.
HABITS: The dark band along the lateral line, which is only hinted at in the accompanying photo, is stark in many cases (especially when the fish is preserved). This is a typical Congo tetra with large shining scales and good aquarium deportment.
WATER CONDITIONS: pH 6.2-6.8 at a temperature of 25-30°C.
SIZE: About 100 mm.
FOOD REQUIREMENTS: Prefers live foods but takes a normal aquarium diet.

Hemigrammopetersius caudalis (Boulenger) • Yellow-tailed Congo Tetra

RANGE: Congo Basin.
HABITS: One of the "super" Congo tetras with very shining, iridescent scales and extremely sexually dimorphic with the males sporting extended fins ray elements on almost all fins. They are wonderful aquarium inhabitants.
WATER CONDITIONS: pH 6.2-6.8 at a temperature of 25-30°C.
SIZE: Up to 100 mm.
FOOD REQUIREMENTS: Prefers live foods but takes a normal aquarium diet.

Hemigrammopetersius intermedius (Blache & Miton) • Short-finned Congo Tetra

RANGE: Amazon Basin.
HABITS: A large-scaled iridescent fish similar in behavior and general appearance to most of the other Congo tetras. Very similar to *H. barnardi* of East Africa. Males are smaller and more colorful than females. The photo shows a pair with the female being larger and more rotund.
WATER CONDITIONS: pH 6.2-6.8 at a temperature of 25-30°C.
SIZE: Up to 95 mm.
FOOD REQUIREMENTS: Prefers live foods but takes a normal aquarium diet.

Hemigrammopetersius rhodesiensis (Ricardo-Bertram) • Rhodesian Tetra

RANGE: Rhodesia (now called Zimbabwe).
HABITS: A small but typical "Congo" tetra that is very rarely imported because Zimbabwe is short on aquarium species. These do make nice aquarium fish when kept in a school.
WATER CONDITIONS: pH 6.2-6.8 at a temperature of 25-30°C.
SIZE: Up to 60 mm.
FOOD REQUIREMENTS: Prefers live foods but takes a normal aquarium diet.

Arnoldichthys spilopterus (Boulenger) • Arnold's Characin, Red-eyed Characin

RANGE: Tropical West Africa, especially the Lagos region and the Niger Delta.
HABITS: A peaceful species which is usually out in front.
WATER CONDITIONS: Soft, neutral to slightly acid water. Temperature 26 to 28°C.
SIZE: Seldom exceeds 6 cm.
FOOD REQUIREMENTS: Has a good appetite and will eat dried food as well as live foods; some live foods should be provided, however.

Ladigesia roloffi Gery • Jelly Bean Tetra

RANGE: Sierra Leone, West Africa.
HABITS: Initially very shy; it will attempt to jump out of tank, so a covered tank is a definite necessity; reasonably hardy and peaceful.
WATER CONDITIONS: Temperature should be from 24 to 26°C, and the pH should be on the acid side, 6.7.
SIZE: To 4 cm.
FOOD REQUIREMENTS: Will accept dry foods after a certain amount of training; freeze-dried foods are accepted willingly and live foods are never refused.

Neolebias ansorgi Boulenger • Ansorge's Neolebias

RANGE: Cameroon to lower Congo basin.
HABITS: Peaceful and very shy in a community tank; should be kept by themselves.
WATER CONDITIONS: Sensitive to hard, alkaline water; water must be well-aged and should never undergo great changes. Temperature 24 to 28°C.
SIZE: To 4 cm.
FOOD REQUIREMENTS: Small live foods only.

Neolebias trewavasae Poll & Gosse • Trewavas's Neolebias

RANGE: Nile to lower Congo River.
HABITS: Peaceful and very shy in a community tank; should be kept by themselves.
WATER CONDITIONS: Sensitive to hard, alkaline water; water must be well aged and the aquarium should never undergo large percentage water changes. Temperature 22 to 28°C.
SIZE: To 5 cm.
FOOD REQUIREMENTS: Small live foods only, of a size comparable to newly hatched brine shrimp.

Distichodus affinis Guenther • Silver Distichodus

RANGE: Lower Congo region.
HABITS: Peaceful; can be trusted with other fishes, but requires a large aquarium.
WATER CONDITIONS: Soft, slightly acid water. Temperature 24 to 27°C.
SIZE: To 13 cm.
FOOD REQUIREMENTS: Large amounts of live or frozen foods, with an addition of vegetable matter like lettuce or spinach leaves.

Citharinus citharus (Geoffroy) • Lined Citharinid

RANGE: Widespread from the Nile to Senegal.
HABITS: Unfortunately the very large body and the disproportionately small head are not clearly visible in this dark photo. The fish is rarely imported because there are very few collectors in its range.
WATER CONDITIONS: Almost neutral water between 6.8-7.2 pH at a temperature of 28-31°C.
SIZE: Probably grows larger than the 72 mm of the specimens with which the author (HRA) has experience.
FOOD REQUIREMENTS: Pokes about in every niche in the aquarium searching for small crustaceans and bits of vegetable matter. An excellent scavenger until it becomes acclimated to normal aquarium fare.

Neolebias unifasciatus Steindachner • One-lined African Tetra

RANGE: From Portuguese Guinea to Gabon.
HABITS: Very common in its range. A wonderful aquarium fish but not very colorful. Has never been bred. Like most African characins, it is difficult or impossible to spawn in the aquarium. Best kept alone in a small tank.
WATER CONDITIONS: Slightly acid warm water with a pH of 6.4-6.8 at 30°C.
SIZE: A midget barely reaching 40 mm.
FOOD REQUIREMENTS: Likes newly hatched brine shrimp but will eat a normal aquarium diet once it becomes acclimated.

Neolebias trilineatus Boulenger • Three-lined Neolebias

RANGE: Congo basin.
HABITS: Peaceful and shy.
WATER CONDITIONS: Not very critical, but the best is slightly acid and soft water. Temperature 23 to 26°C.
SIZE: To 4 cm.
FOOD REQUIREMENTS: Live and frozen foods greatly preferred, but when not available dry foods can be given for a time.
COLOR VARIATIONS: Back brown, sides silvery with three dark horizontal stripes; fins are reddish.

Nannaethiops unitaeniatus Guenther • One-lined African Tetra

RANGE: Equatorial Africa.
HABITS: Peaceful; a good community fish which does not bother plants.
WATER CONDITIONS: Soft and slightly acid. Requires some warmth, about 24 to 26°C.
SIZE: Males 5 to 6 cm; females slightly larger.
FOOD REQUIREMENTS: Live food preferred, but will take dry foods otherwise.

Neolebias ansorgii

Citharinus citharus

Neolebias trewavasae

Neolebias unifasciatus

Nannaethiops unitaeniatus

Neolebias trilineatus

Distichodus affinis

Nannaethiops unitaeniatus

Plate #257

Distichodus lusosso

Distichodus sexfasciatus

Distichodus notospilus

Distichodus noboli

Nannocharax fasciatus

Hemistichodus vaillanti

Hemigrammocharax multifasciatus

Phago maculatus

Plate #258

405

Distichodus lusosso Schilthuis • Long-nosed Distichodus

RANGE: Upper and middle Congo River including Stanley Pool; Angola.
HABITS: A docile fish, but tends to nibble plants.
WATER CONDITIONS: Neutral to slightly acid water of moderate hardness. Temperature 24 to 26°C.
SIZE: To 40 cm in nature, but smaller in the aquarium.
FOOD REQUIREMENTS: In nature it feeds on worms and other bottom-dwelling invertebrates as well as on soft vegetation. It will adapt to most aquarium fare, but should be given small amounts of soft lettuce or spinach as a dietary supplement.

Distichodus notospilus Guenther • Red-finned Distichodus

RANGE: From the southern Cameroons to Angola.
HABITS: Feeds on small crustaceans and bits of algae and vegetation. In the aquarium it has quite a problem adjusting to the normal fare, and small tubificids and live daphnia must be offered to supplement the diet.
WATER CONDITIONS: Cooler waters from 23-26°C at about a neutral pH from 6.8-7.2. They do best in large, well-planted tanks.
SIZE: They probably get a lot larger than the 100 mm specimens the author (HRA) collected in the Cameroons.

Nannocharax fasciatus Guenther • African Characidium

RANGE: Found widely dispersed across central Africa from east to west. Museums have specimens from Liberia, Guinea, Niger and Gabon.
HABITS: Found in shallow, moving creeks where it scoots about on sandy bottoms, usually those bottoms with small stones, searching for tiny micro-life. In the aquarium it makes a good scavenger. Almost indistinguishable superficially from the South American characins of the genus *Characidium*.
WATER CONDITIONS: They thrive under most aquarium conditions.
SIZE: Reaches about 80 mm.
FOOD REQUIREMENTS: Tiny live foods such as brine shrimp nauplii and daphnia suit them well, but they take dried foods, too.

Hemigrammocharax multifasciatus (Fowler) • Checkerboard African Darter Tetra

RANGE: Zambezi River.
HABITS: A bottom-dwelling fish that darts about in short hops searching for food on the interspaces between rocks. Requires an open bottom with sandy patches.
WATER CONDITIONS: pH 6.2-7.2, temperature between 25-30°C. Very well adapted to a scavenger's life in the aquarium and very well camouflaged against sandy bottoms.
SIZE: Reaches about 110 mm.
FOOD REQUIREMENTS: Eats just about everything small enough to ingest, but it does appreciate some live foods from time to time.

Distichodus sexfasciatus Boulenger • Six-barred Distichodus

RANGE: Lower Congo region.
HABITS: Peaceful toward other fishes, but will nibble plants.
WATER CONDITIONS: Neutral to slightly acid. Temperature 24 to 27°C.
SIZE: To 25 cm.
FOOD REQUIREMENTS: Large amounts of live or frozen foods, supplemented with green foods like lettuce or spinach leaves.
COLOR VARIATIONS: Body pinkish to white with six dark bands. Fins are brilliant deep red.

Distichodus noboli Boulenger • Nobol Distichodus

RANGE: Lower Congo River System.
HABITS: Peaceful; a good community tank fish, but requires a large aquarium. Nibbles plants.
WATER CONDITIONS: Soft, slightly acid water. Temperature 24 to 26°C.
SIZE: To 10 cm.
FOOD REQUIREMENTS: Large amounts of live or frozen foods, with an addition of vegetable matter like lettuce or spinach leaves. Will occasionally accept flake food.

Hemistichodus vaillanti Pellegrin • Black-finned Fin-eater

RANGE: Gabon, but probably more dispersed.
HABITS: This fish has a bad reputation for chewing on the fins of its tankmates. Many of its relatives of the subfamily Ichthyborinae are guilty of this intolerable behavior.
WATER CONDITIONS: They thrive under most aquarium conditions, with a pH of 6.3-7.2 at 25-28°C.
SIZE: They may grow larger than the 100 mm known to the authors.
FOOD REQUIREMENTS: It likes to chew on other fishes' fins, but it quickly adjusts to small live foods and bits of fish and meat. Not a good community fish at all.

Phago maculatus Ahl • African Pike Characin

RANGE: West Africa, in the Niger River.
HABITS: A decidedly nasty fish which will kill for the sheer pleasure of killing.
WATER CONDITIONS: Neutral, medium-soft water best. Temperature 23 to 24°C.
SIZE: Up to 20 cm, but usually seen much smaller.
FOOD REQUIREMENTS: Wants plenty of meaty foods, preferably live fishes, although it will also accept dead ones.

Clarias angolensis Steindachner • Black Walking Catfish, Spotted Walking Catfish

RANGE: Widely dispersed over Nigeria, the Congo, Gabon, the Cameroons and Angola.

HABITS: This species is so widely dispersed and so poorly described that the name has been applied to many species. This group needs much more study. The fish shown here has also been called the normally pigmented *Clarias batrachus*. The pattern of small white spots is characteristic of the species.

WATER CONDITIONS: A wide variety of warm waters house this fish at a pH of 6.4-9.0 and temperatures from 22-30°C.

SIZE: Reaches 350 mm.

FOOD REQUIREMENTS: Prefers small fishes but takes almost anything, especially chunks of fish and meat.

Channallabes apus (Guenther) • Eel Catfish

RANGE: Zaire and Angola regions.

HABITS: Mostly nocturnal. Young specimens will not bother the other fishes, but it is best to keep larger ones by themselves.

WATER CONDITIONS: Not critical. Temperature 21 to 24°C.

SIZE: Up to 30 cm.

FOOD REQUIREMENTS: Greedy eaters which will consume great amounts of tubifex worms. Other foods may be substituted, such as beef heart or pieces of fish.

Gymnallabes heterocercalis Loennberg • Fatheaded Eel Catfish #2

RANGE: Cameroons.

HABITS: This fish is identical to *G. typus* in all respects except for its tail, which is turned up giving it the appearance of being heterocercal. All *Gymnallabes* have no bones on the sides of their heads. The dorsal and anal are united with the caudal fin.

SIZE: Reaches over 400 mm.

FOOD REQUIREMENTS: Prefers small living fishes but learns to take other aquarium diets. Not much is known as only a few specimens were collected and imported by the author (HRA).

Clarias mossambicus Peters • Tanganyikan Clarias

RANGE: Very widespread from East Africa, Ethiopia and Lakes Victoria and Tanganyika to the Zambesi.

HABITS: This is another walking catfish; it can be more or less recognized by the dark bands on the sides of the head. The specimen shown here was collected by the author (HRA) in Lake Tanganyika near Burundi.

WATER CONDITIONS: pH high, about 9.0 at 25°C.

SIZE: Grows very large, to about 650 mm.

FOOD REQUIREMENTS: Eats everything but prefers small fishes or chunks of fish or meat.

Gymnallabes typus Guenther • Fatheaded Eel Catfish

RANGE: Lower Niger and Old Calabar coast area, western Africa.

HABITS: An eel-like fish that stays on the bottom and hides during the day, sometimes even buried in the sand. A very active feeder at night, eating any fish small enough to ingest, but it usually pokes about on the bottom, especially in debris.

WATER CONDITIONS: Typical aquarium conditions suit this hardy fish. It was collected in pH 7.1 at 27°C.

SIZE: Reaches 250 mm.

FOOD REQUIREMENTS: Prefers worms and small bottom-dwelling living things, but gradually takes small bits of meat and fish.

Clarias angolensis

Clarias angolensis

Chanallabes apus

Gymnallabes heterocercalis

Clarias mossambicus

Gymnallabes typus

Gymnallabes typus

408

Plate #259

Schilbe marmoratus

Schilbe uranoscopus

Eutropiellus debauwi

Eutropiellus debauwi

Parailia longifilis

Schilbe mystus (juvenile)

Physailia villiersi

Physailia pellucida

Plate #260

409

Schilbe marmoratus Boulenger • African Shoulder-spot Catfish

RANGE: Congo River and its tributaries.
HABITS: Peaceful; inclined to be shy, so hiding places should be provided.
WATER CONDITIONS: Soft, neutral to slightly acid water. Temperature 24 to 27°C.
SIZE: To 16 cm.
FOOD REQUIREMENTS: Prefers live foods, but may possibly be trained to accept frozen foods.

Eutropiellus debauwi (Boulenger) • Three-striped Glass Catfish

RANGE: Stanley Pool region of the Congo River.
HABITS: Very active and peaceful; should be kept in groups rather than singly.
WATER CONDITIONS: Soft, slightly acid water is preferable. Temperature 24 to 26°C.
SIZE: Maximum a little over 7.5 cm.
FOOD REQUIREMENTS: Live foods such as daphnia, tubifex worms and white worms.

Parailia longifilis Boulenger • Speckled African Glass Catfish

RANGE: Upper Congo.
HABITS: The very large eye in the very small head is characteristic of this fish. It is not hardy but does well if given its own aquarium without stress from aggressive fishes.
WATER CONDITIONS: pH 6.4-7.4 at 25-28°C.
SIZE: Reaches 100 mm, but smaller specimens are imported.
FOOD REQUIREMENTS: Live brine shrimp and daphnia are preferred by this and most other aquarium fishes, but they soon learn to eat prepared foods.

Physailia villiersi Boulenger • Dusky African Glass Catfish

RANGE: Chiloango and Lucola Rivers near Cabinda (northern Angola).
HABITS: Hovers in mid-water, preferably in small schools.
WATER CONDITIONS: Clean, neutral to alkaline water over 24°C.
SIZE: 60-70 mm.
FOOD REQUIREMENTS: Likes small crustaceans that stay suspended in the water; prefers not to feed from the bottom.

Schilbe uranoscopus Rueppel • Silver Schilbe Catfish

RANGE: Very widespread from the Lower Nile through East Africa.
HABITS: Never spawned, and nothing is known about their sex differences, if any. They are not nocturnal, as they move about both day and night. Not to be trusted with small fishes.
WATER CONDITIONS: pH 6.0-7.8 at 23-28°C.
SIZE: Reaches 300 mm.
FOOD REQUIREMENTS: Small live foods, especially worms and daphnia. They also take small fishes.

Schilbe mystus Linnaeus • Striped Schilbe Catfish

RANGE: Very widespread through every jungle river in Africa plus the Nile.
HABITS: An active catfish that is very hardy. *Schilbe* is very similar to the genus *Eutropius* except for lacking an adipose fin.
WATER CONDITIONS: Very tolerant of aquarium conditions from pH 5.4-9.0 at 22-30°C.
SIZE: Reaches 340 mm.
FOOD REQUIREMENTS: Eats small fishes and tubifex worms, but probably eats almost anything that once was a living aquatic animal.

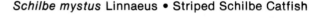

Physailia pellucida Boulenger • African Glass Catfish

RANGE: The upper Nile.
HABITS: Stays motionless in mid-water most of the time, waiting for bits of food to drift or swim by. Never spawned, and nothing is known about sex differences.
WATER CONDITIONS: Prefers clean, clear water that is well aerated, with a pH of 6.2-8.6 at 23-30°C.
SIZE: Reaches at least 93 mm.
FOOD REQUIREMENTS: Prefers daphnia and brine shrimp (living) but quickly learns to accept a normal aquarium diet of dried foods.

Malapterurus electricus (Gemlin) • Electric Catfish

RANGE: Tropical Africa, except for some lake and river systems.

HABITS: Decidedly predatory, so not safe with other species.

WATER CONDITIONS: Neutral water in the medium-soft range is best. Temperature 23 to 28°C.

SIZE: Over 60 cm in nature, but rarely seen at this size when offered for sale.

FOOD REQUIREMENTS: Wants small live fishes which are usually swallowed whole; will also eat plants.

Amphilius platychir Guenther • African Kuhli

RANGE: Tropical Africa including the Great Lakes Tanganyika and Malawi. One of the few Great Lakes fishes not endemic to these lakes.

HABITS: A typical naked catfish that grubs about mostly on the bottom and almost always at night. Its tiny eyes are barely visible on the fish. It is a good scavenger, but you never see them in the aquarium since they hide most of the time the tank is lighted.

WATER CONDITIONS: Slightly hard, alkaline water, pH 6.8-7.8 at 26°C.

SIZE: To 88 mm.

FOOD REQUIREMENTS: They scavenge what they can from the bottom. They like frozen newly hatched brine shrimp that falls to the bottom, where they actively gorge themselves.

Amphilius atesuensis Boulenger • Golden African Kuhli

RANGE: Western tropical Africa, especially Ghana.

HABITS: Spends most of its time hiding from the light. Has never been spawned, and no one seems to know their sexual difference or their reproductive behavior.

WATER CONDITIONS: Water with a pH of 6.8-8.0 at 26°C.

SIZE: To 60 mm.

FOOD REQUIREMENTS: Scrounges small things from the bottom. Seems to enjoy freshly hatched, but frozen, brine shrimp, which it picks off as it falls onto the bottom.

Phractura ansorgei Boulenger • African Whiptail Catfish

RANGE: The lower Niger basin; very common.

HABITS: A widely dispersed catfish that has a very small mouth and is often mistaken for a South American loricariid catfish because of its longitudinal imbricate scutes that are expanded vertebral processes. This is an aquarium favorite and has been spawned on occasion.

WATER CONDITIONS: They enjoy normal aquarium conditions with a pH of 6.2-7.4 at 23-28°C.

SIZE: They are very small, barely reaching 50 mm. The one shown in the illustrations was 49 mm long.

FOOD REQUIREMENTS: Picks small animalcules up from wherever it can find them, but probably eats bits of algae, too.

Malapterurus electricus

Malapterurus electricus

Amphilius platychir

Amphilius atesuensis

Amphilius platychir

Phractura ansorgei

Phractura ansorgei

Phractura ansorgei (fry)

Plate #261

412

Leptoglanis n.sp.

Parauchenoglanis guttatus

Parauchenoglanis macrostoma (juv.)

Parauchenoglanis macrostoma

Auchenoglanis occidentalis (juv.)

Synodontis haugi

Synodontis budgetti

Synodontis frontosus

Plate #262

Leptoglanis sp. • Spotted Mountain Catfish

RANGE: Lake Malawi. This species, which is yet to be named, was discovered hiding in an otherwise empty shell by Dr. Warren E. Burgess.

HABITS: Small enough to take refuge in empty shells, hide under stones and in vegetation, this fish is almost never seen in the aquarium because they are so shy. Their eyes seem to look up giving them a celestial appearance.

WATER CONDITIONS: pH 6.4-7.0 at a temperature of 20-26°C.

SIZE: Up to 45 mm.

FOOD REQUIREMENTS: They are bottom, detritus feeders.

Parauchenoglanis guttatus (Loennberg) • African Flathead Catfish

RANGE: Cameroon; Congo basin.

HABITS: Nocturnal, and shy and retiring, so should be provided with rocks, caves, etc; predatory, so do not keep with fishes that might be swallowed.

WATER CONDITIONS: Not critical; tolerates most local water types quite well, but, as with other fishes, extremes of pH or hardness should be avoided. A temperature range of 21 to 27°C.

SIZE: Up to 30 cm.

FOOD REQUIREMENTS: Prefers earthworms and other live foods but also relishes ground beef heart, chopped fish and other meat- or fish-based foods; some individuals will accept cooked oatmeal (rolled oats).

Parauchenoglanis macrostoma (Pellegrin) • African Spotted Catfish

RANGE: Tropical West Africa (Gabon).

HABITS: Peaceful; usually remains hidden in daylight and comes out at night.

WATER CONDITIONS: Soft, neutral to slightly acid water. Temperature 24 to 27°C.

SIZE: To 25 cm in natural waters; much smaller in the aquarium.

FOOD REQUIREMENTS: All sorts of live or frozen foods.

Auchenoglanis occidentalis (Cuvier & Valenciennes) • Giraffe-nosed Catfish

RANGE: Widespread throughout the central part of Africa from the Niger River to the Congo River and Blue Nile, as well as Lakes Chad, Bangwelu, Mweru, and Tanganyika.

HABITS: A voracious predator which cannot be kept with smaller fishes.

WATER CONDITIONS: Not critical as long as extremes are avoided. Optimum temperatures are about 24 to 28°C.

SIZE: Attains a length of just over 50 cm.

FOOD REQUIREMENTS: Live foods of all kinds preferred. Voracious feeders, so plenty of food must be available.

Synodontis sorex GUNTHER, 506mm

Synodontis afro-fischeri HILGENDORF, holotype, 134mm, Victoria Nyanza

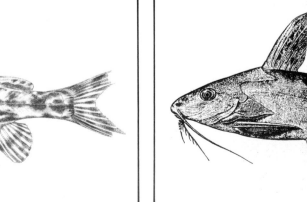

Synodontis robbianus SMITH, holotype, 138mm

The genus SYNODONTIS

Synodontis is a catfish genus of about 100 species that are found throughout Africa except for the Sahara and the waters north of it. The fish are naked, without scales, and are found in most contiguous bodies of water, never being found in intermittent pools. They have dorsal and pectoral spines that are very strong and serrated. These spines make them very easy prey for the fisherman with a net since they become enmeshed in the netting and cannot escape. Of course, the fisherman has his work cut out for him when he tries to remove the fish from its entrapment. The author (HRA) remembers well the first night fishing in the Stanley Pool looking for *Synodontis angelicus* and *S. nigriventris*. A 20-meter by 3-meter seine was pulled through the water at midnight. We collected about 1,200 *Synodontis* in the first haul then spent the rest of the night removing them from the net, finally resorting to cutting pliers to free the fishes by cutting off the three serrated spines (one dorsal and two pectorals). The majority of the fishes lived, even after being out of the water (but in a wet seine) for hours, and then having their spines cut off about halfway down!

The *Synodontis* met by the author in their native habitats have all been nocturnal, and most swim in schools upside down. *S. angelicus*, on the other hand, never schooled but could be found hiding at night inside old tires attached to the docks as bumpers for docking boats. We were able to get a few specimens every night at the yacht club in old Leopoldville (now Kinshasa).

In the aquarium the *Synodontis* species are all peaceful and good scavengers. They are forever on the prowl, searching for food, and they eat everything from flake foods to live foods. They never seem to attack other fishes, but they do caress them from time to time with their three pairs of barbels, making them a pest to other fishes. There have been no concerted spawnings, but random successes have been achieved using hormonal injections of ripe fish.

Dr. Max Poll revised the genus *Synodontis* in 1971, and the authors have relied upon his illustrated descriptions for the identification of the plates. We have also used his black and white drawings to illustrate those fishes for which no color photos were available.

Synodontis eupterus

Synodontis robertsi

Synodontis longirostris

Synodontis longirostris

Synodontis longirostris

Synodontis nigromaculatus

Synodontis nyassae

Synodontis nigromaculatus

416

Plate #263

Synodontis multipunctatus

Synodontis multipunctatus

Synodontis petricola

Synodontis eurystomus

Synodontis acanthomias

Synodontis nigromaculatus

Synodontis nigromaculatus

Synodontis robbianus

Plate #264

417

Synodontis katangae POLL, holotype, 240mm

Synodontis velifer NORMAN, holotype, 214mm

Synodontis centralis POLL, holotype, 116mm

Synodontis ornatus BOULENGER, holotype, 152mm

Synodontis albolineatus PELLEGRIN, holotype, 118mm

Synodontis dorsomaculatus POLL, holotype, 137mm

Synodontis steindachneri BOULENGER, holotype, 172mm, Akonolinga

Synodontis nigrita CUVIER et VALENCIENNES, holotype, 149mm, fleuve Ser

Plate #265

Synodontis caudovittatus BOULENGER, lectotype, 258mm

Synodontis camelopardalis POLL, holotype, 180mm

Brachysynodontis batensoda (RUPPELL), 220mm

Synodontis guttatus GUNTHER, holotype, 700mm

Synodontis filamentosus BOULENGER, holotype, 220mm

Synodontis xiphias GUNTHER, holotype, 670mm

Synodontis koensis PELLEGRIN, holotype, 140mm

Synodontis tessmanni PAPPENHEIM, lectotype, 168mm

Plate #266

Synodontis schoutedeni

Synodontis schoutedeni

Synodontis notatus

Synodontis ocellatus

Synodontis congicus

Synodontis decorus

Synodontis decorus

Synodontis decorus

Plate #267

Synodontis ornatipinnis (juv.)

Synodontis ornatipinnis

Synodontis brichardi

Synodontis flavitaeniata

Synodontis pleurops

Synodontis pleurops

Synodontis pleurops

Synodontis pleurops

Plate #268

421

Synodontis notatus VAILLANT, lectotype, 207mm

Synodontis geledensis GUNTHER, holotype, 307mm

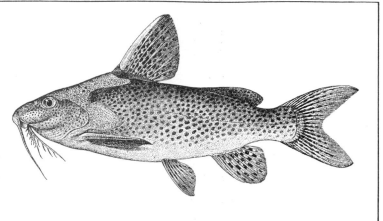

Synodontis woosnami BOULENGER, holotype, 164mm

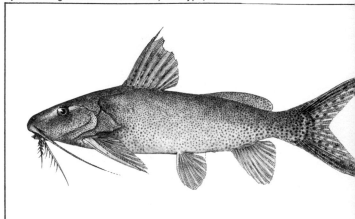

Synodontis punctulatus GUNTHER, lectotype, 222mm

Synodontis eburneensis DAGET, holotype, 281mm

Synodontis khartoumensis ABU GIDEIRI, paratype, 150mm

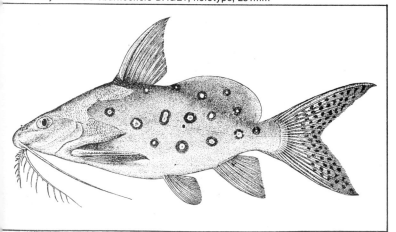

Synodontis ocellifer BOULENGER, lectotype, 225mm

Synodontis pulcher POLL, holotype, 150mm

Plate #269

422

Synodontis polystigma BOULENGER, lectotype, 198mm

Synodontis obesus BOULENGER, lectotype, 275mm

Synodontis leopardinus PELLEGRIN, holotype, 137mm

Synodontis pardalis BOULENGER, lectotype, 229mm

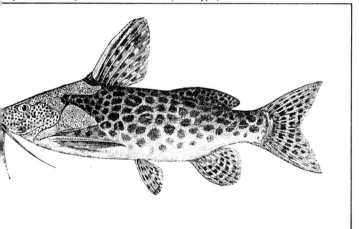

Synodontis macrostigma BOULENGER, lectotype, 171mm

Synodontis punctifer DAGET, holotype, 190mm

Synodontis bastiani DAGET, holotype, 84mm

Synodontis gobroni DAGET, paratype Markala, riv. Niger

Plate #270

Synodontis contractus

Synodontis greshoffi

Synodontis nigriventris

Synodontis nigriventris

Synodontis angelicus

Syndontis angelicus

Synodontis alberti

Synodontis alberti

Plate #271

Phyllonemus typus

Phyllonemus typus

Bagrus ubangensis

Lophiobagrus cyclurus

Chrysichthys brachynema

Chrysichthys sianenna

Gnathobagrus depressus

Chrysichthys ornatus

Plate #272

425

Phyllonemus typus Boulenger • Spatula-barbeled
Catfish

RANGE: Lake Tanganyika.
HABITS: This genus only contains one species. The fish is
easily recognized by the spatulate or leaf-like membrane
on the distal part of the maxillary barbels. There are no
nasal barbels.
WATER CONDITIONS: pH 6.8-7.6 at 25°C.
SIZE: A small catfish that barely reaches 75 mm.
FOOD REQUIREMENTS: A scavenger, as are most catfishes.
Thrives on every normal aquarium diet but prefers to
catch it from the bottom of the tank.

Bagrus ubangensis Boulenger • Ubangi Shovelnose
Catfish

RANGE: Congo.
HABITS: This fish grows very large for the small aquarium
and must be given plenty of room. It swallows tankmates
small enough to ingest in one gulp. This only takes place
at night, in the dark. Normally the fish is much darker
than the small silver specimen shown in the photo.
WATER CONDITIONS: pH 6.2-6.8 at 27°C.
SIZE: Reaches over 300 mm.
FOOD REQUIREMENTS: Small fishes or flake food, which it
learns to gobble.

Lophiobagrus cyclurus Worthington & Ricardo • African
Bullhead

RANGE: Found only in Lake Tanganyika.
HABITS: Not much is known about this species except that it
is difficult to collect and was misidentified as *L. lestradei*
by Poll himself! Recently it has been imported in fair
numbers and has been spawned (accidentally). Reports
that its slime is poisonous to other fishes have not been
confirmed.
WATER CONDITIONS: pH 9.0 at about 25°C.
SIZE: The largest specimen ever collected was 92 mm long.
FOOD REQUIREMENTS: Partially digested small fishes,
shrimps and insects were found in its stomach, so it probably feeds on any small living foods of appropriate size.

Chrysichthys brachynema Boulenger • Salmon Catfish

RANGE: Lake Tanganyika.
HABITS: This is a catfish too large for the home aquarium. Its
red meat has been used to make substitute smoked
salmon for homesick Europeans living on Lake
Tanganyika. The author (HRA) tasted it and it wasn't
bad, especially if you've been on the lake for any length
of time.
WATER CONDITIONS: Alkaline water, pH 9.0 at 25°C.
SIZE: Over 400 mm.
FOOD REQUIREMENTS: Eats smaller fishes but can be
trained to take chunks of fish and meat.

Chrysichthys sianenna Boulenger • Olive-silver Catfish

RANGE: Lake Tanganyika.
HABITS: A nocturnal fish that performs poorly as a scavenger in the home aquarium. Hides most of the time among
dense vegetation.
WATER CONDITIONS: Prefers very alkaline environment
with a pH of 9.0 and a hardness of about DH 10°.
SIZE: Reaches over 220 mm, but smaller specimens are
usually imported for the aquarium trade.
FOOD REQUIREMENTS: Prefers worms and other bottom-
dwelling morsels, but also takes pelleted aquarium
foods.

Gnathobagrus depressus Nichols & Griscom • Long-
jawed Catfish

RANGE: Congo basin.
HABITS: A bottom-dwelling catfish found in low-light areas.
Very similar to *Chrysichthys* except for the long lower
jaw.
SIZE: Reaches at least 200 mm.
FOOD REQUIREMENTS: Probably eats small fishes and
invertebrates found while scavenging at night.

Chrysichthys ornatus Boulenger • Mottled Catfish

RANGE: Upper Congo and Ubangi Rivers.
HABITS: A nocturnal scavenger. Well marked but of limited
interest for aquarists.
WATER CONDITIONS: Tolerates a wide range of conditions
from pH 6.8-9.0 at 25-28°C.
SIZE: Reaches 200 mm.
FOOD REQUIREMENTS: A typical scavenger that feeds from
the bottom. Prefers small worms but takes pelleted
aquarium diets.

AFRICAN BARBS AND OTHER CYPRINIDS

The cyprinids are one of the dominant groups of freshwater fishes, with literally hundreds of species in North America, Asia, Europe, and Africa. There are over 300 species of barbs in Africa alone. Although Asian barbs are a staple of the aquarium hobby, the African species have never become especially popular, although several species have had a short vogue. The butterfly barb, *Capoeta hulstaerti*, for instance, was imported in numbers from the Congo in the 1960's, but it soon faded from sight. The major problem with the African barbs (and the other African cyprinids, for that matter) is that few of them are especially colorful or hardy. Like the cool-water minnows of North America, the males may be colorful when spawning, but this lasts for only a few weeks or months and the rest of the year they are similar to the silvery to tan females. Also, most African barbs that have been imported so far have been like the type usually called *Barbodes vivipara*—silvery with a black lateral band, a few black scale edgings, and a bit of color in the fins. They are seldom imported in numbers, and because they virtually never breed in the aquarium they soon disappear from the hobby until the next importation.

This is not to say that the African barbs are poor aquarium fishes. In fact, in a small tank with clean, slightly acid water and a fairly warm temperature, a small school of barbs can be quite a sight. There is no reason that they cannot be spawned on a regular basis if the aquarist is willing to take the time to do so, as many spawn in much the same manner as do the Asian barbs and American minnows, laying large numbers of eggs that settle into the substrate or plants. The fry are often very small and may require infusoria, but that is seldom held against a popular species. The small mountain stream species from the southern African area are perhaps most colorful, but their colors are best only when spawning; they would tolerate cooler water than the Congo River species that are sometimes imported.

African barbs can be split into two rather vague groups on the basis of adult size. At one extreme are the large species such as *Barbodes capensis* from South Africa. These fishes are usually rather coarse and have more scales in the lateral row than do the smaller species, in this respect resembling the large Eurasian *Barbus* species. Reaching a weight of 10 kilograms or more, the large species are often popular food and sporting fishes. They are predatory on other fishes, frogs, crabs, and just about anything else they can find. When they live in larger, rapid rivers they are good game fishes, taking many types of artificial lures and fighting well. Juveniles of such species would probably outgrow their tanks in a few months and do poorly.

The small species of African barbs (under 150 mm) are found nearly everywhere, from jungle ponds to rapid mountain streams. We at T.F.H. place them in the genera *Barbodes*, *Capoeta*, and *Puntius*, as is correct in most American aquarium literature, but the advanced hobbyist should be aware that, as in so many groups of fishes, there is considerable

Barbodes callipterus

Barbodes guirali

Barbodes camptacanthus

Barbodes camptacanthus

Barbodes trispilos

Barbodes sp.

Barbodes arcislongae

Barbodes sp. cf. robertsi

Plate #273

428

Barbodes fasciolatus

Puntius jae

Barbodes brookingi

Barbodes eutenia

Barbodes macrops

Barbodes nicholsi

Barbodes kerstenii

Barbodes prionocanthus

Plate #274

429

debate about the correct names for our common fishes. Thus the European literature tends to use the name *Barbus* for virtually all the barbs, large and small, while we restrict that name to the large, fine-scaled species of Eurasia. Probably neither system of names is actually correct, as several other generic names, especially *Beirabarbus*, are currently being applied by African ichthyologists. So for the moment we'll stick at least provisionally to *Puntius* for species with no barbels, *Capoeta* with two barbels, and *Barbodes* with four barbels. These differences are purely pedantic, however, as members of all three genera look much alike and are found in the same types of habitats, as well as spawning in a similar manner.

The mountains of south-central Africa have numerous small, colorful species that at first glance would be very difficult to distinguish from the colorful shiners of the southeastern United States. When in spawning colors, the males tend to have bright red and yellow in the fins along with areas of milky white as a contrast. Males of many small barbs develop large breeding tubercles on the head and fins, as in the goldfish and minnows in general. Females and males out of spawning season may have touches of color in the fins and on the body, but they are generally tannish with black lateral bands, like the normal run of African barbs. In southern Africa these small species are kept as native fishes and fare well in aquaria, but they are seldom imported.

Most imported African barbs come from the Great Lakes area or from the western coast, where they are often used as "bag stuffers" by exporters. When an exporter pays for cargo space on an airplane, he may as well put in as many fish bags as he can find, whether they contain premium fishes or not. So after he has packed all his desirable cichlids, catfishes, and oddballs, a few barbs may be added to the shipment to make the best use of the space and maybe make a few extra dollars at the retail end. (Now that most airlines charge by weight, not volume, this practice is ending.) These barbs are seldom very colorful, and rarely is anything really known about their life history or even how to sex them. When the butterfly barb, *C. hulstaerti,* was first imported from the Congo, the colorful specimens were sexed by many "experts," but the fish proved impossible to spawn. Only after many shipments had been imported was it discovered that the first shipments were all males and real females were easily sexed by differences in fin colors. Even today it is doubtful if anyone really knows much about such species as *Barbodes camptacanthus* from the Cameroons and Gabon, although it is imported fairly regularly and has a distinctive color pattern. The species that appear in the hobby only once a decade or so never seem to become established and soon fade from memory.

Although there are over 20 genera of cyprinids (family Cyprinidae) on the most recent checklist of African fishes, only two or three genera other than the barbs are ever imported for the aquarium hobby. Of these *Labeo* is the most familiar, though certainly not common. Like the barbs, African *Labeo* can be divided into large species of 10 kilograms or more that are of most interest as food and game fishes, and small species under 300 mm long that are somewhat suitable for keeping in large aquaria. Of the small species that enter the trade, only *Labeo cylindricus* (southeastern

Africa), *L. forskalii* (Nile drainage), and *L. variegatus* (Congo) are fairly often seen. Of the three, only *L. variegatus* is really small enough (less than 100 mm) for most aquaria, the others often exceeding 300 mm. *Labeo* species feed much like carp, using their ventral mouths and thick lips to extract organic matter, live and dead, plant and animal, from the substrate. Africa has several true dwarf *Labeo* species (under 75 mm long), but they are virtually unknown to ichthyologists, let alone aquarium hobbyists.

Two unusual genera of fishes are rarely imported, *Garra* and *Barilius*. *Garra* is certainly nothing beautiful to look at, the brownish body having nearly parallel surfaces so it looks like a small branch. However, it does make an efficient algae-eater, using the ventral mouth as a scraper. Curiously, this genus is found in both Africa and southern Asia, a distribution pattern shared with *Labeo* and the genera of barbs but found in few other fishes. *Discognathus*, sometimes seen in the aquarium literature, is a synonym of *Garra*.

The species of *Barilius* are streamlined fishes that at first glance look more like South American tetras or marine herring than cyprinids. The silvery bodies are long and slender, and the head is usually pointed and has a large mouth. These fishes are active, schooling species that are predators on small prey and often live in fast waters, though many species are also found in lakes. Some species have recently begun to be imported regularly because they occur in the Great Lakes and are sent as fillers in cichlid shipments. Although most species are not especially colorful (unless you are partial to silvery fishes), the males of a few species, such as *Barilius ubangensis*, are attractively banded and have colored fins. *Barilius* is also an Afro-Asian genus, but recently it was split into two separate genera, *Barilius* proper being restricted to Asian species and *Opsaridium* being used for African species. Regardless of name, remember that these fishes are jumpers in the worst sense of the word and need a covered tank.

Barbodes vivipara

Capoeta hulstaerti

Puntius puellus

Puntius sylvaticus

Barbodes vivipara

Barbodes radiatus aurianticus

Puntius woehlerti

Barbodes sp. cf. greenwoodi

Plate #275

432

Garra ornata

Labeo cylindricus

Labeo rubropunctatus

Labeo variegatus

Barilius ansorgii

Barilius christyi

Barilius microcephalus

Plate #276

Barilius ubangensis

AFRICAN KILLIFISHES

The Germans may call them "eierlegende Zahnkarpfen" (egg-laying toothcarps), but to American and British hobbyists the small, often brightly colored fishes of the Cyprinodontidae are the killifishes. Of the several hundred species, the majority are found in Africa south of the Sahara and have become one of the most sought-after groups of fishes in the entire aquarium hobby. Admittedly, you will seldom see an African killifish for sale in a general petshop (for various reasons they are considered hard to profitably merchandise), but there is a gigantic group of killie specialists who purchase and trade fishes through the international and national mails. Many books on their identification and care have been written (of which one of the most comprehensive on African species is the monumental *Rivulins of the Old World* by Jorgen Scheel), but new species are still being described each year and more unusual species enter the hobbyist market all the time.

African killifishes—particularly the genera *Aphyosemion* (commonly called lyretails although many species lack distinctive tail streamers), *Nothobranchius* (the nothos or fire killies), *Epiplatys* (the panchax, the most plainly marked of the common genera), and *Aplocheilichthys, Procatopus,* and *Lamprichthys* (collectively called lampeyes and ranging in size from under 25 mm to over 125 mm)—are noted for their unusual and often brilliant color patterns in the males (females are usually plain) and especially for their odd spawning habits. Species of *Nothobranchius* (probably all) and *Aphyosemion* (just a few) are annual fishes like the South American *Cynolebias*, the fry developing rapidly into usually brilliantly colored adults that spawn special eggs capable of resting (entering diapause) in the mud bottom of the drying pond for several months before hatching with the next rains. After laying their eggs and fertilizing them, the adults of the first generation die, usually at the age of 8 to 10 months, certainly less than a year. In the aquarium these annual fishes are very popular because the development time of the eggs can be controlled to allow hatching just when the young are wanted. The eggs are also easy to ship as they can be maintained in an almost dry condition for months or perhaps even years.

Lyretails show a great amount of variation in spawning habits, the various species laying their eggs anywhere from the surface to the top layer of the substrate. Although most are probably happiest using spawning mops in midwater, some species will lay their eggs almost anywhere that is available, adapting their behavior to the circumstances within the tank. Most killifishes are best bred in trios, the single aggressive male being allowed to vent his energy on two or even three females (males of many killifishes can and will kill lone females when spawning).

The lampeyes are not seen too often in the aquarium although there are many common species, some of them extremely attractive. Most of the species are small and more iridescent than beautiful, although when kept in schools they look fine in a small tank. The larger types, such as *Proca-*

topus and *Lamprichthys*, are colorful and will spawn in the aquarium, but they tend to be short-lived and not very hardy. Many or perhaps most lampeyes place their eggs in crevices such as floating pieces of natural cork or behind airline tubing in the darkest corner of the tank. Identification of lampeyes is almost impossible even from specimens, and they are poorly covered in available aquarium literature.

On a final and more scientific note, it must be mentioned that the placement of the killifishes in a single family has been in question since a controversial revision by Parenti in 1981. Instead of just the family Cyprinodontidae with several subfamilies, another classification recognizing up to 10 families has begun to establish itself. In this system the lyretails, fire killies, and panchax would be in family Aplocheilidae, the lampeyes in Aplocheilichthyidae, and the American killies would belong to several non-African families, especially Rivulidae (*Cynolebias, Rivulus,* etc.), Fundulidae (*Fundulus, Lucania,* etc.), and Cyprinodontidae (*Cyprinodon, Aphanius, Jordanella,* etc.). Also, there is a recent (and probably justified) trend to consider the African genus *Epiplatys* a synonym of the Asian genus *Aplocheilus*—certainly the two groups of species are superficially and behaviorially very similar and distinguished mainly by geography.

Killifish hobbyists may be among the most satisfied of aquarists because there is so much material available to them at all times. Thanks to a tradition of trading among individuals and groups, literally dozens of African (and American) species are readily available to the specialist and dozens more are available on an occasional basis. No two killies look exactly the same, and their colorful males make even 4-liter tanks bright.

Aphyosemion ogoense ottogartneri

Aphyosemion striatum

Aphyosemion riggenbachi

Aphyosemion bivittatum

Aphyosemion bitaeniatum

Aphyosemion bivittatum

Aphyosemion loennbergi

Aphyosemion loennbergi

Plate #277

436

Aphyosemion mirabile traudae

Aphyosemion gardneri

Aphyosemion gardneri mamfense

Aphyosemion gardneri mamfense

Aphyosemion gardneri clauseni

Aphyosemion gardneri clauseni

Aphyosemion cinnamomeum

Aphyosemion nigerianum X cinnamomeum

Plate #278

437

Aphyosemion bertholdi

Aphyosemion liberiense

Aphyosemion roloffi

Aphyosemion geryi

Aphyosemion chaytori

Aphyosemion brueningi

Aphyosemion guineense

Aphyosemion petersi

Plate #279

438

Aphyosemion franzwerneri

Aphyosemion celiae winifredae

Aphyosemion celiae

Aphyosemion ahli

Aphyosemion calliurum

Aphyosemion calliurum

Aphyosemion australe (gold)

Aphyosemion australe

Plate #280

439

Aphyosemion lujae

Aphyosemion wildekampi

Aphyosemion rectogoense

Aphyosemion christyi

Aphyosemion schioetzi

Aphyosemion gabunense boeinni

Aphyosemion cognatum

Aphyosemion schoutedeni

Plate #281

Aphyosemion puerzli

Aphyosemion ndianum

Aphyosemion exiguum

Aphyosemion elegans X bualanum ??

Aphyosemion bualanum

Aphyosemion rubrifascium

Aphyosemion kiyawense male

Aphyosemion kiyawense female

Plate #282

441

Aphyosemion walkeri

Aphyosemion spurrelli

Aphyosemion arnoldi

Aphyosemion filamentosum X rubrilabiale

Aphyosemion rubrilabiale

Aphyosemion filamentosum-complex

Aphyosemion filamentosum

Plate #283

Aphyosemion filamentosum var.

Aphyosemion

Aphyosemion scheeli

Aphyosemion marmoratum

Aphyosemion marmoratum

Aphyosemion splendopleure

Aphyosemion toddi

Aphyosemion occidentale

Aphyosemion occidentale

Plate #284

443

Aphyosemion sjoestedti

Aphyosemion sjoestedti

Aphyosemion gulare ?

Aphyosemion cameronense

Aphyosemion cameronense

Aphyosemion cameronense

Fundulosoma thierry

Aphyosemion labarrei

Plate #285

444

Nothobranchius palmqvisti

Nothobranchius sp. (Dar es Salaam)

Nothobranchius lourensi

Nothobranchius janpapi

Nothobranchius sp. (Mbeya)

Nothobranchius sp. (Salima)

Nothobranchius kuhntae

Nothobranchius guentheri

Plate #286

Nothobranchius furzeri

Nothobranchius korthausae

Nothobranchius rachovii

Nothobranchius rachovii var.

Nothobranchius rachovii var.

Nothobranchius rachovii blue var.

Nothobranchius kirkii

Nothobranchius kirkii

Plate #287

Nothobranchius patrizii

Nothobranchius steinforti

Nothobranchius lourense

Nothobranchius orthonotus

Nothobranchius melanospilus

Nothobranchius jubbi jubbi

Nothobranchius palmqvisti

Nothobranchius palmqvisti

Plate #288

Pachypanchax playfairii

Pachypanchax playfairii

Pachypanchax homalonotus

Epiplatys huberi

Epiplatys chevalieri

Epiplatys chevalieri

Epiplatys annulatus

Epiplatys annulatus

Plate #289

448

Epiplatys sexfasciatus

Epiplatys sexfasciatus

Epiplatys sexfasciatus

Epiplatys dageti monroviae

Epiplatys dageti monroviae

Epiplatys dageti monroviae

Epiplatys duboisi

Epiplatys duboisi

Plate #290

449

Epiplatys njalaensis

Epiplatys roloffi

Epiplatys macrostigma

Epiplatys macrostigma

Epiplatys macrostigma

Epiplatys macrostigma

Epiplatys grahami

Epiplatys grahami

Plate #291

Epiplatys bifasciatus

Epiplatys bifasciatus

Epiplatys fasciolatus

Epiplatys fasciolatus

Epiplatys spilargyreius

Epiplatys spilargyreius

Epiplatys spilargyreius X fasciolatus

Epiplatys barmoiensis

Plate #292

451

Lamprichthys tanganicanus

Procatopus (?) "Fire-tail"

Procatopus gracilis

Procatopus similis

Procatopus aberrans

Procatopus similis ?

Procatopus nototaenia

Procatopus nototaenia

Plate #293

Aplocheilichthys katangae

Plataplochilus cabindae

Aplocheilichthys macrophthalmus

Aplocheilichthys "Micropanchax" (female)

Aplocheilichthys myersi

Aplocheilichthys rancureli

Aplocheilichthys spilauchen

Aplocheilichthys spilauchen

Plate #294

453

CICHLIDS OF LAKES MALAWI, TANGANYIKA, AND VICTORIA

The African Rift Valley contains a number of lakes that have become important to aquarists mainly as sources of fishes of the family Cichlidae. Two of these, Lake Malawi and Lake Tanganyika, have provided the bulk of the species imported, with Lake Victoria a distant third. Cichlids are the prime targets for the exporters as they constitute the major portion of the fish fauna of all three lakes. Lake Malawi, for example, has more than 250 described species (undoubtedly more to come) of cichlids as compared to fewer than 50 non-cichlid species. Lake Tanganyika is not too different, with about 175 described cichlid species and fewer than 75 non-cichlid species. More cichlids will undoubtedly be described from Lake Tanganyika as well. Lake Victoria follows a similar pattern, with more than 175 cichlid species and only 40 or so non-cichlids.

What also makes these lakes somewhat unique as far as aquarists are concerned is their chemistry, especially the strongly alkaline pH. Normal pH values for these lakes are: Malawi, 7.7-8.6; Tanganyika, 8.6-9.2; and Victoria, 7.1-9.0.

The cichlids of these lakes have undergone an explosive evolution that has become a major research topic among ichthyologists today. The term "species flock" has been applied to the cichlids of these lakes as well as other fishes. The result of the evolutionary trends gives the aquarist a wide variety of diverse species to choose from. In Lake Tanganyika is found the largest cichlid, *Boulengerochromis microlepis,* growing to a length of 90 cm or more. Lake Tanganyika also provides some of the smallest cichlid species that grow no larger than 3.5 cm and live in abandoned snail shells. These shell-dwellers have become very popular in the hobby and are the current rage. Also found in Lake Tanganyika are small cichlids that act much like marine gobies and have for that reason been dubbed the goby cichlids. These are members of the genera *Eretmodus, Tanganicodus,* and *Spathodus.* The most speciose genus in the lake is *Lamprologus,* its more than 40 species providing many aquarium favorites, among which are *L. brichardi, L. compressiceps, L. sexfasciatus,* and the shell-dwellers, all of which belong to this genus. One genus, *Julidochromis,* contains only a half dozen or so species, but all have been imported for the aquarium trade. One of the challenges of Lake Tanganyika is a still rather high-priced species called *Cyphotilapia frontosa.* It has been bred—but not very often—and there is still a demand for the progeny. Perhaps the leading species of Lake Tanganyika cichlid as far as aquarists are concerned is *Tropheus moorii.* This species has evolved a myriad of color patterns, and new color varieties are being imported as fast as they are discovered.

Lake Malawi is no laggard in the provision of aquarium favorites. The cichlid fauna is generally divided (for convenience) into the

Haplochromis species and the mbuna or rock-dwelling cichlids made up of a number of genera. Somewhere in between these are the peacocks of the genera *Aulonocara* and *Trematocranus*. Although more closely related to the *Haplochromis* species, they are found around the rocks and aquarists have given them honorary mbuna status. *Haplochromis moorii* is perhaps comparable to Lake Tanganyika's *Cyphotilapia frontosa* in desirability and providing a challenge to aquarists. The diversity of the *Haplochromis* species surpasses by far that of the *Lamprologus* species of Lake Tanganyika. Malawi boasts more than 100 species of *Haplochromis*, with more in the process of being discovered and described. It is from this genus that the more recent new imports come. They dazzle the aquarist mainly with blues with overtones of violet and green. One species is even referred to as "electric blue." Several species of mbuna have evolved color variations that rival those of *Tropheus moorii*. Of these, perhaps the best known is one of the earlier imports, *Pseudotropheus zebra*; not far behind are *Pseudotropheus tropheops* and the two species of *Labeotropheus*.

The lake cichlids are mostly easy to keep, hardy, and good spawners. As long as aquarists are able to accommodate their need for a very alkaline pH, lots of room, and plenty of rockwork caves (especially for the mbuna), they should have no problem. Food is no problem although it is often forgotten that many of the lake species feed mainly on plant material and should receive at least some vegetable matter in their diets. Tanks with good algal growth are strongly recommended, and rearing tanks with algae are almost a must. Of course there are all kinds of feeding adaptations in the lake cichlids (including scale-eaters, eye-biters, sand-sifters, leaf-scrapers, etc.), but none seems to pose too much of a problem for aquarists.

There are basically two different reproductive types in the lakes, mouthbrooders and substrate-spawners. Mouthbrooders are by far the most common, especially in Lakes Victoria and Malawi. Although Lake Tanganyika has its share of mouthbrooders, most of the species (including all known *Lamprologus* species) are substrate-spawners. The mouthbrooders all spawn in a more or less similar manner, although there are some variations on this theme. The female is courted by the male and a site is selected for egg deposition. All other fishes are generally evicted from the area, in some cases meaning driven from the tank itself or killed outright. The eggs are laid "cichlid fashion" on a flat surface or in a pit in the sand and are fertilized immediately by the male as the two fish circle each other. By the time the female comes back to the eggs she takes them up in her mouth. This continues until all eggs are shed by the female and ensconced in her buccal cavity. Some males will guard the female but others will ignore her once spawning is completed, depending on the species and sometimes even on the individual. Aquarists generally remove the brooding female to a brooding tank where she will be safe from the attacks of other fishes or the advances of the amorous male. In about three weeks the fry are released from the mother's mouth and are able to fend for themselves. The female is ready, at least for a week or so, to accept the fry back into her mouth in the presence of some suspected danger. Most females do not eat during the incubation period, so females should be kept away from the tank containing the males until they have had time to build up their strength again. Aquarists with a nervous disposition or who wish to spare the female the long incubation period will strip the eggs from her mouth and return her to her original tank right away. The eggs are hatched artificially next to gentle aeration. Most spawnings of mouthbrooders do not provide a great number of eggs—somewhere in the neighborhood of 50 or so is relatively common.

The substrate-spawners spawn in a manner typical for cichlids. After courtship and cleaning of a substrate, the female lays a string of eggs and the male follows, fertilizing them. Once the female has become depleted she or the male or both will stand guard over them until they hatch and become free-swimming. The choice of site depends a great deal upon the species involved. Some spawn in depressions or pits dug in the sand, some on a flat portion of a rock or leaf, and some hide their eggs on the roof or floor of caves, well protected from the prying eyes of other fishes.

Haplochromis tetrastigma

Haplochromis tetrastigma

Haplochromis "Electric Blue"

Haplochromis sp.

Haplochromis annectens

Haplochromis "Electric Blue"

Haplochromis fenestratus (female)

Haplochromis fenestratus (male)

Plate #295
(Plates #295 through #325 are of Cichlids of Lake Malawi)

Haplochromis jacksoni

Haplochromis cf. chrysonotus

Haplochromis chrysonotus

Haplochromis cf. chrysonotus

Haplochromis sp.

Haplochromis sp.

Haplochromis nitidus

458

Plate #296

Haplochromis tetrastigma

Haplochromis stonemani

Haplochromis hennydaviesae

Haplochromis auromarginatus

Haplochromis longimanus

Haplochromis eucinostomus

Haplochromis decorus

Haplochromis argyrosoma

Haplochromis nkatae?

Plate #297

459

Haplochromis nototaenia (female)

Haplochromis nototaenia (male)

Haplochromis pholidophorus

Haplochromis woodi

Haplochromis woodi?

Haplochromis modestus

Haplochromis macrostoma (juv.)

Plate #298

Haplochromis macrostoma (adult)

Haplochromis plagiotaenia

Haplochromis sp.

Haplochromis sp.

Haplochromis mollis?

Haplochromis subocularis

Haplochromis lepturus

Haplochromis placodon (female)

Haplochromis placodon (male)

Plate #299

Haplochromis sphaerodon (male)

Haplochromis sphaerodon (female)

Haplochromis obtusus

Haplochromis anaphyrmus

Haplochromis sp.

Haplochromis lateristriga

Haplochromis melanotaenia

Haplochromis sp.

Plate #300

Haplochromis nigritaeniatus

Haplochromis similis (male)

Haplochromis cf *fenestratus*

Haplochromis cf *fenestratus*

Haplochromis spilonotus

Haplochromis strigatus

Haplochromis virginalis

Haplochromis labrosus

Plate #301

463

Haplochromis compressiceps

Haplochromis compressiceps

Haplochromis kiwinge

Haplochromis cf. labridens

Haplochromis labridens

Haplochromis cf. taeniolatus

Haplochromis taeniolatus (female)

Haplochromis taeniolatus

Plate #302

Haplochromis moorii

Haplochromis moorii

Haplochromis electra

Haplochromis electra

Haplochromis johnstoni

Haplochromis callipterus

Haplochromis rostratus (juv.)

Haplochromis tetrastigma

Plate #303

465

Haplochromis venustus

Haplochromis venustus

Haplochromis mloto

Haplochromis mloto

Haplochromis cf. euchilus (juv.)

Haplochromis cf. euchilus (adult)

Haplochromis euchilus (juv.)

Haplochromis euchilus (adult)

Plate #304

Haplochromis livingstoni

Haplochromis livingstoni

Haplochromis fuscotaeniatus (juv.)

Haplochromis fuscotaeniatus

Haplochromis polystigma

Haplochromis polystigma

Haplochromis linni + Haplochromis polystigma

Haplochromis linni

Plate #305

467

All fishes on this page are of the *Labidochromis/Melanochromis textilis/exasperatus/joanjohnsonae* complex.

Plate #306

468

Pseudotropheus tropheops

Pseudotropheus tropheops

Pseudotropheus tropheops (white form)

Pseudotropheus novemfasciatus

Pseudotropheus sp.

Iodotropheus sprengerae

Gephyrochromis lawsi

Gephyrochromis moorii

Plate #307

All photos on this page are of morphs of *Pseudotropheops tropheops*.

Pseudotropheus aurora

Pseudotropheus sp.

Pseudotropheus sp.

Pseudotropheus crabro

Pseudotropheus microstoma

Pseudotropheus tropheops

Pseudotropheus tropheops

Pseudotropheus tropheops

Plate #309

471

Pseudotropheus elongatus (var.)

Pseudotropheus elongatus (var.)

Pseudotropheus elongatus

Pseudotropheus sp.

Pseudotropheus brevis (female)

Pseudotropheus brevis (male)

Pseudotropheus elegans

Pseudotropheus elegans (juv.)

Plate #310

Pseudotropheus lanisticola

Pseudotropheus livingstonii

Pseudotropheus "eduardi"

Pseudotropheus "eduardi"

Pseudotropheus sp.

Pseudotropheus tropheops

Pseudotropheus sp.

Pseudotropheus sp.

Plate #311

473

Pseudotropheus zebra (var.)

Pseudotropheus zebra (var.)

Pseudotropheus zebra (var.)

Pseudotropheus zebra (var.)

Pseudotropheus livingstonii

Pseudotropheus livingstonii

Pseudotropheus lombardoi (female)

Pseudotropheus lombardoi (male)

Plate #312

474

All photos on this page are of morphs of *Pseudotropheus zebra*

Plate #313

Pseudotropheus zebra (male)

Pseudotropheus zebra (male)

Pseudotropheus zebra (female)

Pseudotropheus zebra (female)

Pseudotropheus zebra (albino)

Pseudotropheus zebra (gold)

Pseudotropheus zebra (white)

Pseudotropheus zebra (pale yellow)

Plate #314

Labeotropheus fuelleborni (male)

Labeotropheus fuelleborni (female)

Labeotropheus fuelleborni (male)

Labeotropheus fuelleborni (male)

Labeotropheus fuelleborni (male)

Labeotropheus fuelleborni (female)

Labeotropheus fuelleborni (male)

Labeotropheus fuelleborni (female)

Plate #315

Labeotropheus fuelleborni (male)

Labeotropheus fuelleborni (male)

Labeotropheus trewavasae

Labeotropheus trewavasae

Labeotropheus trewavasae (female)

Labeotropheus trewavasae (female)

Labeotropheus trewavasae (male)

Labeotropheus trewavasae (male)

Plate #316

Labidochromis caeruleus

Labidochromis caeruleus

Labidochromis fryeri

Labidochromis "freibergi"

Labidochromis sp.

Labidochromis sp.

Labidochromis vellicans

Labidochromis mathothoi

Plate #317

Cynotilapia afra

Cynotilapia afra

Cynotilapia sp.

Cynotilapia sp.

Cynotilapia sp.

Cynotilapia afra (var.)

Cynotilapia axelrodi (male)

Cynotulapia axelrodi (female)

Plate #318

480

Melanochromis simulans (male)

Melanochromis simulans (female)

Melanochromis vermivorus (female)

Melanochromis vermivorus (male)

Melanochromis vermivorus

Labidochromis sp.

Labidochromis sp.

Labidochromis sp.

Plate #319

Melanochromis auratus (male)

Melanochromis auratus (female)

Melanochromis auratus (var.) (male)

Melanochromis auratus

Melanochromis chipokee (male)

Melanochromis chipokee (female)

Melanochromis johanni (var.)

Melanochromis johanni (var.) (female)

Plate #320

482

Melanochromis johanni (male)

Melanochromis johanni (female)

Melanochromis johanni (male)

Melanochromis johanni (male)

Melanochromis melanopterus

Melanochromis parallelus

Melanochromis perspicax

Melanochromis perspicax

Plate #321

Chilotilapia rhoadesii

Chilotilapia rhoadesii

Cleithrochromis bowleyi

Hemitilapia oxyrhynchus

Petrotilapia tridentiger

Petrotilapia nigra

Genyochromis mento

Genyochromis mento

Plate #322

Lethrinops lethrinus

Lethrinops parvidens

Lethrinops polli

Lethrinops sp.

Rhamphochromis sp.

Rhamphochromis macrophthalmus

Diplotaxodon argenteus

Doplotaxodon ecclesi

Plate #323

485

Trematocranus sp.

Trematocranus peterdaviesi

Lethrinops aurita

Lethrinops christyi

Lethrinops furcicauda

Lethrinops furcicauda

Lethrinops gossei (male)

Lethrinops gossei (female)

Plate #324

486

Aulonocara nyassae (orange shoulder)

Aulonocara nyassae (female)

Aulonocara nyassae (Peacock Blue)

Aulonocara nyassae (Maleri gold)

Aulonocara sp. (Night Aulonocara)

Aulonocara sp. (white dorsal edge)

Trematocranus jacobfreibergi (male)

Trematocranus jacobfreibergi (female)

Plate #325

487

Astatotilapia bloyeti

Aulonocranus dewindti

Callochromis macrops macrops (female)

Callochromis macrops (Tanzania)

Chalinochromis brichardi

Chalinochromis brichardi

Chalinochromis n. sp.

Chalinochromis n. sp. (juv.)

Plate #326
(Plates #326 through #357 are of Cichlids of Lake Tanganyika)

Julidochromis regani

Julidochromis regani (var.)

Julidochromis regani (melanistic)

Julidochromis regani "Kigoma"

Chalinochromis brichardi

Chalinochromis brichardi

Chalinochromis brichardi "bifrenatus"

Chalinochromis brichardi "Dhoboi"

Plate #327

489

Julidochromis ornatus

Julidochromis ornatus

Julidochromis transcriptus

Julidochromis ornatus/transcriptus

Julidochromis dickfeldi

Julidochromis ornatus/transcriptus

Julidochromis marlieri

Julidochromis marlieri

Plate #328

490

Julidochromis dickfeldi

Julidochromis dickfeldi (southern form)

Julidochromis marlieri (Zaire)

Julidochromis marlieri

Julidochromis ornatus (Uvira form)

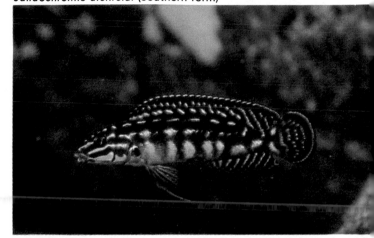

Julidochromis n. sp. (southern coast)

Julidochromis sp. (southern coast)

Julidochromis sp. (southern coast)

Plate #329

Cyphotilapis frontosa

Cyphotilapia frontosa (juv.)

Cyprichromis brieni

Cyprichromis brieni (subadult)

Eretmodus cyanostictus

Cyprichromis brieni (juv.)

Spathodus marlieri

Spathodus erythrodon

Plate #330

Petrochromis fasciolatus

Petrochromis polyodon

Perissodus paradoxus

Perissodus straeleni

Grammatotria lemairei

Perissodus microlepis

Ophthalmochromis ventralis

Ophthalmus ventralis ventralis

Plate #331

493

Petrochromis trewavasae (male)

Petrochromis trewavasae

Petrochromis n. sp. (Nyanza Lac var.)

Petrochromis n. sp.

Petrochromis orthognathus

Simochromis curvifrons

Simochromis curvifrons

Simochromis curvifrons

Plate #332

494

Simochromis babaulti (var.)

Simochromis babaulti

Simochromis curvifrons

Simochromis babaulti

Petrochromis sp.

Simochromis diagramma

Astatoreochromis straeleni

Simochromis dardennei

Plate #333

495

Simochromis diagramma (southern)

Simochromis diagramma (southern)

Simochromis n. sp.

Spathodus marlieri

Telmatochromis bifrenatus (adult)

Telmatochromis bifrenatus (subadult)

Telmatochromis temporalis (freak)

Telmatochromis vittatus

Plate #334

Petrochromis fasciolatus

Petrochromis sp.

Telmatochromis vittatus

Reganochromis calliurus

Telmatochromis bifrenatus?

Telmatochromis caninus

Triglachromis otostigma

Telmatochromis temporalis

Plate #335

Tropheus brichardi

Tropheus brichardi "Blue-eyed Tropheus"

Tropheus duboisi (narrow white band)

Tropheus duboisi (juv.)

Tropheus duboisi (wide yellow band)

Tropheus duboisi (no band)

Tropheus polli

Tropheus polli

Plate #336

Tropheus duboisi (broad band)

Tropheus duboisi (Bemba var.)

Tropheus duboisi (juv.)

Tropheus sp. (Mpulungu var.)

Tropheus moorii ("Moliro" dom. male)

Tropheus moorii ("Moliro" dom. male)

Tropheus moorii kasabae (Kalambo var.)

Tropheus moorii kasabae (Kala var.)

Plate #337

499

Tropheus moorii ("Kigongo-Makobola Bronze" var.)

Tropheus duboisi? ("Blue-faced" var.)

Tropheus moorii "Uvira-Kalunda"

Tropheus moorii? (Flat-nose var.)

Tropheus moorii "Chipimba Cape"

Tropheus moorii "Chipimba Cape"

Tropheus brichardi

Tropheus moorii "Nyanza-Lac" var.?

Plate #338

500

Telmatochromis n. sp. (Kalemie)

Tropheus moorii

Tropheus moorii (green w/orange dorsal)

Tropheus moorii (orange/black var.)

Tropheus moorii (orange/black)

Tropheus moorii (black/red)

Tropheus moorii (cherry-cheek)

Tropheus moorii (Cape Banza var.)

Plate #339

Tropheus moorii (Kiriza var.)

Tropheus moorii (Kiriza male)

Tropheus moorii (Kiriza or Kaiser II)

Tropheus moorii (Kiriza female)

Tropheus moorii (Bemba orange)

Tropheus moorii (fed on algal diet!)

Tropheus moorii "annectens" (juv.)

Tropheus moorii "annectens" (Kaniosha)

Plate #340

Tropheus moorii "annectens" (Kaniosha)

Tropheus moorii "annectens" (Kaniosha juv.)

Tropheus moorii "annectens" (Musimu)

Tropheus moorii "annectens"

Tropheus moorii "annectens" (canary cheek)

Tropheus moorii "annectens" (juv.)

Tropheus moorii "annectens" (Kaniosha)

Tropheus moorii "annectens" (Kitas a var.)

Plate #341

503

Tropheus moorii "Bemba Orange"

Tropheus moorii ("Red/Black" var.)

Tropheus moorii "Kamba Bay"

Tropheus moorii "Kamba Bay" (juv.)

Tropheus moorii

Tropheus moorii "Rainbow" or "Chaitika Cape"

Tropheus moorii (SW type)

Tropheus moorii "Kabeyeye"

504

Plate #342

Tropheus moorii ("Murago" var.)

Tropheus moorii (juv. 4 cm. long)

Tropheus moorii ("Murago" adult)

Tropheus sp. (green var.)

Tropheus moorii (lemon striped)

Xenotilapia sp.

Xenotilapia flavipinnis

Xenotilapia melanogenys

Plate #343

Xenitilapia spilopterus

Aulonocranus dewindti

Xenotilapia flavipinnis

Xenotilapia sima

Xenotilapia ochrogenys

Xenotilapia sp. (flavipinnis?)

Pierre Brichard and fish photo setup

Rocky point of land in one of the Rift Lakes

Plate #344

506

Haplochromis pfefferi

Tanganicodus irsacae

Haplochromis horei

Haplochromis benthicola

Limnochromis auritus

Cardiopharynx schoutedeni?

Lobochilotes labiatus

Lobochilotes labiatus

Plate #345

507

Haplochromis burtoni

Aulonocranus dewindti

Boulengerochromis microlepis

Bathybates ferox

Callochromis macrops melanostigma

Callochromis pleurospilus

Cardiopharynx schoutedeni

Ophthalmochromis ventralis

Plate #346

508

Cyprichromis leptosoma (southern)

Cyprichromis nigripinnis

Cardiopharynx schoutedeni

Trematocara n. sp.

Haplochromis benthicola (female)

Haplochromis benthicola (male)

Haplotaxodon microlepis

Haplotaxodon microlepis (male)

Plate #347

Lamprologus brichardi

Lamprologus brichardi

Lamprologus sp. "Magarae"

Lamprologus brevis

Lamprologus callipterus

Lamprologus attenuatus (nuptial colors)

Lamprologus toae

Lamprologus caudopunctatus

Plate #348

Lamprologus brichardi (var.)

Lamprologus brichardi (Ubwari)

Lamprologus buscheri

Lamprologus cunningtoni

Lamprologus n. sp.

Lamprologus n. sp.

Lamprologus calvus

Lamprologus compressiceps (Ubwari)

Plate #349

Lamprologus compressiceps

Lamprologus calvus

Lamprologus compressiceps (var.)

Lamprologus falcicula

Lamprologus furcifer (orange var.)

Lamprologus leleupi melas

Lamprologus leleupi?

Lamprologus leleupi

Plate #350

Lamprologus elongatus

Lamprologus cunningtoni

Lamprologus furcifer

Lamprologus sp.

Lamprologus leleupi

Lamprologus leleupi

Lamprologus meeli

Lamprologus lemairei

Plate #351

Lamprologus niger

Lamprologus obscurus

Lamprologus moorii (yellow form)

Lamprologus moorii (black form)

Lamprologus niger?

Lamprologus mustax

Lamprologus falcicula

Lamprologus mondabu

Plate #352

Lamprologus lemairei (juv.)

Lamprologus mondabu

Lamprologus mustax (female)

Lamprologus mustax (male)

Lamprologus multifasciatus

Lamprologus niger

Lamprologus ocellatus

Lamprologus ocellatus w/parasite

Plate #353

Perissodus straeleni

Lamprologus tretocephalus

Lamprologus tretocephalus (subadult)

Cyphotilapia frontosa

Cyphotilapia frontosa

Lamprologus tretocephalus

Cyphotilapia frontosa (juv.)

Lamprologus fasciatus

Plate #354

516

Lamprologus tetracanthus

Lamprologus tetracanthus

Lamprologus savoryi

Lamprologus sexfasciatus

Lamprologus pleuromaculatus

Lamprologus prochilus

Lamprologus ocellatus

Lamprologus ornatipinnis

Plate #355

This remarkable series of photographs shows spawning behavior of *Lamprologus brevis*, one of the shell-dwelling cichlids of Lake Tanganyika. The two upper photos at left show a sub-adult male posturing, and in the two photos above right a fully adult male is shown with his spawning partner immediately before (upper photo) and after the female has begun to enter the shell. Below left the male is shown before entering the shell himself, while below right he is shown during stages of his entrance.

Lamprologus n. sp.

Lamprologus sexfasciatus (yellow race)

Lamprologus attenuatus

Lamprologus elongatus

Lamprologus profundicola

Lamprologus profundicola (juv.)

Ophthalmochromis nasutus

Ophthalmochromis nasutus

Plate #357

Haplochromis macrognathus

Haplochromis sauvagei

Haplochromis dichrourus

Haplochromis cinereus

Haplochromis riponianus

Haplochromis brownae

Haplochromis lacrimosus

Haplochromis lacrymosus

Plate #358
(All cichlids shown on this plate are from Lake Victoria)

Pseudocrenilabrus philander male

Pseudocrenilabrus philander female

Pseudocrenilabrus multicolor male

Pseudocrenilabrus multicolor female

Tylochromis lateralis

Tylochromis polylepis

Stomatepia mariae

Serranochromis robustus

Plate #359

521

Pseudocrenilabrus philander (Weber) • South African
Mouthbrooder

RANGE: Throughout southern Africa.
HABITS: Aggressive; should be kept with species of similar
size and temperament.
WATER CONDITIONS: Not critical.
SIZE: 8 to 11 cm.
FOOD REQUIREMENTS: All foods accepted eagerly.

Pseudocrenilabrus multicolor (Hilgendorf) • Dwarf
Egyptian Mouthbrooder

RANGE: All over eastern Africa south to the lower Nile.
HABITS: Fairly safe in the community aquarium.
WATER CONDITIONS: Not critical. Temperature between
24 and 27°C.
SIZE: Males to 8 cm; females slightly smaller.
FOOD REQUIREMENTS: Live and frozen foods preferred;
dry foods are taken.

Tylochromis lateralis (Boulenger) • Congo Tylochromis

RANGE: Congo basin.
HABITS: A maternal mouthbrooder. Habits are probably
very similar to those of *T. polylepis*.
WATER CONDITIONS: Not critical. Temperatures between
about 23 and 28°C are suitable.
SIZE: Attains a length of about 28 cm.
FOOD REQUIREMENTS: Probably a snail-eater (it has
crushing pharyngeal teeth), but it will accept a variety of
other meaty foods. Vegetable matter should be included
in their diet.

Tylochromis polylepis (Boulenger) • Lake Tanganyika
Tylochromis

RANGE: Endemic to Lake Tanganyika.
HABITS: Juveniles are most often seen around the coastal
areas and are gregarious. The adults cruise over the
open sandy stretches, usually by themselves.
Mouthbrooders (maternal).
WATER CONDITIONS: Hard, alkaline with temperatures be-
tween 23 and 28°C preferred.
SIZE: Attains a length of about 33 cm.
FOOD REQUIREMENTS: Will accept a variety of aquarium
foods but should also be given some vegetable matter.
Feeds on snails in nature.

Stomatepia mariae (Holly) • Barombi Tilapia

RANGE: Endemic to Lake Barombi-ma-Mbu, a crater lake in
the Cameroons.
HABITS: Not well known. This species apparently shares a
common ancestor with a *Tilapia* species and probably
has similar habits. It differs from *Tilapia* by having a
larger mouth and essentially conical outer teeth.
WATER CONDITIONS: Not critical. Normal aquarium
temperatures of 23 to 28°C are sufficient. Virtually
unknown in the hobby.
SIZE: Attains a length of about 10 cm.
FOOD REQUIREMENTS: Accepts a variety of meat and
vegetable foods.

Serranochromis robustus (Guenther) • Banded
Largemouth; Nembwe

RANGE: South-central and southwestern Africa, including
Lakes Bangweulu and Malawi.
HABITS: A riverine species. A maternal mouthbrooder that is
very aggressive in defense of the brood, it is piscivorous,
so tankmates must be large and able to care for
themselves.
WATER CONDITIONS: Not critical, but generally slightly
hard and alkaline water is preferred, especially those
imported from Lake Malawi. Temperatures between 23
and 28°C are preferred.
SIZE: A large species possibly exceeding 40 cm in length.

TILAPIA

Tilapia is a rather complicated genus containing over 75 species, many of which contain subspecies. In 1968, Dr. Thys van den Audenaerde produced an annotated bibliography of *Tilapia* that included a listing of the species under various groupings, some of which were named subgenera. Dr. E. Trewavas of the British Museum (Natural History) has been investigating the genus and has written papers elevating some of the subgenera to full generic status. Thus we see combinations such as *Sarotherodon mossambica* or *Oreochromis hornorum* popping up in hobbyist and scientific literature. These moves have not been universally accepted (this may be just a matter of time, however) and you might still see those species names as *Tilapia mossambicus* and *T. hornorum*, etc. This rather confusing situation will probably continue for a while.

A number of species have what has now been called the "*Tilapia* spot." This is a blackish spot on the soft dorsal fin base just behind the spiny portion. It is visible in many of the accompanying photos.

The name *Tilapia* comes from the Bechuana word "thlape," which means simply "a fish." It is a common genus in Africa and, because of its economic importance and ability to adapt to many ecological conditions, has been introduced into many different countries as a basic source of protein. *Tilapia* culture is quite advanced, and it is not unusual to find almost every available lake or pond in the tropics stocked with one or more species of this genus . . . much to the detriment of the local native species.

Aquarists have not really taken species of *Tilapia* into their tanks in great numbers. Regulations in certain countries actually prohibit keeping any of them, mostly for fear of their getting free and colonizing local waters as they have done in so many instances. Most species are plain in color and grow rather large for a small tank. A few species are kept, however, and bred. It has been found that there are two major modes of reproduction in *Tilapia*, mouthbrooding and substrate-spawning. This behavioral difference was used by Dr. Trewavas along with several morphological characteristics in originally separating *Sarotherodon* (mouthbrooders) from other *Tilapia* (substrate-spawners). Many of the species are relatively peaceful, except when spawning; others are just plain mean and nasty, like many other cichlids. The tank conditions are not critical as most species are easily adaptable to aquarium life. Large tanks are recommended for these often large fishes, with plenty of hiding places for females. Plants may be used, but there is a risk with certain species that they may be uprooted or even destroyed. Feeding is not difficult as most species of *Tilapia* will accept a variety of aquarium foods. Some will rid your aquarium of snails; others will require at least some vegetable matter in their diet. A well-balanced diet is therefore recommended.

Tilapia kottae

Sarotherodon grahami

Tilapia shirana

Tilapia shirana

Tilapia pungo

Tilapia kumba

Tilapia aurea

Tilapia leucosticta

Plate #360

524

Tilapia mariae

Tilapia mariae

Tilapia tholloni

Tilapia sp.

Tilapia rendalli

Tilapia nilotica

Tilapia sp.

Tilapia sp.

Plate #361

525

Sarotherodon mossambicus

Sarotherodon mossambicus

Tilapia ovalis

Tilapia sp.

Tilapia sp.

Tilapia sp.

Tilapia sp.

Tilapia sp.

Plate #362

526

Steatocranus casuarius

Steatocranus casuarius

Steatocranus gibbiceps juv.

Steatocranus sp.

Teleogramma brichardi

Teleogramma brichardi

Steatocranus tinanti

Steatocranus tinanti

Plate #363

527

Steatocranus casuarius Poll • Lionhead Cichlid

RANGE: Stanley Pool, Zaire.
HABITS: Fairly peaceful for a cichlid.
WATER CONDITIONS: Should have hard, alkaline water.
    Temperature 24 to 28°C.
SIZE: About 10 cm.
FOOD REQUIREMENTS: Will rarely accept dry foods, al-
    though some frozen foods, particularly frozen adult brine
    shrimp, are taken.

Steatocranus gibbiceps Boulenger • Lionhead Cichlid II

RANGE: Congo Basin.
HABITS: Males develop a large fatty hump on the head. Pos-
    sibly identical with *S. casuarius* and have similar habits
    and needs. Generally peaceful but should have caves or
    other secure places.
WATER CONDITIONS: Not critical. Temperatures between 23
    and 28°C.
SIZE: Attains a length of 9 to 10 cm, females slightly smaller.
FOOD REQUIREMENTS: Prefers live foods but will accept
    frozen foods as well. Not too fond of dry foods.

Steatocranus sp. • Lion head Cichlid

The Congo drainage has numerous species of lion head cichlids, some of which appear only as rare unidentified imports. Since the taxonomy of this genus is somewhat confused and the species all look much alike, it is often impossible to put a "good" name on a single fish. The fish shown has been identified as *S. mpozoensis*, but there is no way of telling for certain until more fish are imported. All the lion heads have much the same requirements as the common *S. casuarius*.

Teleogramma brichardi Poll • Brichard's Slender Cichlid

RANGE: Congo basin.
HABITS: Playful, but sometimes quarrelsome with members
    of its own species.
WATER CONDITIONS: Medium-soft, slightly acid water best;
    tank should have plenty of rocks and caves to make the
    fish feel at home. Temperature 21 to 27°C.
SIZE: About 10 cm.
FOOD REQUIREMENTS: Live foods much preferred, although
    some frozen foods are accepted.

Steatocranus tinanti (Boulenger) • Slender Lionhead Cichlid

RANGE: Central Africa, especially the Congo River area.
HABITS: A bottom-dweller that spends most of its time in
    hiding.
WATER CONDITIONS: Prefers water that is warm (27°C) and
    neutral, the closer to pH 7.0 and a hardness of 3 degrees,
    the better.
SIZE: A maximum size of 15 cm is rare.
FOOD REQUIREMENTS: Will only eat live foods, though some
    pelleted dried foods and frozen brine shrimp serve well.

Nanochromis dimidiatus

Nanochromis dimidiatus

Nanochromis dimidiatus

Nanochromis dimidiatus

Nanochromis splendens females?

Nanochromis splendens male

Nanochromis parilius

Nanochromis parilius

Plate #364

529

Nanochromis dimidiatus (Boulenger) • Dimidiatus

RANGE: Congo basin.
HABITS: Usually very peaceful in the community aquarium.
WATER CONDITIONS: Soft, slightly acid water. Temperature
    24 to 26°C.
SIZE: Males 9 cm; females 6 cm.
FOOD REQUIREMENTS: All sorts of live foods, preferably
    those which sink to the bottom; frozen foods also ac-
    cepted.
COLOR VARIATIONS: Body dusky with a purplish sheen; hori-
    zontal dark line may be present; back part of dorsal fin
    and top of caudal fin bright red.

Nanochromis splendens (Boulenger) • Congo Dwarf
Cichlid

RANGE: Congo basin.
HABITS: Apt to be a bit quarrelsome at times; best kept by
    themselves.
WATER CONDITIONS: Soft, slightly acid water is best.
    Temperature 24 to 26°C.
SIZE: Up to 8 cm for males; females about 2 cm smaller.
FOOD REQUIREMENTS: Live foods of all kinds; at times
    when none is available, frozen foods may be provided
    temporarily.
COLOR VARIATIONS: Sides of body blue, belly bright green;
    dorsal fin is orange with a black tip and white edge; up-
    per half of tail striped.

Nanochromis parilius Roberts & Stewart • Bar-tailed
Nudiceps

RANGE: Congo basin.
HABITS: A secretive fish that needs many caves or other
    hiding places. Flowerpots are commonly used. Readily
    spawned, with the sexes easily distinguished by color and
    the rounded appearance of the female's abdomen. Eggs
    are usually placed in a sheltered position and guarded by
    the female.
WATER CONDITIONS: Prefers higher temperatures, in the
    range of 27-30°C, with spawning occurring in the upper
    part of the range. Otherwise slightly acid and moderate-
    ly soft water is recommended.
SIZE: Attains a length of about 8-9 cm.
FOOD REQUIREMENTS: Will accept a variety of aquarium
    foods. For spawning, live foods, especially tubificid
    worms, are generally needed.

Pelvicachromis roloffi (Thys van den Audenaerde) •
Roloff's Kribensis

RANGE: Sierre Leone and eastern Guinea.
HABITS: Generally peaceful, even tending to be shy.
WATER CONDITIONS: Neutral to slightly acid (pH 6.5) water
at a temperature of 24 to 26°C for keeping, slightly higher
for breeding.
SIZE: Attains a maximum length of a little over 7.5 cm.
FOOD REQUIREMENTS: Will accept a variety of aquarium
fare but prefers live food.

Pelvicachromis taeniatus (Boulenger) • Striped Kribensis

RANGE: Lower Niger River, West Africa.
HABITS: Generally peaceful, even timid except when breeding.
WATER CONDITIONS: Soft, slightly acid water is best; the
tank should be well planted and provide hiding places.
Temperature 24 to 26°C.
SIZE: Male 8 cm; female slightly smaller.
FOOD REQUIREMENTS: Live foods are preferred, but finely
chopped beef heart is also accepted and even relished.

Pelvicachromis subocellatus Guenther • Ocellated Krib

RANGE: Coastal regions of western Africa from Gabon to
the Moanda region of Angola; this includes the lower
Congo.
HABITS: Relatively peaceful, but will establish and defend a
territory, especially when ready to spawn.
WATER CONDITIONS: Not critical. A temperature   23 to
25°C is adequate.
 SIZE: Attains a maximum size of about 12 cm.
FOOD REQUIREMENTS: Will accept a variety of foods including daphnia, tubifex, bloodworms, and even **prepared
foods**.

Pelvicachromis roloffi

Pelvicachromis roloffi

Pelvicachromis taeniatus "klugei"

Pelvicachromis taeniatus "klugei"

Pelvicachromis taeniatus striped anal

Pelvicachromis subocellatus ?

Pelvicachromis taeniatus ?

Pelvicachromis taeniatus ?

Plate #365

Pelvicachromis pulcher male yellow form

Pelvicachromis pulcher male red form

Pelvicachromis pulcher female yellow

Pelvicachromis pulcher female red

Pelvicachromis sp. aff. *pulcher*

Pelvicachromis sp. aff. *pulcher*

Pelvicachromis pulcher pink var.

Pelvicachromis pulcher

Plate #366

Pelvicachromis pulcher (Boulenger) • Kribensis

RANGE: Tropical West Africa, especially the Niger Delta.
HABITS: Peaceful; does some digging, but mostly under rocks, and plants are seldom uprooted.
WATER CONDITIONS: Not critical. Temperature 23 to 25°C.
SIZE: Males up to 8 cm; females to 6 cm.
FOOD REQUIREMENTS: Live and frozen foods.

Chromidotilapia batesii (Boulenger) • Bates's Chromidotilapia

RANGE: Two forms (possibly different species), one from the Rio Muni and vicinity and the other from Fernando Po.
HABITS: The two forms are similar when preserved, but live colors are different. The southern form has blood red on the upper part of the caudal fin. The northern form picks up the eggs immediately while the southern form delays a day before picking them up for incubation.
WATER CONDITIONS: Hard, alkaline water preferred, especially if spawning is attempted. Temperatures 23-28°C.
SIZE: Apparently not much more than about 7-10 cm.
FOOD REQUIREMENTS: Accepts a variety of aquarium foods, especially meaty and live foods, but including frozen and flake foods.

Chromidotilapia guentheri (Sauvage) • Guenther's Mouthbrooder

RANGE: West Africa, Sierra Leone to Cameroon.
HABITS: Aggressive, especially to others of its own species.
WATER CONDITIONS: Hard, alkaline water preferred and best for spawning. Temperature 24 to 27°C.
SIZE: 15 cm; smaller specimens most usually offered for sale.
FOOD REQUIREMENTS: Accepts all meaty live, frozen and freeze-dried foods.

Chromidotilapia kingsleyi Boulenger • Kingsley's Chromidotilapia

RANGE: Lower Gabon.
HABITS: A mouthbrooder. May be aggressive, so it is best to keep only a single pair.
WATER CONDITIONS: Seems to prefer hard, alkaline water at temperatures between 23 and 28°C. Some salt can be added.
SIZE: Attains a length of up to 25 cm.
FOOD REQUIREMENTS: Should be fed a variety of meaty foods, living if possible, along with frozen and flake foods.

Thysia ansorgi (Boulenger) • Five-spot African Cichlid

RANGE: Liberia to Nigeria, in fresh and brackish waters.
HABITS: Peaceful for a cichlid; does some digging, usually around rocks, but plants are seldom uprooted.
WATER CONDITIONS: Slightly alkaline, with an addition of about a teaspoonful of salt per 4 liters of water; tank should be well planted. Temperature 24 to 26°C.
SIZE: Males to about 10 cm; females a little smaller.
FOOD REQUIREMENTS: Live foods preferred, but they will also take frozen foods.

Chromidotilapia batesii

Chromidotilapia batesii

Chromidotilapia guentheri

Chromidotilapia guentheri

Chromidotilapia guentheri var.

Chromidotilapia kingsleyi

Thysia ansorgii

Thysia ansorgii

Plate #367

536

Hemichromis lifalili

Hemichromis lifalili

Hemichromis bimaculatus (female)

Hemichromis bimaculatus (male)

Hemichromis bimaculatus var.

Hemichromis bimaculatus var.

Hemichromis thomasi

Hemichromis thomasi

Plate #368

Hemichromis lifalili Loiselle • Hemichromis Bimac II;
Lifalili

RANGE: Congo basin.
HABITS: Males grow larger than the females and may show a
frontal gibbosity with age. This species occurs in a wide
variety of riverine habitats, ox-bow lakes, marshes, and
swamps. Does not like rapids or swampy areas low in oxygen. Very aggressive and known to rearrange
aquarium decor.
WATER CONDITIONS: Not critical. Temperatures should be
about 23-28°C.
SIZE: Males to 8.2 cm, females to 6.2 cm.
FOOD REQUIREMENTS: Eats a variety of aquarium foods,
but live foods are preferred.

Hemichromis bimaculatus Gill • Jewel Cichlid

RANGE: West and central Africa.
HABITS: Besides being very pugnacious, it has the nasty
habit of digging up plants.
WATER CONDITIONS: Not critical. Temperature should be
quite high, about 27°C.
SIZE: To about 15 cm; usually smaller.
FOOD REQUIREMENTS: Live foods preferred; frozen foods
accepted.

Hemichromis thomasi (Boulenger) • African Butterfly
Cichlid

RANGE: Sierra Leone, southeast Guinea and west Liberia.
HABITS: Relatively peaceful.
WATER CONDITIONS: Not critical. Temperature 25°C.
SIZE: Males up to 10 cm; females to 8 cm.
FOOD REQUIREMENTS: Live, frozen or freeze-dried foods
are accepted.

Hemichromis fasciatus Peters • Five-spotted
Hemichromis

RANGE: West Africa, widely distributed from Senegal to the
    Congo.
HABITS: Very quarrelsome toward other fishes; should be
    kept by themselves.
WATER CONDITIONS: Occurs in both fresh and brackish
    waters. In the aquarium they adapt to any water condi-
    tion.
SIZE: Fully grown, about 30 cm.
FOOD REQUIREMENTS: Will consume any unwanted fish or
    will settle for chunks of fish or beef heart.

Hemichromis elongatus (Guichenot) • Elongate
Hemichromis

RANGE: Southeastern Guinea, Sierra Leone, southwestern
    Liberia, and Togo to northern Angola, including the
    Niger Delta, Congo basin, and Upper Zambezi basin.
HABITS: Found in a variety of habitats with the exception of
    violent rapids and the open waters of large lakes.
    Generally aggressive and may tear up the tank decora-
    tions. A substrate spawner.
WATER CONDITIONS: Not critical. Can tolerate some salt in
    the water. Temperatures between 22 and 28°C are best.
SIZE: Attains a length of about 14 cm.
FOOD REQUIREMENTS: Will accept a variety of foods but
    should get a heavier proportion of meaty foods.

Lamprologus mocquardi Pellegrin • Ubangi Lionhead
Cichlid

RANGE: Upper Ubangi.
HABITS: Little is known about this species as it does not get
    into the hobby often. Commonly confused with *L. con-*
    golensis, with which it shares similar habits and needs.
WATER CONDITIONS: Not critical. Temperatures in the
    range of 23 to 28°C are sufficient.
SIZE: Attains a length of about 10 cm.
FOOD REQUIREMENTS: Best to furnish live foods, but frozen
    foods may also be accepted.

Lamprologus congolensis Schilthuis • Congo Lionhead
Cichlid

RANGE: Congo basin.
HABITS: The head of this species develops a fatty padding
    giving it (and certain other cichlids) the "lionhead" ap-
    pearance. A substrate-spawner. Territorial and thus
    should have a number of hiding places (caves, flower-
    pots, etc.). Very aggressive.
WATER CONDITIONS: Not critical. Temperatures between 23
    and 28°C are acceptable.
SIZE: Attains a length of about 10 cm.
FOOD REQUIREMENTS: Prefers living foods but accepts a
    variety of other aquarium foods, except perhaps flakes
    or other dry foods.

Hemichromis fasciatus

Hemichromis fasciatus

Hemichromis elongatus

Hemichromis elongatus

Hemichromis elongatus? juvenile

Hemichromis elongatus

Lamprologus mocquardi

Lamprologus congolensis

Plate #369

540

Ctenopoma acutirostre

Ctenopoma acutirostre

Ctenopoma ansorgii

Ctenopoma ansorgii

Ctenopoma congicum

Ctenopoma congicum

Ctenopoma multispinis

Ctenopoma kingsleyae

Plate #370

541

Ctenopoma acutirostre Pellegrin • Leopard Ctenopoma

RANGE: Middle and lower Congo River tributaries.
HABITS: Predatory; should never be kept with fish they can swallow. Peaceful with larger fishes; inclined to be shy in small tanks.
WATER CONDITIONS: Not critical. Temperature 25 to 28°C.
SIZE: To 15 cm; usually much smaller in captivity.
FOOD REQUIREMENTS: Any food with a high meat or fish content; very fond of smaller live fish, pieces of earthworm, etc. Frozen brine shrimp is excellent.

Ctenopoma ansorgei (Boulenger) • Ornate Ctenopoma

RANGE: Tropical West Africa.
HABITS: Peaceful when given plenty of space and kept with fishes of the same size or larger.
WATER CONDITIONS: Not critical, but the water must be kept warm, 25 to 29°C.
SIZE: To 7 cm.
FOOD REQUIREMENTS: Large live foods, preferably small living fish. Cut-up earthworms or pieces of beef heart are also taken greedily.
COLOR VARIATIONS: Body brownish, with 6 or 7 bluish to greenish bars on the sides, extending into the dorsal and anal fins.

Ctenopoma congicum (Boulenger) • Congo Ctenopoma

RANGE: Lower Congo River.
HABITS: Fairly peaceful with larger fishes. Likes a large, well-planted tank.
WATER CONDITIONS: Not critical, but temperature should be kept high, about 25°C.
SIZE: To 8 cm.
FOOD REQUIREMENTS: Large live foods, small living fishes preferred. They can be trained to accept pieces of fish, shrimp, etc.

Ctenopoma multispinis Peters • Many-spined Ctenopoma

RANGE: Upper and Lower Zambezi River system; apparently absent from the Middle Zambezi. Prefers swamps and backwaters.
HABITS: A predatory species that should not be kept with smaller species. This species has been reported to bury itself in the sand of an aquarium as it was being emptied and to later come out and move around the tank bottom in the damp sand. In nature it crosses "dry" land to better conditions.
WATER CONDITIONS: Not critical. Temperatures should be in the upper end of the normal range for tropical fishes.
SIZE: Reaches a length of about 16 cm.
FOOD REQUIREMENTS: Accepts many aquarium foods. Should be given regular feedings of live foods such as small guppies.

Ctenopoma kingsleyi (Guenther) • Kingsley's Ctenopoma

RANGE: Widely scattered from Senegal to the Congo region.
HABITS: Very predatory and nasty; should not be kept with other fishes.
WATER CONDITIONS: Not critical, but temperature should be high, about 25°C.
SIZE: To 20 cm.
FOOD REQUIREMENTS: Will eat just about everything, but prefers living fish.

Ctenopoma maculata Thominot • Single-spot Ctenopoma

RANGE: Southern Cameroons to the Congo.
HABITS: A predatory species that should only be kept with fishes that can take care of themselves. Floats like a dead leaf when frightened. Spawns in typical anabantoid fashion, the eggs floating to the surface. The eggs hatch after about a day and the fry become free-swimming after three more days.
WATER CONDITIONS: Seem to prefer slightly acid water (but this is not critical) at a temperature of 23-28°C.
SIZE: 20 cm according to Boulenger, but usually no more than half that in captivity.
FOOD REQUIREMENTS: Will take a variety of aquarium foods, especially small guppies.

Ctenopoma nanum Guenther • Dwarf Ctenopoma

RANGE: Cameroons to Congo.
HABITS: Males are generally larger and have more pointed dorsal and anal fins than females. Assumes a dark blue to almost black spawning livery. A predatory species, so tankmates must be carefully chosen.
WATER CONDITIONS: Not critical, but slightly acid water at a temperature of 23-25°C seems to suit them fine.
SIZE: Males reach a size of about 7.5 cm; females are some 10 mm smaller.
FOOD REQUIREMENTS: Accepts both living and prepared foods readily.

Ctenopoma muriei (Boulenger) • Nile Ctenopoma

RANGE: Extends from the White Nile south to the Rift Lake area and west to the Chad basin.
HABITS: Found in low oxygen content pools with the main vegetation grasses. May produce as many as 2,000 eggs per spawning. Not to be trusted with smaller fishes.
WATER CONDITIONS: Not critical. Slightly acid water at a temperature between 23 and 25°C is recommended.
SIZE: Males reach a length of about 8.5-9.0 cm, females about 10 mm larger.
FOOD REQUIREMENTS: Accepts a variety of aquarium foods. Live foods should be offered on a regular basis for best results.

Ctenopoma nigropannosum Reichenow • Two-spotted Ctenopoma

RANGE: Gabon and the Congo.
HABITS: Its rather large size and unspectacular colors make it generally unwelcome in home aquaria. It is also quite aggressive and not sociable.
WATER CONDITIONS: Slightly acid water with a temperature range of 22-28°C is recommended.
SIZE: Attains a length of about 17 cm.
FOOD REQUIREMENTS: Not a fussy eater. In fact, it will feed on small fishes placed in the aquarium as well as on frozen food and chopped fish and shrimp.

Ctenopoma oxyrhynchus (Boulenger) • Mottled Ctenopoma

RANGE: Tributaries of the lower Congo River.
HABITS: Peaceful with fishes of the same size or larger.
WATER CONDITIONS: Not critical, but temperatures should be kept high, 26 to 29°C.
SIZE: To 10 cm.
FOOD REQUIREMENTS: Larger live foods preferred, especially living fishes.

Ctenopoma ocellatum Pellegrin • Bullseye Ctenopoma

RANGE: Congo region.
HABITS: A fast-water species that can also be found in the immediate vicinity of waterfalls.
WATER CONDITIONS: Slightly acid water with temperatures of 20-24°C is sufficient. A higher than normal aeration is recommended.
SIZE: Attains a length of about 14 cm.
FOOD REQUIREMENTS: Live foods are preferred, but it will accept a variety of aquarium foods.

Ctenopoma maculata (juv.)

Ctenopoma maculata

Ctenopoma nanum

Ctenopoma nanum

Ctenopoma muriei

Ctenopoma nigropannosum

Ctenopoma oxyrhynchus

Ctenopoma ocellatum

Plate #371

544

Channa obscurus

Glossogobius giuris

Periophthalmus papilio

Periophthalmus barbarus

Periophthalmus barbarus

Periophthalmus barbarus

Lates niloticus

Lates microlepis

Plate #372

Channa obscurus (Guenther) • Square-spotted African Snakehead

RANGE: Most major drainages of northern and central tropical Africa.
HABITS: Like Asian snakeheads, this is a species of rivers and ponds as well as lakes that can survive droughts through breathing atmospheric air.
WATER CONDITIONS: Totally amenable to any warm-water conditions.
SIZE: To at least 35 cm in length, probably larger.
FOOD REQUIREMENTS: Like the other snakeheads, this is a vicious predator that will take any type of live food of large size. Will also scavenge and thus will adapt to almost any type of food.

Periophthalmus papilio Bloch & Schneider • Butterfly Mudskipper

RANGE: Western Africa from Senegal to the Congo.
HABITS: Cannot be maintained with any other class of fishes; they soon overcome their initial shyness.
WATER CONDITIONS: Water must have a salt content, about a ½ teaspoon to the liter; areas must be provided for the fish to climb out onto a dry perch.
SIZE: Attains a size of 16 cm.
FOOD REQUIREMENTS: Living insects or small earthworms; tubifex worms are also welcome; can be trained to take other foods.

Periophthalmus barbarus (Linnaeus) • Mudskipper

RANGE: East Africa to Australia.
HABITS: Cannot be combined with any other group of fishes; shy at first, but later can be tamed effectively.
WATER CONDITIONS: Water must have salt, ½ teaspoon to the liter, added; there should be an area where the fish can climb out. Temperature 24 to 27°C.
SIZE: To 15 cm.
FOOD REQUIREMENTS: Worms and living insects.

Lates niloticus (Linnaeus) • Nile Perch

RANGE: Widely distributed in rivers and lakes of tropical Africa, including the Nile, Niger, Senegal, Volta, and Congo Rivers and Lakes Chad, Albert, and Rudolf.
HABITS: Grows too large for home aquaria, so only young specimens are kept. Not a good community tank fish. Very aggressive and predatory.
WATER CONDITIONS: Not critical. Accepts a wide variety of aquarium conditions.
SIZE: Attains a length of at least 180 cm and a record weight of close to 200 kilos.
FOOD REQUIREMENTS: Meaty foods are necessary and the addition of live fishes to the diet is recommended.

Glossogobius giuris (Hamilton-Buchanan) • Flathead Goby

RANGE: Coastal and estuarine areas from eastern Africa through southern Asia to Australia and the Pacific Islands. Often enters fresh water by ascending rivers.
HABITS: Like many other large gobies, it lurks in debris and roots waiting for passing prey. Utilized as a foodfish in some areas.
WATER CONDITIONS: Warm, hard water is best, preferably with some salt added.
SIZE: Very large for a goby, to at least 35 cm.
FOOD REQUIREMENTS: Can be a vicious predator of smaller fishes, but also scavenges and might even accept some vegetable matter in the diet.

Lates microlepis Boulenger • Small-scaled Nile Perch

RANGE: Endemic to Lake Tanganyika.
HABITS: Lives in schools and preys on clupeids roaming the lake. Apparently breeds close to the shores. Not a good community tank fish.
WATER CONDITIONS: Hard, alkaline water is necessary. Temperatures between 23 and 28°C are best.
SIZE: Reaches a length of about 85 cm.
FOOD REQUIREMENTS: Young individuals feed on crustaceans and small fishes. Similar aquarium foods are suitable.

MASTACEMBELIDAE (SPINY EELS)

The spiny eels are not true eels. Anyone that looks closely at one will quickly see that. The body is long and eel-like, but that is where the resemblance ends. The anterior part of the dorsal fin consists of up to 40 or more separate, movable spines. The second (soft) portion of the dorsal is joined to the caudal fin, as is the anal fin (these are generally separate in Asiatic species). There are about 50 species in the family, most contained in the genus *Mastacembelus*. However, work currently in progress is sure to change things around a bit.

Several African species are quite colorful and are somewhat readily available in the aquarium trade. Unfortunately for aquarists, these are light-shy species, and during the day they are usually buried in the sand or hiding under some part of the aquarium decor. Mostly just the head is visible sticking out of the sand. At night they become more active and go about searching for food. The water conditions do not seem to be critical, but the addition of a little bit of salt is sometimes recommended. Periodic partial water changes are useful. Temperatures between 23 and 28°C are adequate. Feeding may be a problem with certain species or even individuals. Live food, especially worms and insects (chironomid larvae), are your best bet. Although a few species have been spawned, it is a rare event in aquaria and aquarists usually do not attempt to spawn their charges.

Enneacampus ansorgii Boulenger • African Freshwater Pipefish

RANGE: Congo region in Africa.
HABITS: Peaceful.
WATER CONDITIONS: Should be maintained in slightly salty to brackish water. Temperature about 25°C.
SIZE: 10 cm.
FOOD REQUIREMENTS: Usually refuses to eat anything but small living foods, although floating frozen foods may be picked at; aquatic crustaceans and baby livebearers are preferred.

Mastacembelus frenatus

Mastacembelus moorii

Mastacembelus reticulatus

Mastacembelus ophidium

Mastacembelus ellipsifer

Mastacembelus tanganicae

Enneacampus ansorgii

Enneacampus ansorgii

Plate #373

548

Chonerhinus naritus (juv.)

Chonerhinus naritus

Tetraodon mbu

Tetraodon miurus

Tetraodon schoutedeni

Tetraodon schoutedeni

Tetraodon duboisi

Bedotia geayi

Plate #374

Chonerhinus naritus (Richardson) • Bronze Puffer

RANGE: Southeast Asia, primarily Burma, the Malay Peninsula and Thailand. Also occurs in the Congo drainage, Africa, based on a single specimen collected in the last century.

HABITS: A fin-nipper and not to be trusted, even with fishes much larger than itself.

WATER CONDITIONS: Softness and acidity factors not critical as long as extremes are avoided, but the addition of non-iodized salt at the rate of about one teaspoonful for every 8 liters of tank capacity will help the fish. This is a warmth-loving species.

SIZE: Up to 30 cm in nature.

FOOD REQUIREMENTS: Live foods, especially tubificid worms are best, but meaty prepared foods are accepted.

Tetraodon mbu Boulenger • Giant Puffer

RANGE: Congo basin to the Malagarazi near Lake Tanganyika.

HABITS: Sluggish swimmers but quite nippy. Able to crush shellfish with their powerful teeth shaped like parrot beaks.

WATER CONDITIONS: Not critical. Temperatures from 23-28°C are recommended.

SIZE: Probably the largest African freshwater puffer, reaching a length of at least 67 cm.

FOOD REQUIREMENTS: Will eat a variety of meaty foods, but clams and other shellfish are closer to their natural diet.

Tetraodon schoutedeni Pellegrin • Schouteden's Puffer;
Leopard Puffer

RANGE: Lower Congo.

HABITS: Generally less nippy than the other puffers and does well in a community aquarium with fishes lacking tempting flowing fins. It is an open-water spawner where one or more males bite into the female's ventral side during mating.

WATER CONDITIONS: Not critical. Normal aquarium temperature of 23-28°C should prevail.

SIZE: Attains a length of about 10 cm, with the male slightly smaller.

FOOD REQUIREMENTS: Meaty foods are acceptable, and snails are also eaten.

Tetraodon duboisi Poll • Stanley Pool Puffer

RANGE: Known only from Stanley Pool, Zaire, and its vicinity.

HABITS: A bottom-dwelling puffer that buries itself in the sand. Prefers well-oxygenated water. Described only in 1959, it is similar to *T. schoutedeni* but has an obviously different pattern that fits it for disappearing into the sand.

WATER CONDITIONS: Not critical.

SIZE: About 60-70 mm long.

FOOD REQUIREMENTS: Like most puffers, it will eat almost anything, especially living crustaceans and snails. It will also attack smaller fishes.

Tetraodon miurus Boulenger • Congo Puffer

RANGE: Middle and lower Congo River; found in fresh water only.

HABITS: A dangerous fish in the community aquarium; should be given a tank by itself or with others of its own kind.

WATER CONDITIONS: Soft, slightly acid water. Temperature 24 to 27°C.

SIZE: To 10 cm.

FOOD REQUIREMENTS: Living small fishes, fully grown brine shrimp or pieces of earthworms; they enjoy snails.

Bedotia geayi Pellegrin • Madagascar Rainbow

RANGE: Madagascar.

HABITS: Peaceful and active; never molest their tankmates.

WATER CONDITIONS: Somewhat alkaline water required, about pH 7.3 or 7.4. Temperature 24 to 26°C.

SIZE: 6 to 7 cm.

FOOD REQUIREMENTS: Not a fussy eater; will eat dried foods readily, but should get live food occasionally.

Southeast Asian Region

Scleropages formosus (silver form)

Scleropages formosus (gold form)

Scleropages formosus

Dermogenys pusillus?

Nomorhamphus liemi (female)

Nomorhamphus liemi (male)

Nomorhamphus liemi

Xenentodon cancila

Plate #375

553

Scleropages formosus (Mueller & Schlegel) •
Barramundi; Asiatic Arowana

RANGE: Southeastern Thailand, Sumatra, Borneo and
  Bangka.
HABITS: Will eat small fishes; excellent jumper.
WATER CONDITIONS: Not critical. A temperature between
  22 and 28°C should suffice.
SIZE: To 90 cm and a weight of over 7 kilograms.
FOOD REQUIREMENTS: Surface feeder in nature on insects
  but will also take small fishes and crustaceans (shrimp,
  etc.); smaller individuals will take daphnia, brine
  shrimp, etc.

Dermogenys pusillus van Hasselt • Malayan Halfbeak

RANGE: Malaysia, Sumatra, Borneo and Thailand.
HABITS: Should be kept by themselves; if more than one
  male is put into a tank, they will fight continually.
WATER CONDITIONS: Water should have an addition of one
  quarter teaspoon of salt to every liter of water.
  Temperature 23 to 26°C.
SIZE: Males to 5 cm; females to 6.5 cm.
FOOD REQUIREMENTS: Living foods like daphnia or mosquito
  larvae.

Nomorhamphus liemi Voget • Black-finned
Celebes Halfbeak

RANGE: Celebes.
HABITS: Generally peaceful but will eat fishes small enough
  to swallow; should probably be kept by themselves.
WATER CONDITIONS: On the hard side with a pH of 7.0 or
  higher; regular water changes are recommended.
  Temperature should be around 23 to 28°C.
SIZE: May reach 10 cm.
FOOD REQUIREMENTS: Must have live foods such as Guppies
  or brine shrimp.

Xenentodon cancila (Hamilton-Buchanan) • Silver
Needlefish

RANGE: Southeastern Asia.
HABITS: Surface-swimmer and will jump out of tank if it is
  not covered; at times it appears to be motionless, as if
  hanging in air.
WATER CONDITIONS: An addition of some sea-salt would be
  beneficial. Temperature range from 22 to 26°C.
SIZE: Up to 30 cm.
FOOD REQUIREMENTS: Prefers live foods including all kinds
  of smaller fishes.

Acanthophthalmus javanicus Bleeker • Javanese Loach

RANGE: Java and Sumatra.

HABITS: Peaceful and able to slither into almost inaccessible places and pick up food other fishes cannot reach.

WATER CONDITIONS: Clean water. Temperature about 24 to 28°C.

SIZE: About 8 cm.

FOOD REQUIREMENTS: They pick up most uneaten foods but are very fond of tubifex and white worms.

Acanthophthalmus kuhli • (Cuvier & Valenciennes) Coolie Loach, Leopard Eel

RANGE: Northeastern Bengal, Assam, Malaysia, Burma, Java, Sumatra, Borneo, Singapore and Malacca.

HABITS: A peaceful little fish found on muddy bottoms in its native water. Hides from bright light and becomes active at night.

WATER CONDITIONS: They prefer clean, clear water with a temperature of 24 to 28°C. The use of coarse gravel should be avoided.

SIZE: 8 cm; matures at 7 cm.

FOOD REQUIREMENTS: A good scavenger which can be counted on to pick up much of the food other fishes leave uneaten.

Acanthophthalmus semicinctus Fraser-Brunner • Half-banded Loach

RANGE: Sunda Islands.

HABITS: Peaceful; often remains hidden when the light is bright and comes out at night.

WATER CONDITIONS: Clean, clear water with a temperature of 24 to 27°C. Do not give them a bottom with coarse gravel.

SIZE: A little over 7.5 cm.

FOOD REQUIREMENTS: An excellent scavenger which will pick up uneaten food, but should get its share of live food, too.

Acanthophthalmus shelfordi Popta • Shelford's Loach

RANGE: Borneo.

HABITS: Peaceful. Usually remains hidden during the day and comes out at night. When feeding time arrives it may come out even though it is light.

WATER CONDITIONS: Although quite tolerant of varied conditions, optimum would be medium soft (about 5 DH) and slightly acid to neutral pH. Temperature should be 21 to 24°C.

SIZE: To about 8 cm.

FOOD REQUIREMENTS: Not critical. Foods that sink to the bottom, like worms, can be used.

Acanthophthalmus anguillaris Vaillant • Worm Kuhli Loach

RANGE: Borneo to Thailand.

HABITS: A peaceful fish that usually remains hidden during the day, coming out at night to feed. Very hardy and will breed in captivity without the aquarist's help (and most times without his knowledge.)

WATER CONDITIONS: Able to withstand a variety of aquarium conditions and even survives through many adverse conditions. Slightly acid water at 23-28°C suits them very well.

SIZE: Attains a length of about 9 cm or more.

FOOD REQUIREMENTS: Will eat a variety of materials that are added to the tank in the evenings and that fall to the bottom. Seems to be able to find little things to eat even without formal feedings, though like all scavengers it must be fed regularly.

Acanthophthalmus myersi Harry • Slimy Myersi

RANGE: Southeastern Thailand.

HABITS: A nocturnal swimmer; prefers hiding during the day, so wholesalers use inverted, split coconut shells in their aquaria.

WATER CONDITIONS: Prefers soft, acid water with a pH of 6.2. Temperature 26 to 28°C.

SIZE: Less than 7.5 cm.

FOOD REQUIREMENTS: Worms, frozen brine shrimp and anything that will fall to the bottom and not require teeth to chew.

Acanthophthalmus javanicus

Acanthophthalmus anguillaris

Acanthophthalmus kuhlii

Acanthophthalmus myersi

Acanthophthalmus semicinctus

Acanthophthalmus shelfordi

Acanthophthalmus shelfordi

Acanthophthalmus myersi var.

Plate #376

Botia beauforti

Botia berdmorei

Botia dario

Botia dario

Botia lohachata

Botia hymenophysa

Botia macracantha

Botia macracantha

Plate #377

Botia beauforti Smith • Beaufort's Loach

RANGE: Thailand.
HABITS: Generally peaceful toward other fishes; mostly nocturnal. Will remain mostly in the darker portions of the aquarium.
WATER CONDITIONS: Soft, slightly acid water, well-aerated. Tank should have a number of hiding places and be dimly lighted. Temperature 23 to 26°C.
SIZE: 20 cm.
FOOD REQUIREMENTS: Live foods, especially tubifex or white worms preferred; frozen and prepared foods also eaten, and food left by other fishes.

Botia berdmorei Blyth • Berdmore's Loach

RANGE: Burma.
HABITS: Peaceful toward other fishes if kept in a group; mostly nocturnal.
WATER CONDITIONS: Soft, slightly acid water, well-aerated. Tank should have a number of hiding places and be dimly lighted. Temperature 23 to 25°C.
SIZE: To 8 cm.
FOOD REQUIREMENTS: Live foods, especially tubifex and white worms, preferred; frozen and prepared foods also eaten, and food left by other fishes.

Botia dario (Hamilton-Buchanan) • Bengal Loach

RANGE: Bengal and Assam, India.
HABITS: A typical loach inhabiting the bottom layers of the tank. Peaceful enough for a community tank.
WATER CONDITIONS: Seems to prefer soft, slightly acid water with temperatures between 23 and 28°C.
SIZE: A small loach of about 8-10 cm in length.
FOOD REQUIREMENTS: Usually feeds off the bottom. Tubifex worms are preferred, but it will scavenge around for any leftovers from the other fishes in the tank.

Botia lohachata Chaudhuri • Pakistani Loach

RANGE: India and Pakistan.
HABITS: A typical loach with bottom-dwelling habits.
WATER CONDITIONS: Prefers very soft, slightly acid water with high temperatures in the high 20's (°C).
SIZE: Seldom larger than 10 cm in length.
FOOD REQUIREMENTS: This species often starves in an aquarium, for they must have worms in their diet, preferably tubifex.

Botia hymenophysa (Bleeker) • Banded Loach

RANGE: Malaysia, Thailand, Singapore, Java, Sumatra and Borneo.
HABITS: Occurs in flowing streams of fresh water. Mostly nocturnal; shuns light and stays in the darker portions of the aquarium.
WATER CONDITIONS: Should be given clean, well-oxygenated water. Temperature 24 to 27°C.
SIZE: In captivity about 15 cm; wild specimens are said to attain 30 cm.
FOOD REQUIREMENTS: Will take any living foods, including small fishes. Will also rummage around the bottom for uneaten leftovers.

Botia macracantha (Bleeker) • Clown Loach

RANGE: Sumatra, Borneo and the Sunda Islands.
HABITS: Peaceful, not quite as nocturnal as some of the other species.
WATER CONDITIONS: Clean, well-aerated water. Temperature should not exceed 24°C.
SIZE: 30 cm maximum, but most specimens do not exceed 10 cm.
FOOD REQUIREMENTS: They like to grub for leftover morsels at the bottom, but should also get some living foods.

Botia lecontei Fowler • Leconte's Loach

RANGE: Thailand.
HABITS: A peaceful species that will fit fairly well into a community tank. Possibly nocturnal. Similar to *B. modesta* but easily distinguishable by fin color.
WATER CONDITIONS: Soft, slightly acid water is preferred. Temperatures between 23 and 28°C are sufficient.
SIZE: Attains a length of about 10 cm.
FOOD REQUIREMENTS: A variety of food is accepted as they scour the bottom for tidbits, but tubifex worms are preferred.

Botia modesta Bleeker • Orange-finned Loach

RANGE: Thailand, Vietnam, Malaysia.
HABITS: Peaceful; a community aquarium fish. Nocturnal.
WATER CONDITIONS: Does best in water at a pH of 6.6 in very soft water. Prefers high temperatures of about 28°C.
SIZE: To 10 cm.
FOOD REQUIREMENTS: Prefers tubifex worms, but as a scavenger it probes the bottom for almost any kind of food.
COLOR VARIATIONS: The orange fins may become yellow if they do not have insects or shrimp in their diet.

Botia morleti Smith • Hora's Loach

RANGE: Thailand.
HABITS: Peaceful, mostly nocturnal. Will remain mostly in the darker portions of the aquarium.
WATER CONDITIONS: Soft, slightly acid water, well-aerated. Tank should have a number of hiding places and not be brightly lighted. Temperature 23 to 25°C.
SIZE: To 10 cm; usually smaller.
FOOD REQUIREMENTS: Live foods, especially tubifex or white worms, preferred; frozen and prepared foods also eaten, and food left by other fishes.

Botia sidthimunki Klausewitz • Dwarf Loach

RANGE: Thailand.
HABITS: Peaceful, playful, seem to be less nocturnal than the other species.
WATER CONDITIONS: Soft, alkaline water, well-aerated. Temperature 23 to 25°C.
SIZE: 4 cm.
FOOD REQUIREMENTS: Small live foods preferred; other foods accepted.

Botia lecontei

Botia modesta

Botia morleti (juvenile)

Botia morleti

Botia sidthimunki

Botia sidthimunki

Botia sidthimunki (var.)

Botia sidthimunki (var.)

Plate #378

Botia hymenophysa juv.

Botia morleti juv.

Botia hymenophysa? (var.)

Botia striata

Lepidocephalus thermalis

Lepidocephalus berdmorei

Lepidocephalus guntea

Lepidocephalus jonklaasi

Plate #379

561

See plate #377

See plate #378

Botia striata Rao • Zebra Loach

RANGE: Southern India.
HABITS: Peaceful and lively; likes to be in a group of its own
species.
WATER CONDITIONS: Soft, slightly acid water best, but does
well in a variety of conditions. Temperature 20 to 25°C.
SIZE: Attains a length of about 6 cm in the aquarium; grows
larger (10 cm) in nature.
FOOD REQUIREMENTS: Live foods, especially tubificid
worms, are preferred, but it will accept normal
aquarium substitutes.

See plate #377

Lepidocephalus thermalis (Valenciennes) • Lesser Loach

RANGE: Over all of Sri Lanka below 1,600 feet and also southern India.
HABITS: Fond of still pools with an abundance of leaf debris
in which it can burrow. Also found (? accidentally) in hot
springs. One of the last fishes to die when a pool dries up.
WATER CONDITIONS: Not choosy. Should have clean, warm
water but otherwise will tolerate most aquarium conditions.
SIZE: 40-50 mm.
FOOD REQUIREMENTS: Eats mostly small vegetable matter
and debris, but will adjust to small insects and worms in
the aquarium.

Lepidocephalus berdmorei (Blyth) • Berdmore's Loach

RANGE: Apparently known only from Thailand and Burma.
HABITS: Likes to burrow into the bottom material and is not
seen very often. A peaceful fish for a community
aquarium.
WATER CONDITIONS: Slightly acid water of average hardness is acceptable. Water temperatures should be between 23 and 28°C. Water changes are recommended.
SIZE: Attains a length of at least 8 cm.
FOOD REQUIREMENTS: Mostly insect larvae (chironomids
and mosquito larvae in aquaria) and worms are preferred.

Lepidocephalus guntea (Hamilton-Buchanan) • Gunte

RANGE: India to the Near East.
HABITS: A shy fish that likes to burrow in the substrate.
Peaceful and can be added to a community tank.
WATER CONDITIONS: Clean water that is slightly acid and
medium hard is sufficient. Temperatures of 23-28°C are
best. Water changes on a regular basis are beneficial.
SIZE: Attains a length of about 8-10 cm.
FOOD REQUIREMENTS: Feeds from the bottom, mainly on
insects and their larvae (chironomids) and worms
(tubificid worms).

Lepidocephalus jonklaasi Deraniyagala • Jonklaas's Loach

RANGE: Endemic to Sri Lanka, where it is found in the
Akuressa forest.
HABITS: Peaceful and suitable for a community tank. Likes
to burrow and should have a suitable substrate. In nature
it is found in shaded pools in hill streams where the bottoms have much leaf debris.
WATER CONDITIONS: Not critical. Slightly acid water at
normal aquarium temperatures are sufficient. Regular
water changes are recommended.
SIZE: Attains a length of about 7-9 cm.
FOOD REQUIREMENTS: A variety of foods that fall to the
bottom are acceptable. Tubifex worms and chironomid
larvae are preferred, and it should also have vegetable
matter.

Noemacheilus notostigma Bleeker • Fighting Loach

RANGE: Sri Lanka.
HABITS: Best kept by themselves in pairs or several pairs in a large tank with a number of hiding places.
WATER CONDITIONS: Not critical, but the water should be clean. Temperature 24 to 27°C.
SIZE: To 8 cm.
FOOD REQUIREMENTS: Any kind of food accepted, but there should be live foods given at times.

Nemacheilus botia (Hamilton-Buchanan) • Mottled Loach

RANGE: Upper India.
HABITS: Peaceful toward other fishes and will not harm plants. Are useful in cleaning up unwanted algae and food left by other fishes.
WATER CONDITIONS: Water should be slightly alkaline but not very hard. Temperature 75 to 80°.
SIZE: To 4½ inches.
FOOD REQUIREMENTS: Not at all fussy about foods. Should have some soft algae to pick at in addition to their regular diet.

See Plate #379

Misgurnus mizolepis Guenther • Chinese Fine-scaled Loach

RANGE: Occurs over much of southern China south into northern Southeast Asia.
HABITS: A typical weatherfish, occurring in every type of waterbody from rivers to ditches. Survives drying well, as it can burrow into the bottom and also breathe atmospheric air.
WATER CONDITIONS: Although this species ranges south into tropical Asia, it is basically a cooler water fish and will survive well at 18°C and higher. Water conditions unimportant, but best kept clean.
SIZE: 10 to 21 cm. There are many described subspecies and varieties that differ greatly in adult size and color pattern.
FOOD REQUIREMENTS: Prefers small crustaceans, insect larvae, and worms, but will adjust to almost any type of diet. Some vegetable matter should be tried as well.

Noemacheilus fasciatus (Cuvier & Valenciennes) • Barred Loach

RANGE: Sumatra, Java, Borneo.
HABITS: Best given a tank of their own; chooses and defends its own territories.
WATER CONDITIONS: Soft, slightly acid water. Temperature 24 to 26°C.
SIZE: To 9 cm.
FOOD REQUIREMENTS: Likes worms and other live foods, but not a fussy eater.

563

Noemacheilus notostigma (var.)

Noemacheilus notostigma

Noemacheilus cf. *notostigma*

Noemacheilus botia

Lepidocephalus thermalis

Lepidocephalus thermals (var.)

Noemacheilus fasciatus

Misgurnus mizolepis

Plate #380

Vaillantella euepipterus

Acanthopsis choirorhynchus

Acanthopsis choirorhynchus

Homaloptera cf. zollingeri

Pseudogastromyzon myersi

Pseudogastromyzon myersi

Pseudogastromyzon cf. myersi

Plate #381

565

Vaillantella euepipterus (Vaillant) • Chocolate
Long-finned Loach

RANGE: Rivers of Borneo. A secretive fish that is seldom
collected.
HABITS: In nature this odd species is a burrower in rapid
streams, so it is not too easy to keep in the aquarium. The
substrate must be of gravel smooth and soft enough to
allow burrowing, yet there must be a current to provide
heavily oxygenated water. Nocturnal, shy, and delicate;
imported only by accident.
WATER CONDITIONS: Not choosy as long as it is clean and
well-oxygenated. Can probably stand lower temperature
than most loaches because of its stream habitat.
SIZE: 60-80 mm.
FOOD REQUIREMENTS: Feeds well on live tubifex worms
and bloodworms of appropriate size.

Acanthopsis choirorhynchus (Bleeker) • Long-
nosed Loach

RANGE: Southeastern Asia, Sumatra, Borneo, Java; occurs
in fresh water only.
HABITS: Mostly nocturnal; in the daylight hours it usually
remains buried in the gravel with only its eyes showing.
WATER CONDITIONS: Neutral to slightly acid water. Temperature between 24 and 30°C.
SIZE: Wild specimens attain a length of 18 cm; in captivity
they remain smaller.
FOOD REQUIREMENTS: Living foods only: tubifex worms,
white worms, daphnia, etc.

Homaloptera cf. *Zollingeri* Bleeker • Zollinger's
Hillstream Loach

RANGE: Occurs at least in Java, Sumatra, and Thailand.
HABITS: Peaceful and suitable for a community tank of non-
aggressive fishes. Clings to hard surfaces where it
scraps algae from rocks in swift currents.
WATER CONDITIONS: Not critical, but there should be above-
average aeration and filtration for this current-loving
species. Normal aquarium temperatures are sufficient.
SIZE: Attains a length of about 10 cm.
FOOD REQUIREMENTS: An algae-eater that should be supplied with sufficient amounts of vegetable matter. The
diet can be supplemented with various other aquarium
foods.

Pseudogastromyzon myersi Herre • Myers' Hillstream
Loach; Hong Kong Plecostomus

RANGE: Hong Kong Island.
HABITS: Peaceful and suitable for a community tank. Generally useful as an algae-eater.
WATER CONDITIONS: Not critical, but sufficient aeration
and regular water changes are recommended.
SIZE: A rather small species attaining a length of only about
5 cm.
FOOD REQUIREMENTS: This is an algae-eater and should
have sufficient quantities of vegetable matter.

SOUTHEAST ASIAN CYPRINIDS

To the aquarist the countries of Southeast Asia are the true home of the cyprinids (family Cyprinidae), with hundreds of species of barbs, rasboras, sharks, and related fishes that are suitable for the home aquarium. In fact, the great majority of aquarium cyprinids come from Southeast Asia, as the African species are only sporadically imported and seldom bred, while the American and European species cannot take warm water temperatures. Many Southeast Asian barbs and danios are common bread-and-butter fishes of the hobby and can be found in every petshop regardless of its size.

The danios *(Danio* and *Brachydanio)* are perennial beginner's fishes because they spawn so easily under the most spartan aquarium conditions, are bred in huge numbers on fish farms, and are cheap. Additionally, their spotted and striped patterns and constant activity make them a center of attention in a small aquarium. Like virtually all the Asian cyprinids, the danios have an active chasing spawning ritual that results in hundreds or thousands of eggs flying around the tank to end up in the substrate or the plants. Also like most other cyprinids, danios have a reputation as egg-eaters, and often elaborate measures—such as special grills or layers of glass beads—must be taken to prevent the parents from eating their own eggs. The eggs develop in a day or two into small fry that are hardy and will feed on fine live or prepared foods. Strained egg yolk and sifted crushed flake foods are often successfully used to raise danio and other cyprinid fry, making these fishes especially satisfying when the aquarist has neither the experience nor the time to raise live foods.

The literally dozens of Southeast Asian barbs fall into the same three major genera as the African barbs—*Barbodes, Capoeta,* and *Puntius*—and are just as impossible to separate on the barbel characters. Additionally, there are numerous other genera that are barb-like in at least some ways and are occasionally imported, though these oddballs are seldom bred and usually disappear soon after each importation. Many species of barbs that have never become well-established in the hobby even though they seem suitable prove to be the young of larger species. Several Indian and tropical Asian barbs grow to over a meter in length and are important food fishes and may even be popular game species.

Also often reaching large sizes are the various species of sharks, *Labeo* and *Morulius* and a few other genera, which often are more common in village fish markets than aquaria. Fortunately, some of the most colorful species of Asian sharks are also relatively small, even the adults not reaching 25 cm, and these are among the most popular aquarium species. The name "shark" as applied to the cyprinids is of course misleading and probably never should have been used to begin with, but after 50 years it is hard to break an old habit. In aquarium jargon, "shark" applies to any cyprinids with streamlined bodies, long heads, and high, erect dorsal fins. This would include not only such things as the red-tailed black shark and the black shark, but also the Apollo sharks (*Luciosoma*), which admittedly don't look much like a *Labeo* species. Although until recently it has proved almost impossible to spawn sharks in the aquarium (or even in ponds), the technique of induced spawning after injection of pituitary hormones may eventually change this and allow anyone willing to do the work to spawn the common sharks.

The rasboras are a complicated and large group that is poorly understood both scientifically and aquaristically. Only the harlequin rasbora (*Rasbora heteromorpha*) and its close relatives are truly common in the aquarium, and they are also the most distinctively shaped and patterned of the familiar species, with the deep body and black "pork chop" pattern setting them off from the other common species. Although about a dozen species of rasboras are imported on a sporadic basis, some of them attractive and simple to breed, only the harlequins persist in the hobby. Many rasboras are silvery fishes that lack any type of personality, which certainly accounts for their absence from the hobby. By the way, the genus *Rasbora* is now being split. The group of large silvery species related to *Rasbora daniconius* and *R. cephalotaenia* is now placed in the genus *Parluciosoma,* for instance.

Certainly one of the most neglected of the Southeast Asian cyprinids must be the White Cloud Mountain minnow, *Tanichthys albonubes.* One of the smallest yet most colorful of common aquarium fishes, many people consider it to be *the* beginner's fish. Sometimes it seems that the fish is almost impossible to kill unless you let the tank dry up or boil over. Actually, this little stream fish prefers water at lower temperatures than usually maintained in the aquarium.

A word about the Siamese algae-eater is necessary in any discussion of Southeast Asian cyprinids, although technically it belongs to a different family than the other fishes we've talked about. The genus *Gyrinocheilus* (there are several described species but they are all very much alike and probably impossible to distinguish in life) belongs to its own family, Gyrinocheilidae, because of modifications of the gills and operculum. While adhering to stones and wood at the bottom of rivers and streams in order to rasp algae, it takes water into its gills and then exhales it through special openings at the upper edge of the operculum where the gill covers connect to the side of the head. Although this may seem like a minor difference from the normal cyprinids, it is a drastic change in a very fundamental body process. Algae-eaters are of course staples of the aquarium trade, though they are usually seen only at small sizes (few get enough algae to reach maturity in the aquarium).

Chela dadiburjuri

Chela caeruleostigmata

Chela "Pseudobarilius"

Chela laubuca (Burma)

Chela laubuca

Chela sp.

Esomus metallicus

Esomus danricus

Plate #382

Rasbora vaterifloris

Rasbora pauciperforata

Rasbora borapetensis

Rasbora agilis

Rasbora urophthalma

Rasbora maculata

Rasbora brittani (male)

Rasbora brittani (female)

Plate #383

Rasbora heteromorpha espei

Rasbora heteromorpha espei

Rasbora heteromorpha

Rasbora heteromorpha

Rasbora meinkeni

Rasbora elegans

Rasbora sumatrana

Rasbora sumatrana var.

Plate #384

Rasbora trilineata

Rasbora trilineata

Rasbora caudimaculata

Rasbora dorsiocellata

Rasbora myersi

Rasbora somphongsi

? Rasbora

Rasbora einthoveni

Plate #385

Parluciosoma cephalotaenia

Rasbora "Pike Rasbora"

Parluciosoma daniconius

Rasbora sp.

Rasbora "Nondescript"

Rasbora sp.

Rasbora kalochroma

Rasborichthys altior

Plate #386

Danio aequipinnatus

Danio aequipinnatus (pair)

Danio malabaricus

Danio malabaricus (pair)

Brachydanio albolineatus

Brachydanio frankei

Brachydanio kerri

Brachydanio nigrofasciatus

Plate #387

Brachydanio rerio (var.)

Brachydanio rerio

Luciosoma bleekeri

Luciosoma setigerum

? Luciosoma

Leptobarbus melanopterus

Leptobarbus hoeveni (juv.)

Plate #388

Leptobarbus hoeveni

Zacco macrolepis

Zacco macrolepis

Zacco platypus (juv.)

Barilius nanensis

Zacco platypus (male)

Hemigrammocypris lini

Probarbus julienni

Leptobarbus hoeveni

Plate #389

Barbodes binotatus

Barbodes binotatus

Puntius sp. "Odessa Barb"

Puntius sp. "Odessa Barb"

Puntius filamentosus (juv.)

Puntius filamentosus

Puntius naryani

Puntius naryani

Plate #390

577

Puntius ticto

Puntius ticto

Puntius conchonius

Puntius conchonius

Puntius conchonius

Puntius conchonius

Puntius conchonius (longfin)

Puntius conchonius (veilfin)

Plate #391

Puntius nigrofasciatus

Puntius nigrofasciatus (male)

Puntius nigrofasciatus

Puntius nigrofasciatus (var.)

Capoeta semifasciolatus

Capoeta semifasciolatus

Puntius sachsi (albino)

Puntius sachsi

Plate #392

579

Capoeta

Capoeta

Capoeta chola

Puntius amphibius

Puntius pleurotaenia

Capoeta chola

Puntius dorsalis (bronze var.)

Puntius dorsalis (red var.)

Plate #393

580

Puntius somphongsi

Capoeta cf *binotatus*

Capoeta cf *binotatus*

Capoeta "Bigscale"

Capoeta sp.

Capoeta oligolepis

Capoeta oligolepis (male)

Capoeta oligolepis (albino)

Plate #394

581

Barbodes pinnauratus

Barbodes pinnauratus

Barbodes schwanenfeldii

Barbodes schwanenfeldii

Barbodes daruphani

Barbodes fasciatus

Barbodes everetti

Barbodes everetti

Plate #395

Capoeta tetrazona varieties

Plate #396

583

Capoeta arulius (juv.)

Capoeta arulius

Capoeta titteya (female)

Capoeta titteya (male)

Barbodes lateristriga

Puntius lineatus

Barbodes binotatus

Barbodes binotatus

Plate #397

584

Barbodes pentazona?

Barbodes pentazona hexazona

Barbodes pentazona rhomboocellatus

Barbodes pentazona pentazona

Tanichthys albonubes (Brown form)

Tanichthys albonubes

Tanichthys albonubes (longfin var.)

Plate #398

Tanichthys albonubes (Blue form)

585

Cyclocheilichthys apogon (juv.?)

Cyclocheilichthys apogon

Cyclocheilichthys apogon

Osteocheilus sp.

Hampala macrolepidota

Rohtee alfrediana

Osteochilus hasseltii

Osteochilus vittatus

Plate #399

586

Balantiocheilos melanopterus (var.)

Balantiocheilos melanopterus

Barbichthys laevis

Barbichthys laevis

Labeo bicolor

Labeo bicolor

Labeo erythrurus

Labeo erythrurus

Plate #400

587

Labeo frenatus

Labeo frenatus

? Barbichthys laevis

? Labeo

Labeo forskali

Labeo frenatus ?

Morulius chrysophekadion

Morulius chrysophekadion

Plate #401

Epalzeorhynchus siamensis

Epalzeorhynchus kalopterus

Epalzeorhynchus siamensis?

Gyrinocheilos aymonieri

Gyrinocheilos aymonieri

Gyrinocheilos aymonieri

Paracrossocheilus vittatus

Crossocheilus oblongus

Plate #402

SPAWNING IN SOUTHEAST ASIAN
AQUARIUM CYPRINIDS

Most of the Southeast Asian cyprinids that have come onto the aquarium scene fall into the category of "egg-scatterers" as far as their spawning habits are concerned. They vary from species to species in such particulars as the degree of adhesiveness of the eggs (the eggs range from not sticky at all to very sticky), the degree to which the parent fish rely on the presence of plants to both set the spawning mood and to act as receivers of the eggs (some species will not normally spawn unless live plants or reasonable facsimiles of live plants are present in the tank, whereas others will spawn readily in completely bare tanks), the time of day at which spawning normally commences (some preferring the dawn and others the dusk) and other relatively small considerations. But in the main the term "egg-scatterer" is nicely apt: the main run of Southeast Asian aquarium cyprinid species scatter the eggs and let them lie where they fall, whether that means stuck in a clump of plants or strewn over the bottom stratum, and they give them no heed at all except perhaps to eat them.

A definite exception to the rule of who-cares-where-the-eggs-go is the popular *Rasbora heteromorpha* (and its closely allied species/races), a cyprinid that exhibits cichlid-like solicitude in the choosing of a spot upon which to deposit the eggs—even if, unlike the cichlids, it doesn't pay much attention to the eggs after they're laid. The spawning pattern of *Rasbora heteromorpha* is much less specialized than the spawning of cyprinids such as the bitterlings, but it is a departure from the norm nonetheless.

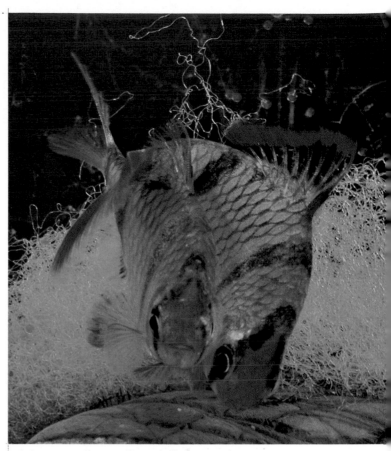

Above: views from the front and rear of a pair of *Capoeta tetrazona* as they go through their spawning gyrations prior to actual release of the eggs during this spawning, eggs, visible in the artificial spawning grass, have already been released during previous clinches.

Below: The male (in background in both photos) is more colorful than the female and has both a greater intensity of red in his fins and a greater area of red coloration during the spawning. The photos show the trembling of the fish and their side-to-side posture immediately before the eggs are expelled and fertilized.

Plate #403

591

The male in this pair of *Rasbora* of the *R. heteromorpha/espei/hengeli* complex is closely following the female, who has taken up her position near the leaf chosen as the site for the eggs.

The spawning partners have now slid under the leaf and positioned themselves upside down.

The male is now beginning to curve his body around the female, who keeps her belly glued to the leaf.

Fully in the embrace of the male, the female is attaching the eggs to the underside of the leaf.

Plate #404

Bagrichthys hypselopterus

Bagrichthys sp.

Leiocassis siamensis

Leiocassis siamensis

Mystus vittatus

Mystus vittatus

Mystus micracanthus

Glyptothorax callopterus

Plate #405

Bagrichthys hypselopterus (Bleeker) • Black Lancer

RANGE: Sumatra and Borneo; probably through much of the Indonesian area.

HABITS: This striking riverine catfish is highly prized by enthusiasts because of the odd pattern and the high dorsal fin. In large adults the length of the dorsal spine may be almost equal to the length of the body.

WATER CONDITIONS: Neutral, warm water is preferred, but this fish is not too choosy. It is, however, very subject to fungal infections from any cause—whether too acid water or scratches from rough substrates.

SIZE: Reaches at least 40 cm, though usually seen at only half or less that size. Seldom matures in the aquarium.

FOOD REQUIREMENTS: Eats almost any type of aquarium food that settles to the bottom. A nocturnal feeder as typical of most catfishes.

Leiocassis siamensis Regan • Barred Siamese Catfish

RANGE: Thailand.

HABITS: Peaceful toward fishes it cannot swallow; mostly nocturnal in its habits.

WATER CONDITIONS: Soft, slightly acid water which has been aged for at least a week. Temperature 22 to 25°C.

SIZE: To 16 cm.

FOOD REQUIREMENTS: All sorts of live or frozen foods.

Mystus vittatus (Bloch) • Striped Catfish

RANGE: India, Burma, Thailand and Sri Lanka.

HABITS: A peaceful, active catfish. Tends to be shy at first in bright light.

WATER CONDITIONS: Can be kept in a wide variety of water conditions but seems to prefer slightly acid, soft water. Temperature 24 to 28°C.

SIZE: Reaches a length of 21 cm.

FOOD REQUIREMENTS: Will take most aquarium foods offered if they sink to the bottom. Prefers worms.

Mystus micracanthus (Bleeker) • Two-spot Catfish

RANGE: Southeast Asia from Thailand to the islands of Sumatra, Java and Borneo.

HABITS: Generally peaceful, especially when young. Active swimmer although shy in the presence of bright light.

WATER CONDITIONS: Not critical as long as extremes are avoided, but seems to prefer slightly acid water. Temperature 24 to 28°C.

SIZE: Reaches a length of about 15 cm.

FOOD REQUIREMENTS: Will eat a wide variety of aquarium foods that sink to the bottom.

Bagrichthys sp. • False Black Lancer

RANGE: Imported from Borneo.

HABITS: Assumedly also a river-dweller, but actually little is known about this fish. It may be *B. macropterus* or an undescribed species. It lacks the white line of the true black lancer and has a lower dorsal fin.

WATER CONDITIONS: Like the black lancer, not choosy but subject to infections.

SIZE: At least 30 cm.

FOOD REQUIREMENTS: Not critical.

Glyptothorax callopterus Smith • Band-finned Torrent Catfish

RANGE: Thailand and probably adjacent countries.

HABITS: A highly specialized catfish that adheres to boulders in torrential streams by means of a sucking disc on the chest.

WATER CONDITIONS: Relatively cool, flowing, well-oxygenated water is preferred.

SIZE: 60-75 mm.

FOOD REQUIREMENTS: Must have some vegetable matter in the diet; also eats small crustaceans and insect larvae.

Heteropneustes fossilis (Bloch) • Asian Stinging Catfish

RANGE: Much of tropical Asia, from India to Southeast Asia.
HABITS: An eel-like catfish of ponds, ditches, and rice paddies. Since it is able to breathe air, it is often found in drying situations. Infamous for its barbed pectoral spines that have large venom glands. This fish has caused human deaths and should not be handled.
WATER CONDITIONS: Not at all choosy, as in nature it can live in almost any type of habitat. Must be kept warm, however.
SIZE: Usually about 20 cm long, but reaches at least 30 cm and perhaps more.
FOOD REQUIREMENTS: Feeds on invertebrates, smaller vertebrates including fishes, and will also scavenge.

Platytropius siamensis (Sauvage) • False Siamese Shark

RANGE: Thailand, in the Menam Chao Phya River and its drainages.
HABITS: A riverine species also found in canals. Poorly known, although aquarium specimens tend to school and are constantly active. A large tank is preferred or they will repeatedly batter their snouts against the glass.
WATER CONDITIONS: Not critical. The water should be clean and well-oxygenated.
SIZE: 15-25 cm long.
FOOD REQUIREMENTS: Shy, but will eventually take most aquarium foods with high meat content, live or frozen.

Kryptopterus bicirrhis (Cuvier & Valenciennes) • Glass Catfish

RANGE: Thailand to Indonesia.
HABITS: Peaceful; should not be kept singly, and should also not be kept with very active fishes.
WATER CONDITIONS: Water should be slightly alkaline and have a hardness which does not surpass 10 DH. Temperature about 24°C.
SIZE: To 10 cm.
FOOD REQUIREMENTS: Should be given living foods such as tubifex worms, white worms, daphnia, etc.

Ompok bimaculatus (Bloch) • One-spot Glass Catfish

RANGE: Sri Lanka, Indo-China, Thailand, Burma, Java and Sumatra.
HABITS: Only small specimens are adaptable to aquaria, and they should not be kept singly; single fish are short-lived.
WATER CONDITIONS: Very adaptable to practically any clean water. Temperature 23 to 28°C.
SIZE: To 46 cm in native waters; about half that in the aquarium.
FOOD REQUIREMENTS: Live or frozen foods preferred.

Chaca bankanensis Bleeker • Chocolate Frogmouth Catfish; Chocolate Angling Catfish

RANGE: Southern Malaysia, Sumatra, and Borneo; apparently absent from Thailand and northern Malaysia.
HABITS: A nocturnal, sedentary lurker that should not be kept with small fishes. The Indian *Chaca chaca* is a distinct species that is seldom imported. Both lure small fishes with their maxillary barbels.
WATER CONDITIONS: Not critical. Temperatures between 23 and 28°C are best.
SIZE: 15 to 20 cm.
FOOD REQUIREMENTS: Will take most living foods, but prefers small fishes and earthworms. Can engulf fishes up to half its own length.

Pangasius sutchi Fowler • Siamese Shark

RANGE: Malay Peninsula.
HABITS: Relatively peaceful, but will eat fishes small enough to swallow.
WATER CONDITIONS: Not critical, but soft acid water preferred. Temperature 22 to 27°C.
SIZE: 18 cm, but usually smaller.
FOOD REQUIREMENTS: Prefers live or frozen foods.

Ompok sabanus Inger & Chin • Tawny Glass Catfish

RANGE: Northern Borneo.
HABITS: Found in nature in muddy rivers from the mouths to smaller tributary streams. Attracted to offal.
WATER CONDITIONS: Not critical. Should be able to stand a broad range of temperatures (as long as at least warm) and hardness.
SIZE: 10-18 cm.
FOOD REQUIREMENTS: Takes insects, crustaceans, and small vertebrates.

Heteropneustes fossilis

Chaca bankanensis

Platytropius siamensis

Pangasius sutchi

Kryptopterus bicirrhis

Kryptopterus bicirrhis

Ompok bimaculatus ?

Ompok sabanus

Plate #406

596

Aplocheilus blocki

Aplocheilus blocki

Aplocheilus dayi

Aplocheilus dayi

Aplocheilus lineatus

Aplocheilus lineatus

Aplocheilus panchax

Aplocheilus panchax

Plate #407

597

Aplocheilus blocki (Arnold) • Dwarf Panchax, Green
Panchax, Panchax from Madras

RANGE: Madras, India.
HABITS: Peaceful, but should not be kept with large fishes.
WATER CONDITIONS: Well-aged water which is soft and
slightly acid. Temperature 21 to 25°C.
SIZE: Males 5 cm; females slightly smaller.
FOOD REQUIREMENTS: Will eat dried foods, but this *must* be
supplemented with live foods.

Aplocheilus dayi (Steindachner) • Day's Panchax,
Singhalese Panchax

RANGE: Sri Lanka.
HABITS: Will not annoy anything it cannot swallow. May be
kept in company with larger fishes.
WATER CONDITIONS: Neutral to slightly acid. Temperature
24.5 to 25.5°C.
SIZE: 8.5 cm; females only a little smaller.
FOOD REQUIREMENTS: Dried food will be taken, but live
food should be supplemented at least occasionally.

Aplocheilus lineatus (Cuvier & Valenciennes) •
Panchax Lineatus, Striped Panchax

RANGE: Malabar and Madras, India, and Sri Lanka.
HABITS: Best kept by themselves; although usually peaceful
except with small fishes, they sometimes harass other
fishes.
WATER CONDITIONS: Neutral to slightly acid soft water.
Temperature 24 to 27°C.
SIZE: 10 cm; will begin to spawn at 6 cm.
FOOD REQUIREMENTS: Live foods such as daphnia, tubifex
worms, enchytrae and grown-up brine shrimp. Dried
foods may be fed occasionally.

Aplocheilus panchax (Hamilton-Buchanan) •
Panchax Panchax, Blue Panchax

RANGE: India, Burma, Malay Peninsula, Thailand,
Indonesia.
HABITS: Will not bother anything they cannot swallow, and
may be kept in community aquaria which do not contain
small fishes.
WATER CONDITIONS: Soft, slightly acid water, preferably
well aged. Temperature 24 to 26°C.
SIZE: 6 to 8 cm; will begin spawning when three-fourths
grown.
FOOD REQUIREMENTS: Mostly living foods such as daphnia,
enchytrae or tubifex worms. Frozen or dried foods may
be given occasionally.

Oryzias javanicus (Bleeker) • Javanese Rice Fish

RANGE: Java and Malaysia.
HABITS: Peaceful toward other fishes and will not harm plants.
WATER CONDITIONS: Water should be neutral to slightly
  alkaline, with a little salt added. Keep at 26 to 29°C.
SIZE: Males to 3 cm; females to 4 cm.
FOOD REQUIREMENTS: Live foods greatly preferred; other
  foods are not picked up once they fall to the bottom.

Oryzias latipes (Schlegel) • Medaka

RANGE: Japan and nearby islands.
HABITS: Active and peaceful, although a male will occasion-
  ally rough up a female; a very good community fish.
WATER CONDITIONS: Slightly soft, acid water desirable.
SIZE: Females about 5 cm; males slightly smaller.
FOOD REQUIREMENTS: Takes all foods.

Oostethus brachyurus Rueppel • Indian Freshwater Pipefish

RANGE: Sri Lanka and India.
HABITS: Peaceful with any fish that cannot be swallowed.
WATER CONDITIONS: Should have brackish water, although
  the salt can vary in concentration from light to heavy;
  tank should not be too heavily aerated. Temperature 24
  to 29°C.
SIZE: About 13 cm.
FOOD REQUIREMENTS: In the home aquarium, this fish will
  accept only newborn livebearers.

Doryichthys "Red-belly" • Red-bellied Freshwater Pipefish

RANGE: Southeast Asia. Even the generic identity of this
  pipefish is in doubt, and the species currently cannot be
  determined.
HABITS: Found in purely freshwater habitats as well as
  estuarine areas. Prefers weeded aquaria. Seldom survives for long in the aquarium and should not be kept
  with other fishes.
WATER CONDITIONS: Hard, alkaline water, preferably with
  a teaspoon of salt added per 4 liters. Temperature 25-30°C.
SIZE: About 100-150 mm.
FOOD REQUIREMENTS: Must have small, preferably living,
  foods, such as young and adult brine shrimp or the fry of
  livebearers.

Indostomus paradoxus Prashad & Mukerji • Paradox Fish

RANGE: Lake Indawgyi, northern Burma.
HABITS: Peaceful; given to resting on the bottom for long
  periods or drifting through the water slowly.
WATER CONDITIONS: Soft water; pH about 6.8. Temperature
  20 to 24°C.
SIZE: About 2.5 cm.
FOOD REQUIREMENTS: Live baby brine shrimp preferred,
  but it may be trained to accept substitutes.

Oryzias javanicus

Oryzias javanicus

Oryzias latipes

Oryzias latipes

Oostethus brachyurus

Doryichthys "Red-belly"

Oostethus brachyurus

Plate #408

Indostomus paradoxus

600

Badis badis badis

Badis badis badis

Badis badis badis (female)

Badis badis burmanicus

Pristolepis fasciatus

Pristolepis fasciatus (juvenile)

Nandus nandus

Nandus nandus

Plate #409

Badis badis badis (Hamilton-Buchanan) • Badis, Dwarf Chameleon Fish

RANGE: India.
HABITS: Peaceful, but will hide a great deal when kept in a community aquarium.
WATER CONDITIONS: Not critical; a well-planted aquarium should be provided, with several small flowerpots laid on their sides.
SIZE: Up to 8 cm; will begin breeding at 5 cm.
FOOD REQUIREMENTS: Live foods only, in sizes tiny enough for their small mouths.

Badis badis burmanicus (Ahl) • Burmese Badis

RANGE: Burma.
HABITS: Peaceful, but will hide a great deal if kept in the community aquarium.

WATER CONDITIONS: Not critical; should have a well-planted aquarium with a number of hiding places.
SIZE: About 6 cm.
FOOD REQUIREMENTS: Small live foods only.

Pristolepis fasciata (Bleeker) • Small-mouthed Leaffish

RANGE: Southeast Asia.
HABITS: In nature it is found in weeded, muddy lakes, rivers and ponds. Probably territorial and should be treated as such in the aquarium.

WATER CONDITIONS: Not too choosy as long as the water is warm, over 25°C. Will tolerate a broad range of pH.

SIZE: Usually under 100 mm, but may exceed 210 mm.
FOOD REQUIREMENTS: Takes live foods of an appropriate size, especially small fishes and larger insects, as well as shrimp.

Nandus nandus (Hamilton-Buchanan) • Nandus

RANGE: India, Burma and Thailand.
HABITS: A voracious species which will eat any fish up to three-fourths of its own size.

WATER CONDITIONS: Soft, acid water is optional. Temperature 22 to 26°C.

SIZE: Up to 20 cm.
FOOD REQUIREMENTS: Live fishes; some can be trained to take worms and beef.

Channa asiatica (Linnaeus) • Northern Green Snakehead

RANGE: Found over a wide area of Asia, from the USSR and China to Japan and northern Southeast Asia.

HABITS: Found in all types of habitats from ponds and lakes to rivers, streams, and rice paddies. Like the other members of the genus, it builds and guards a nest for its eggs. Note the absence of the ventral fins.

WATER CONDITIONS: Not choosy. Will tolerate quite a bit of pollution, but of course prefers clean water.

SIZE: A rather small species seldom exceeding 250 mm in length. Juveniles under 100 mm have a more contrasting pattern.

FOOD REQUIREMENTS: Will take almost any living food, especially fishes, shrimp, insects, and even a bit of vegetable matter.

Channa micropeltes (Cuvier & Valenciennes) • Red Snakehead

RANGE: Southeast Asia, into India.

HABITS: A voracious, greedy species, but not everything that it kills is destined to serve as food, as it often kills without eating the fishes it has destroyed.

WATER CONDITIONS: Not critical; this is a very hardy and adaptable fish.

SIZE: Up to 1 meter; usually offered for sale at 8 to 10 cm.

FOOD REQUIREMENTS: Eats most meaty (living and non-living) foods when young; in larger sizes prefers live fishes and amphibians but will take chunks of meat.

Channa striatus (Bloch) • Chevron Snakehead

RANGE: Virtually all of tropical Asia, from India to southern China, Southeast Asia, and to the Indonesian area. Widely introduced because of its commercial importance as a food fish.

HABITS: Found in most sluggish or still waters and even buries itself deeply in the mud when the water dries. The parents build a nest in shallow water and lay floating eggs that hatch in just 3 days.

WATER CONDITIONS: A warm-water fish that thrives under virtually all conditions.

SIZE: The fish shown are juveniles under 10-15 cm long. As the species grows the color pattern virtually disappears and the fish becomes wholly dark brown. Adults reach at least a full meter in length.

FOOD REQUIREMENTS: Will eat anything that comes close enough to grab, including fishes, invertebrates, snakes, frogs, and small mammals.

Chanda baculis Hamilton-Buchanan • Pla Kameo or Burmese Glassfish

RANGE: Burma, India and Thailand in the Sikuk River, in the headwaters of the Menam Chao Phya, in the lower Menam Nan and in the Bung Borapet.

HABITS: A dainty but beautiful small fish; peaceful.

WATER CONDITIONS: Strictly a freshwater species which prefers the higher temperatures in the upper 20's °C.

SIZE: The smallest of the large genus *Chanda*. Rarely larger than 5 cm.

FOOD REQUIREMENTS: Prefers live foods, but accepts frozen brine shrimp and some dry foods in pellet form. Requires copious amounts of live food such as microworms and daphnia.

Channa orientalis Bloch & Schneider • Ceylonese Green Snakehead

RANGE: Sri Lanka.

HABITS: A rather delicate species that likes clean water and is often found in pools near mountain streams. Young fish are often found with their parents. Like *C. asiatica*, this species lacks ventral fins.

WATER CONDITIONS: Will take almost any water conditions in the aquarium, but because of its small size it is more sensitive to poor water.

SIZE: Probably the smallest member of the family, adults barely reaching 100 mm in length.

FOOD REQUIREMENTS: Will take almost any living food of reasonable size.

Channa argus (Cantor) • Spotted Snakehead

RANGE: A mostly northern fish with several subspecies in Russia, China, Japan, and northern Southeast Asia. Likely to be found almost anywhere in subtropical Asia.

HABITS: One of the larger but more colorful snakeheads, this species is found in almost any type of water body, from ponds to rivers. Like the other snakeheads, the presence of air cavities above the gills (like the labyrinth organs of gouramis) allows it to survive in very oxygen-depleted waters and even to travel overland when a pond dries up.

WATER CONDITIONS: Not choosy. Perhaps should be kept a bit cooler than most other snakeheads because of the more northern distribution (22-26°C).

SIZE: Reaches at least 40 cm in length, but seldom exceeds 25 cm in much of its range.

FOOD REQUIREMENTS: Eats almost anything.

Chanda ranga Hamilton-Buchanan • Glassfish, Glass Perch

RANGE: Northern India, Bengal to Burma.

HABITS: Very numerous in rice paddies and other shallow bodies of water in their habitat; peaceful in the aquarium.

WATER CONDITIONS: Requires somewhat hard water with a light salt content. Once established in an aquarium, they should be moved as little as possible. Temperature about 26°C.

SIZE: 5 cm; in nature they become slightly larger.

FOOD REQUIREMENTS: Some prepared foods are unwillingly accepted, but the bulk of foods given should be alive.

COLOR VARIATIONS: Body light amber with a glassy transparency. In the males, the soft dorsal fin and the anal fin have a bright blue edge.

Channa asiatica

Channa orientalis

Channa micropeltes

Channa argus

Channa striatus

Channa striatus

Chanda baculis

Chanda ranga

Plate #410

604

Datnioides quadrifasciatus

Datnioides microlepis

Datnioides microlepis

Monodactylus argenteus

Toxotes chatareus

Toxotes jaculator

Scatophagus argus

Scatophagus argus

Plate #411

605

Datnioides quadrifasciatus (Sevastianov) • Many-Barred
Tiger Fish

RANGE: Thailand, India, Burma and the Indo-Australian
Archipelago.
HABITS: Peaceful; will not molest other fishes, but will swal-
low those which are small enough to be eaten.
WATER CONDITIONS: Neutral to slightly acid. Temperature
23 to 26°C.
SIZE: To 38 cm in their natural waters.
FOOD REQUIREMENTS: Larger live foods, chunks of shrimp
or raw fish.
COLOR VARIATIONS: Yellowish to coppery in color with 8 to
10 dark brown bars, some of which unite as the fish grows
older.

Datnioides microlepis Bleeker • Siamese Tiger Fish

RANGE: Thailand, Sumatra and Borneo.
HABITS: Peaceful; will not harm any fish it cannot swallow.
WATER CONDITIONS: Neutral to slightly acid. Temperature
23 to 26°C.
SIZE: To 38 cm in its natural waters; much smaller in the
aquarium.
FOOD REQUIREMENTS: Larger live foods or chunks of shrimp
or raw lean beef.
COLOR VARIATIONS: Body yellow to cream or pinkish, with
black vertical bars.

Monodactylus argenteus (Linnaeus) • Mono

RANGE: Coastal waters from eastern Africa to Fiji.
HABITS: Shy and often gets panicky when frightened; best
kept in a small group in a roomy tank.
WATER CONDITIONS: Slightly alkaline water with about a
quarter teaspoon of salt to each liter is acceptable.
Temperature 23 to 25°C.
SIZE: Wild specimens attain 23 cm; seldom exceed half that
in captivity.
FOOD REQUIREMENTS: All sorts of live foods.
COLOR VARIATIONS: Body silvery, with a golden sheen
above; two black vertical bars, one through the eye and
the other through the pectoral base.

Toxotes chatareus (Hamilton-Buchanan) • Seven-spotted
Archer Fish

RANGE: India to the New Hebrides (including the Indo-Australian Archipelago, Thailand, Vietnam, Philippines,
New Guinea and northern and northeastern Australia).
HABITS: Peaceful to slightly aggressive; best kept with other
brackish water fishes.
WATER CONDITIONS: Although pure fresh or pure salt water
can be tolerated, brackish water is best. Temperature 22
to 28°C.
SIZE: A maximum size of about 20 cm is attained; usually
smaller in aquaria.
FOOD REQUIREMENTS: Live foods, especially insects, are
best; other foods, even hamburger meat, are also accepted.

Toxotes jaculator (Pallas) • Archer Fish

RANGE: India, Burma, Malaysia, Philippines, East Indies
and Thailand.
HABITS: Usually peaceful, but individual specimens can be
aggressive; not a good community fish unless kept with
other fishes liking slightly brackish water.
WATER CONDITIONS: Water should be slightly salty; tank
should be large. Temperature 23 to 29°C.
SIZE: Over 15 cm, but always sold at a much smaller size.
FOOD REQUIREMENTS: Best food is live insects which the
fish captures for itself, but it will accept meaty
substitutes; some hobbyists claim that it will accept dry
food, but this depends on the individual fish.

Scatophagus argus (Gmelin) • Spotted Scat

RANGE: Tropical Indo-Pacific region along the coasts.
HABITS: Peaceful toward other fishes, but will graze on
aquatic plants right down to the roots.
WATER CONDITIONS: Fairly hard, alkaline water with a
teaspoon of salt per four liters of water added.
Temperature 23 to 26°C.
SIZE: To 33 cm in their home waters; about half that in
captivity.
FOOD REQUIREMENTS: Live foods of all kinds, with the
addition of vegetable substances like lettuce or spinach
leaves; will also eat frozen foods.

Etroplus suratensis (Bloch) • Banded Chromide

RANGE: India and Sri Lanka; in the mouths of streams and bays.
HABITS: Somewhat quarrelsome; should be trusted only with fishes of its own size or bigger.
WATER CONDITIONS: Requires a generous addition of salt to the water, a tablespoonful for every 4 liters, or 10% sea water added.
SIZE: Wild specimens may measure up to 40 cm, but we seldom see them more than 8 cm in length.
FOOD REQUIREMENTS: Should be generously fed with a variety of live foods or frozen full-grown brine shrimp.

Etroplus maculatus (Bloch) • Orange Chromide

RANGE: India and Sri Lanka.
HABITS: Fairly peaceful with fishes of its own size, but cannot be trusted completely.
WATER CONDITIONS: Water should be fresh and clean, with about a quarter teaspoon of salt added to each liter.
SIZE: About 8 cm.
FOOD REQUIREMENTS: Should be provided with living or frozen foods; dried food taken only when very hungry.

Gnatholepis knighti Jordan & Everman • Pond Goby

RANGE: Pacific islands to Southeast Asia. As with most gobies, the identification of this species is somewhat doubtful.
HABITS: A brackish water species usually found in sea-side ponds and the mouths of rivers. Can be adapted to fresh-water aquaria.
WATER CONDITIONS: Warm, alkaline water with salt added is necessary.
SIZE: 30-45 mm.
FOOD REQUIREMENTS: Like most small gobies, it will take small live foods such as daphnia and cyclops, as well as the standard brine shrimp. Some will adjust to taking prepared foods as well.

Ctenogobius schultzei (Herre) • Redneck Goby

RANGE: Hong Kong to the Philippines.
HABITS: Found in clear, running water over sand bottoms as well as in estuarine areas, so quite adaptable. Spawns readily in the aquarium. Females are very plain and lack the enlarged, brightly colored gill areas of the breeding males.
WATER CONDITIONS: Temperature 25°C and higher. Some salt should be added to the water, at least at first.
SIZE: 50-60 mm.
FOOD REQUIREMENTS: Likes cyclops, daphnia, brine shrimp nauplii, and most other small live foods.

Etroplus suratensis

Etroplus suratensis

Etroplus maculatus

Etroplus maculatus

Etroplus maculatus (var.)

Etroplus maculatus (var.)

Gnatholepis knighti

Ctenogobius schultzei

Plate #412

608

Stigmatogobius sadanundio

Mugilogobius valigouva

Awaous grammepomus

Sicyopterus "Jonklaas"

Periophthalus barberus

Parapocryptes serperaster

Brachygobius doriae

Brachygobius doriae

Plate #413

609

Stigmatogobius sadanundio (Hamilton-Buchanan) • Knight Goby

RANGE: Indonesia, Burma, India and the Philippines.
HABITS: A bottom-dwelling fish which requires live food.
WATER CONDITIONS: Originally from brackish water areas, this fish is not at home in soft water conditions. Add salt to the water, at least one tablespoon for 8 liters.
SIZE: Up to about 9 cm.
FOOD REQUIREMENTS: Must have copious feedings of live foods, preferably worms; frozen brine shrimp is eagerly taken.

Awaous grammepomus (Bleeker) • Stippled River Goby

RANGE: Tropical Indo-West Pacific from India and Sri Lanka to the Philippines and Java.
HABITS: Although sometimes found in estuarine areas, it is typically a goby of large, often fast-flowing rivers on tropical islands. Here it is found on sandy to rocky substrates and uses the large head and lips to look for food under rocks.
WATER CONDITIONS: Warm, hard water is preferred; salt may be added to ensure the right chemistry.
SIZE: One of the larger gobies, often reaching 100 mm in length and approaching 150 mm. In some areas it is large enough to use for food.
FOOD REQUIREMENTS: Will take anything small enough to swallow—the size of the mouth should indicate that it is not to be trusted with small fishes. Some vegetable matter is also taken.

Periophthalmus barbarus (Linnaeus) • Mudskipper

RANGE: East Africa to Australia.
HABITS: Cannot be combined with any other group of fishes; shy at first, but later can be tamed effectively.
WATER CONDITIONS: Water must have salt, ½ teaspoon to the liter, added; there should be an area where the fish can climb out. Temperature 24 to 27°C.
SIZE: To 15 cm.
FOOD REQUIREMENTS: Worms and other living insects.

Brachygobius doriae (Guenther) • Doria's Bumblebee Goby

RANGE: Borneo and the Malayan Archipelago.
HABITS: Should be kept by themselves in a small aquarium. Hiding places should be provided.
WATER CONDITIONS: Water should have an addition of one heaping teaspoonful of table salt per 4 liters. Temperature 24 to 26°C.
SIZE: Up to 2.5 cm.
FOOD REQUIREMENTS: Small live foods exclusively.

Mugilogobius valigouva (Deraniyagala) • Mullet-headed Goby

RANGE: Sri Lanka.
HABITS: A small estuarine goby of unimpressive colors. It can be adapted to freshwater aquaria on occasion.
WATER CONDITIONS: Since this species is estuarine, it must have salt added to the water. Hard, alkaline water is necessary, as for most other brackish water species.
SIZE: Small, only 15-20 mm long.
FOOD REQUIREMENTS: The small adult size and small mouth mean that only the finest foods will be taken. Related species also will eat a bit of algae as part of their diet.

Sicyopterus "Jonklaas" • Jonklaas's Mountain Goby

RANGE: Sri Lanka.
HABITS: Peaceful; clings to glass or rocks with sucker-like pelvic fins.
WATER CONDITIONS: Requires cool (21°C), well-aerated, clear water.
SIZE: Average 15 cm; females larger than males.
FOOD REQUIREMENTS: Prefers a lush growth of algae on rocks and aquarium glass; will also eat prepared foods containing a large amount of vegetable matter.

Parapocryptes serperaster (Richardson) • Slim Mudskipper

RANGE: Southeast Asia from India to China, most numerous in Malayan Archipelago.
HABITS: Aggressive.
WATER CONDITIONS: Warm, brackish water required. Temperature 24 to 27°C.
SIZE: To about 25 cm.
FOOD REQUIREMENTS: Will accept only rich, meaty foods, in most cases only living foods; tubifex worms, earthworms and small live fishes are accepted, and will gladly take softbodied insects.

Anabas testudineus (Bloch) • Climbing Perch

RANGE: India, Sri Lanka, Burma, Southeast Asia, southern China, Philippine Islands and Malaysia.

HABITS: Aggressive; should be kept by themselves. Large aquarium should be provided and kept covered.

WATER CONDITIONS: Not critical. Has a wide temperature tolerance, 18 to 30°C.

SIZE: Up to 25 cm; becomes mature at 10 cm.

FOOD REQUIREMENTS: Eats almost anything; in the absence of live foods, canned dog food with a high beef content is an acceptable substitute.

COLOR VARIATIONS: Dirty gray to greenish, with a dark spot at the caudal base and another just behind the gill plate.

Osphronemus goramy Lacepede • Giant Gourami

RANGE: Great Sunda Islands; introduced in other places as a food fish.

HABITS: Peaceful; because of their size they should be kept only with large fishes.

WATER CONDITIONS: Not critical as long as the water is clean. Temperature 23 to 28°C.

SIZE: Up to 60 cm in natural waters; about half that in the aquarium.

FOOD REQUIREMENTS: Should get large amounts of shrimp, clams, mussels, etc., to which is also added vegetable matter such as boiled oatmeal.

Helostoma temmincki Cuvier and Valenciennes • Kissing Gourami

RANGE: Thailand, Indonesia, Sumatra, Borneo, Java, Malay Peninsula and Cambodia.

HABITS: Prefer a large aquarium. Plants are not necessary though they do enjoy "chomping" on them to remove whatever has fallen onto them or grown over them. They are easily overcrowded and unless they are given plenty of room their growth is stunted, they develop a "hollow belly" and they die.

WATER CONDITIONS: The water conditions are not critical, but they do much better in slightly hard water with a pH of 7.0. Temperature 26°C.

SIZE: Up to 30 cm.

FOOD REQUIREMENTS: A greedy eater which never tires of looking for food. Their major diet should consist of frozen brine shrimp and worms now and then. They seem to get along very well on salmon eggs (the dried prepared form available as fish food) and shredded shrimp, though this usually fouls the water.

Belontia signata (Guenther) • Combtail

RANGE: Sri Lanka.

HABITS: Vicious toward smaller fishes; should be kept only with those which are able to take care of themselves.

WATER CONDITIONS: Large tank is required. Water not critical. Temperature should be at least 25°C.

SIZE: 12.5 cm.

FOOD REQUIREMENTS: Very greedy; will take coarse dried foods, but prefers chunks such as pieces of earthworms or lean raw beef.

COLOR VARIATIONS: Sides are a reddish brown, lighter in the belly region; outer edge of the tail is fringed.

Anabas testudineus (xanthistic)

Anabas testudineus

Osphronemus goramy (juvenile)

Osphronemus goramy (adult)

Helostoma temmincki (green)

Helostoma temmincki (pink)

Belontia signata

Belontia signata

Plate #414

Parosphromenus deissneri

Parosphromenus filamentosus

Trichopsis pumilus

Trichopsis schalleri

Betta bellica

Trichopsis vittatus

Betta imbellis

Betta brederi

Plate #415

613

Parosphromenus deissneri (Bleeker) • Licorice Gourami

RANGE: Bangka, Sumatra and Malay Peninsula.
HABITS: Peaceful, but unsuitable for the community tank because of its shy temperament ; needs shelter of some sort for its well-being.
WATER CONDITIONS: Soft, acid water is recommended (some aquarists use a small peat filter so that the water turns an amber color but remains very clear and clean) at a temperature of about 24 or 25°C.
SIZE: One of the dwarf species reaching a length of only 4 cm.
FOOD REQUIREMENTS: Live foods such as daphnia, cyclops, Grindal worms and mosquito larvae are best.

Parosphromenus filamentosus Vierke • Spike-tailed Licorice Gourami

RANGE: Endemic to southern Borneo near Kalimantan.
HABITS: A quiet and peaceful species.
WATER CONDITIONS: Not critical. Soft water is better than hard. Temperatures from 24° to 30°C are acceptable.
SIZE: Attains a maximum length of about 4 cm (only 2.5 cm without the tail).
FOOD REQUIREMENTS: Not choosy about its food as long as it is live.

Trichopsis pumilus (Arnold) • Pygmy Gourami

RANGE: Vietnam, Thailand, Malaysia and Sumatra.
HABITS: Peaceful, but because it is shy it is best to keep them only with their own kind.
WATER CONDITIONS: A large aquarium is not required, 26°C is good; for spawning 29°C.
SIZE: Males about 3 cm; females slightly smaller.
FOOD REQUIREMENTS: Will take prepared as well as the smaller live foods.

Trichopsis schalleri (Ladiges) • Three-striped Croaking Gourami

RANGE: Thailand.
HABITS: Peaceful; emits a faint croaking sound, especially during spawning activity.
WATER CONDITIONS: Soft, slightly acid water. Temperature 23 to 25°C.
SIZE: About 6 cm.
FOOD REQUIREMENTS: Live or frozen foods of all kinds; dry foods would probably be accepted.

Betta bellica Sauvage • Slender Betta

RANGE: Perak, in Malaysia.
HABITS: Not a good fish for the community tank. Although there is not the aggressiveness between males as with *B. splendens*, they are best kept alone.
WATER CONDITIONS: Not critical, but a high temperature (25 to 30°C) must be maintained.
SIZE: About 10 cm.
FOOD REQUIREMENTS: Should get living foods, with occasional supplements of dried foods.

Trichopsis vittatus (Cuvier & Valenciennes) • Croaking Gourami

RANGE: Vietnam, Thailand, Malaysia, Sumatra, Java and Borneo.
HABITS: Peaceful and shy; should be kept by themselves because of their high temperature requirements.
WATER CONDITIONS: A well-covered, well-heated aquarium is necessary or this fish may prove to be sensitive. A temperature of 27 to 29°C should be maintained.
SIZE: Males a little over 6 cm; females slightly smaller.
FOOD REQUIREMENTS: Will take dried foods if hungry, but prefers live foods, especially white worms.

Betta imbellis Ladiges • Peaceful Betta, Crescent Betta

RANGE: Malaysia.
HABITS: Peaceful among themselves or other species.
WATER CONDITIONS: Neutral water of moderate hardness. Temperature 23 to 27°C.
SIZE: About 5 cm.
FOOD REQUIREMENTS: Will take a variety of live, frozen or prepared foods.
COLOR VARIATIONS: Males dark brown with a bright orange border along the posterior edge of the caudal fin and on the distal tips of the anal and pelvic fins. Females are a dull mottled brown with orange pelvic fin tips and a less intense orange border on the caudal fin.

Betta brederi Myers • Breder's Betta

RANGE: Java and Sumatra.
HABITS: Although they are not vicious, it is best to keep this species by themselves.
WATER CONDITIONS: Not critical, as long as the tank is clean. Temperature about 25°C.
SIZE: To 8 cm.
FOOD REQUIREMENTS: Live foods exclusively.

Betta macrostoma Regan • Brunei Beauty; Peacock Betta

RANGE: Sarawak and Brunei, Borneo.
HABITS: Apparently peaceful toward other fishes, but males are extremely aggressive toward one another.
WATER CONDITIONS: Not critical, but frequent water changes are suggested. The pH should be about neutral and the temperature about 20-25°C.
SIZE: Attains a length of about 10-12 cm, the females remaining a bit smaller.
FOOD REQUIREMENTS: A variety of live foods such as daphnia, bloodworms, brine shrimp, and mosquito larvae are best. They will accept frozen and prepared foods designed for aquarium fishes.

Betta akarensis Regan • Sarawak Betta

RANGE: Known definitely from the Akar River, Sarawak, but probably more widely distributed on the island of Borneo.
HABITS: Virtually nothing is known of this obscure species, but it occurs in rivers and streams.
WATER CONDITIONS: Uncertain, but can probably be kept like any other riverine betta.
SIZE: Reaches at least 52 mm in length.
FOOD REQUIREMENTS: Will take live foods of appropriate size and can probably be supplemented with prepared aquarium foods.

Betta taeniata Regan • Banded Betta

RANGE: The various fish assigned (somewhat doubtfully) to this species are found in Malaya, Sumatra, Borneo, and Thailand.
HABITS: Found in nature in many types of waters, from ditches to rivers. Adapts well to aquarium culture and can be treated much like *Betta splendens*. A mouth-brooder.
WATER CONDITIONS: Not choosy as long as the water is fairly warm (24°C or over) and not dirty.
SIZE: 60-80 mm.
FOOD REQUIREMENTS: Prefers live foods (insects, crustaceans), but takes prepared foods.

Betta pugnax (Cantor) • Mouth-brooding Betta

RANGE: Thailand and Malaya.
HABITS: In nature it is found in small, rather swiftly flowing sand-bottomed streams, but it adapts well to aquarium conditions. Likes a heavily planted environment.
WATER CONDITIONS: The water should be relatively cool (21-25°C) and on the soft side (often will spawn only in soft water). Quite tolerant of pH between 6.4 and 7.8.
SIZE: One of the larger bettas, often exceeding 80 mm and reaching at least 100 mm.
FOOD REQUIREMENTS: Loves small crustaceans and insect larvae but will adapt to a diet consisting at least partially of prepared foods.

Betta unimaculata (Popta) • One-spot Betta

RANGE: Borneo.
HABITS: Generally peaceful. Males are aggressive toward one another, but fighting is mostly ritualistic.
WATER CONDITIONS: Not critical. Neutral water of about 7 DH at a temperature range of 23 to 28°C should be used. Regular partial water changes are recommended.
SIZE: Attains the rather large size for a *Betta* of 11 cm in males (females reach only 9 cm).
FOOD REQUIREMENTS: Should be given a well-rounded diet of all live foods including mosquito larvae, brine shrimp, daphnia, etc.

Betta smaragdina Ladiges • Emerald Betta

RANGE: Known from Thailand near the Laotian border. Many authorities consider this species doubtfully distinct from *B. splendens*, with which it agrees in almost all features of its natural history.
HABITS: Slowly flowing rivers, ditches, and rice paddies. Likes a great amount of plant cover. Very territorial.
WATER CONDITIONS: Not choosy. The water should be relatively warm (25°C and more).
SIZE: Females to about 60 mm, males to at least 75 mm.
FOOD REQUIREMENTS: Takes both live foods and prepared foods.

Betta macrostoma (male)

Betta macrostoma (female)

Betta akarensis

Betta macrostoma (male) var.

Betta taeniata

Betta pugnax

Betta unimaculata

Betta smaragdina

Plate #416

616

All fish on this page are forms of *Betta splendens*.

Plate #417

Betta splendens Regan • Betta, Siamese Fighting Fish

RANGE: Thailand, Malaysia, Southeast Asia.
HABITS: Usually peaceful with other fishes of its own size, but two males in the same aquarium will fight until one retreats.
WATER CONDITIONS: Not critical; breathing atmospheric air as they do, they can be kept in very small containers. Temperature should not go below 25°C.
SIZE: 5 to 6 cm.
FOOD REQUIREMENTS: Will take dried foods, but should get an occasional meal of live foods.
COLOR VARIATIONS: Many colors have been developed: red, green, blue and combinations of these colors.

Macropodus concolor Ahl • Black Paradise Fish

RANGE: Not specifically known. Said to come from the East Indies.

HABITS: Not as aggressive as *M. opercularis.* Two males will normally fight, and plants may be torn up.

WATER CONDITIONS: Prefers neutral to slightly acid water and a temperature between 20 and 25°C.

SIZE: Males attain a length of about 12 cm, females only 8 cm.

FOOD REQUIREMENTS: Live foods are preferred (glass worms, daphnia, tubifex worms, etc.).

Macropodus opercularis (Linnaeus) • Paradise Fish

RANGE: China and Formosa.

HABITS: Very quarrelsome, even toward their own kind.

WATER CONDITIONS: Very adaptable to any water conditions. An unheated aquarium suffices, and for breeding 21 to 24°C is high enough.

SIZE: About 8 cm.

FOOD REQUIREMENTS: A greedy eater which should be fed often and generously; all kinds of foods are accepted.

Pseudosphromenus cupanus cupanus (Cuvier) • Spike-tail Paradise Fish

RANGE: Southern India and Sri Lanka.

HABITS: Generally peaceful.

WATER CONDITIONS: Water should be fairly soft and acidic. 23 to 26°C is the best temperature range; slightly higher for breeding.

SIZE: To about 8 cm.

FOOD REQUIREMENTS: Accepts all standard aquarium foods.

Malpulutta kretseri Deraniyagala • Malpulutta

RANGE: Sri Lanka.

HABITS: Peaceful; should be kept only with small species.

WATER CONDITIONS: Soft, slightly acid water is optional. Temperature 24 to 27°C.

SIZE: About 4 cm.

FOOD REQUIREMENTS: Mosquito larvae eagerly taken; can be trained to take frozen and freeze-dried foods.

Belontia hasselti (Cuvier & Valenciennes) • Java Combtail

RANGE: Java, Bali, Borneo, Sumatra.

HABITS: Peaceful for a large anabantoid.

WATER CONDITONS: Composition of water not critical, but temperature is; the temperature should not be allowed to fall below 24°C.

SIZE: Up to 10 cm in the aquarium; probably larger in the wild.

FOOD REQUIREMENTS: Accepts all standard aquarium foods.

COLOR VARIATIONS: The spot at the base of the rear of the dorsal fin on males varies in size and intensity from fish to fish; over-all body color ranges from golden to light brown.

Pseudosphromenus cupanus dayi (Koehler) • Day's Paradise Fish

RANGE: Southeast Asia.

HABITS: Peaceful and easy to keep.

WATER CONDITIONS: Not critical as long as clean and warm. Temperature 24 to 28°C.

SIZE: Up to 8 cm.

FOOD REQUIREMENTS: Not at all choosy; will thrive on most foods (prepared, frozen, etc.).

Macropodus concolor

Belontia hasselti

Macropodus opercularis (blue)

Macropodus opercularis

Pseudosphromenus cupanus

Macropodus opercularis (albino)

Malpulutta kretseri

Pseudosphromenus cupanus dayi

Colisa chuna (female)

Colisa chuna (male)

Colisa labiosa (pair)

Colisa fasciata (male)

Colisa lalia (female)

Colisa lalia (male)

Sphaerichthys osphromenoides

Colisa lalia (var. sunset)

Plate #419

621

Colisa chuna (Hamilton-Buchanan) • Honey Gourami

RANGE: India.
HABITS: Peaceful and shy.
WATER CONDITIONS: Soft, slightly acid water desirable.
 Temperature 24 to 28°C.
SIZE: 6 cm.
FOOD REQUIREMENTS: Will accept some dry foods, but
 prefers small living foods, especially crustaceans.

Colisa labiosa (Day) • Thick-lipped Gourami

RANGE: India and Burma.
HABITS: Peaceful and rather shy; a good fish for the com-
 munity aquarium.
WATER CONDITIONS: Requires warmth, otherwise not criti-
 cal as to water conditions if extremes are avoided.
 Temperature about 25°C.
SIZE: 10 cm; usually somewhat smaller.
FOOD REQUIREMENTS: Live foods preferred, but in the
 absence of these, prepared foods are acceptable.

Colisa fasciata (Bloch & Schneider) • Giant Gourami

RANGE: India: Coromandel Coast, Northwest and North
 Provinces, Assam.
HABITS: Peaceful; a good community fish.
WATER CONDITIONS: Not critical; they like warm water.
 Temperature 25 to 26°C.
SIZE: Males about 12 cm; females a little smaller.

Colisa lalia (Hamilton-Buchanan) • Dwarf Gourami

RANGE: India, Bengal and Assam.
HABITS: Very peaceful; likely to be shy and retiring if kept
 with fishes which annoy it.
WATER CONDITIONS: Water should be neutral to slightly
 acid; enjoys a tank which gets a good amount of sunlight.
 Temperature 24 to 27°C.
SIZE: Largest males never exceed 6 cm; females 5 cm.
FOOD REQUIREMENTS: Not a fussy eater. Dried foods ac-
 cepted, but should be alternated with live foods.

Sphaerichthys osphromenoides Canestrini • Chocolate Gourami

RANGE: Malaysia and Sumatra.
HABITS: Peaceful and very shy; better kept by themselves.
WATER CONDITIONS: Very soft, slightly acid water. Tem-
 perature should never drop below 24°C, and should be
 around 28°C.
SIZE: 5 cm; usually a bit smaller.
FOOD REQUIREMENTS: Live foods should be fed at all times;
 this fish shows little interest in dried or frozen foods.

Trichogaster microlepis (Guenther) • Moonbeam
Gourami

RANGE: Thailand.
HABITS: A fairly peaceful fish, but large specimens tend to
be bullies, at least with others of their species.
WATER CONDITIONS: Soft, slightly acid water best, but this
is not of great importance. Temperature 24 to 29°C.
SIZE: Up to 15 cm.
FOOD REQUIREMENTS: Takes prepared, frozen and live
foods.

Trichogaster leeri (Bleeker) • Pearl Gourami,
Leeri, Mosaic Gourami

RANGE: Thailand, Malayan Peninsula, Penang, Sumatra
and Borneo.
HABITS: Peaceful and inclined to be a bit shy; may be kept
in any community aquarium.
WATER CONDITIONS: Not critical, but water should be rather warm, about 26°C. A full-grown pair should be kept in
a good-sized tank, at least 60 liters.
SIZE: 10 cm.
FOOD REQUIREMENTS: Will eat any kind of dried foods,
but should also get live foods occasionally.

Trichogaster pectoralis (Regan) • Snakeskin Gourami

RANGE: Southeastern Asia.
HABITS: Peaceful and entirely harmless to other fishes,
even young ones.
WATER CONDITIONS: Soft, slightly acid water. Temperature
24 to 27°C.
SIZE: To 26 cm in their home waters; mature at 10 cm.
FOOD REQUIREMENTS: Not choosy as to food; dry food
accepted as well as frozen and live foods.

Trichogaster trichopterus (Pallas) • Three-spot
Gourami, Blue Gourami

RANGE: Southeastern Asia and the Indo-Malaysian Archipelago.
HABITS: Peaceful in a community tank with fishes which
are not too small.
WATER CONDITIONS: Not critical, but slightly acid, soft
water is best. Temperature 24 to 28°C.
SIZE: To 15 cm.
FOOD REQUIREMENTS: Takes any food, dried as well as live
or frozen.

Trichogaster microlepis

Trichogaster leeri

Trichogaster trichopterus (wild)

Trichogaster pectoralis

Trichogaster trichopterus

Trichogaster trichopterus (cosby)

Trichogaster trichopterus (gold)

Trichogaster trichopterus (white)

624

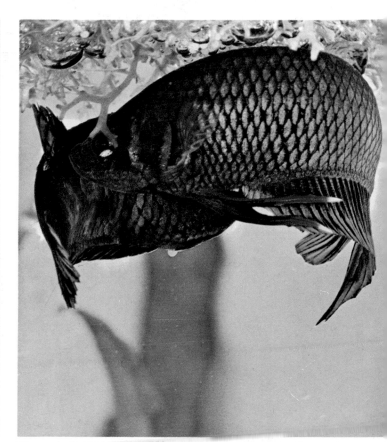

The female waits under the nest for the approach of the male. Her obviously egg-laden condition is a good sign that she is ready to spawn, and the white "pimple" at her vent is further proof.

The male (longer fins) sidles up to the female under the nest (which is seen to contain eggs from previous embraces during this same spawning) and will soon wrap his body around the female's.

Having expelled and fertilized the eggs (visible at the female's vent and right under the head of the male), the spawning partners separate. The male recovers more quickly than the female and will collect the eggs while the female remains semi-paralyzed for a few moments.

The *Betta* fry shown here have hatched and will soon attempt to leave the nest, but at this stage they're not quite ready to swim freely yet.

Plate #421

BREEDING BEHAVIOR OF THE SIAMESE FIGHTING FISH

The Siamese Fighting Fish, *Betta splendens*, is one of the most popular of all tropical fish species kept by aquarists, and it's also one of the easiest species to induce to spawn. Assuming that the potential spawning partners are not physically deficient as the result of abuse or genetic deformity, *Betta splendens* usually will spawn if the sexes are separated before spawning and the temperature of the water in which the potential parents are kept is brought up to within a degree or two of 27°C.

The male's readiness to spawn is evidenced by his construction of the nest of bubbles into which the eggs will be placed during and immediately after the spawning itself; the female's readiness is indicated by her general plumpness in the belly area.

At the beginning of the spawning ritual, the male chases the female around the tank with much blustering and fin-slapping and gill-flaring, accompanied by occasional nips (and, unfortunately, an occasional beating to death in cases in which the male and female are simply incompatible or the female is unable to signify willingness to spawn). Once the parents come into agreement and settle down to spawn they position themselves under the nest, and the male wraps his body around the female, who turns belly-up during the nuptial embrace. The female then releases a group of eggs, which are fertilized by the clouds of sperm released by the male. The eggs slowly sink to the bottom of the tank, and the male follows to retrieve them; some he catches on the fly, before they've reached the bottom, and others he picks up after they've hit the bottom. After being retrieved, the eggs are ejected from the male's mouth into the bubblenest; the eggs generally stay put once they're in the nest, but sometimes eggs fall out and have to be placed back into the nest by the male. (The female, incidentally, sometimes helps in the egg-retrieval process.)

The spawning embrace/egg release/egg retrieval sequence is repeated until the female is depleted of eggs or the spawning breaks off for some other reason, but in any event the female should be removed after it has become plain that she is no longer welcome in the spawning tank. The male often will make that plain enough, but in some cases the parents can be left together in the spawning tank with no fighting at all. The male should be left in the tank at least for the first day or two after the spawning so that he can tend the nest and eggs; at the 27°C temperature suggested as proper for spawning it usually takes a little longer than a day for the eggs to hatch, and it takes about another day and a half before the fry become capable of wandering away from the nest area.

Other nest-building anabantoids have spawning patterns similar in the main to that exhibited by *Betta splendens*, although variations in the pattern are of course shown from species to species. The variations for the most part consist of differences regarding whether the eggs rise or sink, whether the male allows the female to play any part in retrieving the eggs or tending the nest, the extent and thickness of the nest and the degree to which it incorporates vegetation, how badly the male beats up on the female and things like that—but regardless of which species is involved and regardless of whether the aquarist will make any attempt at all to raise the fry, the spawning act itself is fascinating to watch.

Macrognathus siamensis (Guenther) • Spot-finned Spiny Eel

RANGE: Thailand.

HABITS: Fairly peaceful with fishes its own size or not too much smaller, but it has been known to attack tiny species and half-grown individuals of large species.

WATER CONDITIONS: Soft, slightly acid water is best. Temperature 24 to 29°C.

SIZE: Up to 25 cm.

FOOD REQUIREMENTS: Usually reluctant to accept dry foods, although will sometimes pick these up from the bottom; tubifex worms are eagerly accepted.

Mastacembelus circumcinctus Hora • Half-banded Spiny Eel

RANGE: Thailand.

HABITS: Found in lakes and sluggish rivers. Although generally peaceful, it should not be trusted with small fishes.

WATER CONDITIONS: Not choosy as long as the water is relatively warm (to about 26 or 27°C) and clean.

SIZE: Probably reaches at least 200 mm, but most specimens under 150 mm.

FOOD REQUIREMENTS: Like other spiny eels, it prefers living foods of small to medium size, especially worms and crustaceans. Can be adapted to prepared foods.

Mastacembelus "Smith" • False Armatus Spiny Eel

RANGE: Southeast Asia.

HABITS: A small, peaceful eel that is not yet identified. The rows of spots along the middle of the back and at the base of the dorsal fin seem to resemble the variable *M. armatus,* but the rest of the pattern of the body and head is quite distinctive. Spiny eels are often hard to identify and their variability makes the situation even more complex.

WATER CONDITIONS: Likes warm, clean water, like other spiny eels.

SIZE: Seems to be a small species, under 150 mm in length.

FOOD REQUIREMENTS: Prefers live foods but will take some prepared foods.

Mastacembelus zebrinus Blyth • Zebra Spiny Eel

RANGE: Burma.

HABITS: A generally peaceful fish, but not above eating baby fishes.

WATER CONDITIONS: Not critical if extremes are avoided. Temperature 22 to 26°C.

SIZE: Up to 46 cm in the wild; usually seen at no more than 13 cm.

FOOD REQUIREMENTS: Small moving live foods are preferred, but prepared foods are readily accepted, provided pieces are not too large.

Mastacembelus armatus (Lacepede) • White-spotted Spiny Eel

RANGE: India, Sri Lanka, Thailand and Sumatra.

HABITS: Mostly nocturnal; should have places where it can hide.

WATER CONDITIONS: Not important as long as the water is clean. Temperature 24 to 27°C.

SIZE: To 76 cm in native waters.

FOOD REQUIREMENTS: Living or frozen foods, especially worms.

Mastacembelus erythrotaenia Bleeker • Spotted Fire Eel

RANGE: Java, Borneo and Sumatra.

HABITS: Mostly nocturnal and a bit shy at first; hiding places should be provided.

WATER CONDITIONS: Not important as long as the water is clean. Temperature 24 to 26°C.

SIZE: To 46 cm.

FOOD REQUIREMENTS: Very fond of worms and other live foods such as daphnia and brine shrimp.

Macrognathus siamensis

Mastacembelus armatus

Mastacembelus circumcinctus

Mastacembelus circumcinctus

Mastacembelus "Smith"

Mastacembelus armatus

Mastacembelus zebrinus

Mastacembelus erythrotaenia

Plate #422

628

Tetraodon cutcutia

Tetraodon cutcutia

Tetraodon palembangensis

Tetraodon palembangensis

Carinotetraodon somphongsi (female)

Carinotetraodon somphongsi (male)

Tetraodon fluviatilis

Carinotetraodon lorteti

Plate #423

Tetraodon cutcutia Hamilton-Buchanan • Malayan Puffer

RANGE: Malaysia and parts of India, in fresh and brackish
   waters.
HABITS: Quarrelsome toward other fishes and even among
   themselves.
WATER CONDITIONS: Hard, alkaline water with salt added,
   one teaspoonful per 4 liters. Temperature 24 to 27°C.
SIZE: To 15 cm.
FOOD REQUIREMENTS: Live foods in the larger sizes or
   chopped-up pieces of table shrimp; crushed snails are a
   delicacy.

Tetraodon palembangensis Bleeker • Figure-eight Puffer

RANGE: Southeastern Asia and Malaysia Peninsula.
HABITS: A fin-nipper; tends to be pugnacious.
WATER CONDITIONS: Does best in water to which a teaspoon
   of salt per 4 liters has been added.
SIZE: Up to 18 cm.
FOOD REQUIREMENTS: Prefers larger live foods like fishes
   or shrimp.

Carinotetraodon somphongsi (Klausewitz)•
Somphongs' Puffer

RANGE: Tachin River system of Thailand.
HABITS: Peaceful toward fishes other than puffers.
WATER CONDITIONS: For best results the water should be
   neutral to slightly alkaline and moderately hard. The
   recommended temperature range is 23 to 26°C.
SIZE: Attains a length of at least 7 cm in aquaria, possibly
   larger in the wild.
FOOD REQUIREMENTS: Live foods, especially snails are
   preferred, but pieces of frozen foods are accepted.

Tetraodon fluviatilis Hamilton-Buchanan • Round-
spotted Puffer

RANGE: Widespread from India to the Philippines, including
   Southeast Asia and the East Indies.
HABITS: In nature this is a fish of the estuarine areas, sometimes ascending larger rivers. Although commonly
   found in pure fresh water, it is more typically a brackish
   water fish. Like all other puffers, it is a fin-nipper and
   can be dangerous to any other fishes in the aquarium.
WATER CONDITIONS: Warm water with a good bit of salt
   added (at least one teaspoon per 4 liters) is best, but the
   fish is actually quite adaptable.
SIZE: Reaches at least 150 mm in length, but usually smaller.
FOOD REQUIREMENTS: Takes most live foods and also prepared foods. Crustaceans and molluscs are sometimes
   preferred.

Carinotetraodon lorteti (Tirant) • Red-bellied Puffer

RANGE: Thailand and adjacent areas.
HABITS: An estuarine to riverine fish that is almost strictly
   freshwater. Males are distinguished by the red fold of
   skin on the belly and the bright red markings at the bases
   of the fins. Peaceful.
WATER CONDITIONS: Moderately hard and warm water
   (25°C) is recommended.
SIZE: Seldom exceeds 50-60 mm in the aquarium.
FOOD REQUIREMENTS: Live foods are accepted over prepared foods, but the fish will eventually adapt to frozen
   or freeze-dried preparations.

Australasian Region

Anguilla marmorata

Anguilla marmorata

Anguilla bicolor

Ophisternon sp.

Gymnothorax polyuranodon

Scleropages jardinii

Nematalosa sp. cf. papuensis

Thryssa scratchleyi

Plate #424

633

Anguilla marmorata Quoy & Gaimard • Giant Long-finned Eel

RANGE: Widely distributed in the Indo-Pacific region.
HABITS: Occurs mostly in coastal freshwater streams. Although most of their life is spent in fresh water, they migrate to the sea to spawn. Small individuals can be kept in aquaria, but they are very adept at getting out of the tank and wandering across the floor. Therefore a good tank cover is needed.
WATER CONDITIONS: Not critical as long as extremes are avoided.
SIZE: Attains a length of up to 2 meters.
FOOD REQUIREMENTS: Eels accept a wide variety of meaty foods and pose no feeding problems in home aquaria.

Anguilla bicolor McClellend • Short-finned Freshwater Eel

RANGE: Philippines through the East Indies to New Guinea and the Bismarck Archipelago.
HABITS: Inhabits coastal freshwater streams. Migrates to the sea to spawn and die. Tanks must be well covered as these eels are masters at getting out. The anterior nostrils may be orange.
WATER CONDITIONS: Not critical. The surroundings must be relatively clean.
SIZE: Attains a length of about a meter.
FOOD REQUIREMENTS: Carnivorous (at least in adults) and will accept a variety of foods. Not to be trusted with smaller fishes.

Gymnothorax polyuranodon (Bleeker) • Freshwater Moray Eel

RANGE: East Indies to New Guinea and the Fiji Islands.
HABITS: Occurs in rivers near the mouths. Like other morays, this one has sharp teeth and must be handled with care.
WATER CONDITIONS: Not critical. Can withstand some salt in the water.
SIZE: Attains a length of about 70 cm.
FOOD REQUIREMENTS: Morays feed on small fishes and invertebrates. Squid normally is a favorite food.

Nematalosa cf. *Papuensis* (Munro) • Golden-cheek Herring, Fly River Threadback Herring

RANGE: Apparently endemic to New Guinea.
HABITS: A schooling fish that occurs at least in the Fly River of New Guinea. Probably not suitable for home aquaria.
WATER CONDITIONS: Should have plentiful aeration. Otherwise, not much is known about the keeping of this species.
SIZE: Attains a length of at least 22 cm.
FOOD REQUIREMENTS: This is a filter-feeder and should receive as food small filterable material that is floating in the water.

Ophisternon sp. • Dusky One-gilled Eel

RANGE: Not known, but inhabits at least New Guinea.
HABITS: An estuarine eel that enters fresh waters. Like other species in the family Synbranchidae, this eel has a single gill opening on the lower surface of the throat.
WATER CONDITIONS: Can be maintained in fresh, brackish, or salt water.
SIZE: Not known, but probably 50 cm or more.
FOOD REQUIREMENTS: Normally feeds on small fishes and invertebrates. Aquarium foods are usually accepted.

Scleropages jardini (Kent) • Northern Spotted Barramundi

RANGE: Northern Australia and New Guinea.
HABITS: Normally a surface-feeder that will eat smaller fishes as well. Must be kept in a relatively large tank. A buccal incubator.
WATER CONDITIONS: Not critical, although the species may be a bit sensitive to temperature changes. No salt should be added to the water.
SIZE: Attains a length of at least 50 cm.
FOOD REQUIREMENTS: Primarily small fishes and crustaceans. Larger individuals will even take frogs.

Thryssa scratchleyi (Ramsay & Ogilby) • Fly River Anchovy

RANGE: Known only from freshwater rivers of New Guinea.
HABITS: A fairly common species in the Upper, Middle, and Lower Fly River. They possibly are catadromous (migrating to the sea to spawn). The identification is somewhat doubtful.
WATER CONDITIONS: Anchovies are usually extremely delicate fishes that do not do well in aquaria. Many species die as soon as they are touched by a net. Normal aquarium conditions can be tried.
SIZE: One of the largest species of the family, with the maximum known length 37.1 cm.
FOOD REQUIREMENTS: Apparently feeds on fishes in nature. These can be easily supplied in aquaria along with other meaty fare.

THE SEA CATFISHES, FAMILY ARIDAE

The sea catfishes, as their name implies, are predominantly marine or estuarine catfishes, although some of the species are restricted to fresh water. The species that are encountered in New Guinea are mostly freshwater catfishes, with some species found in brackish or fully marine environments.

Identification of the various species (or even genera) of sea catfishes is very difficult, leading to a lot of confusion among workers in the group and aquarists who wish to keep them. Fortunately, the differences between the various species as far as keeping them in captivity is concerned or their life histories are not great enough to be of any consequence. One of the main problems with these catfishes (and many other catfishes as well) that aquarists should be aware of is the potential of the dorsal and pectoral spines for inflicting nasty wounds. These spines are strong, sharp, and serrated, and with the fish thrashing about in the net or in one's hand with these spines extended there are bound to be accidents. That they could also become entangled in the aquarium net is obvious.

One of the most interesting aspects of the life history of the sea catfishes is their method of brooding eggs. The eggs are quite large, approximately 15 mm in diameter, and are retained in the mouth of the male parent for the duration of the incubation period. The male does not eat at all during this time, which may last for approximately two weeks. As usual for mouthbrooders with large, yolky eggs, the number of eggs per spawning is somewhat limited. An average seems to be in the neighborhood of some 200 to 300 eggs.

Some species are relatively small (15-20 cm) but others can grow quite large (to a meter). Only the smaller species or the young of the larger species can readily be kept in the size tanks normally maintained by aquarists. A 200-liter tank would not be overly large for any of these fishes. The water conditions are not critical, and these fishes can be kept in freshwater tanks quite easily. They can stand the addition of salt to the tank, but it must be remembered that the New Guinea species are mostly riverine in habitat.

Feeding ariid catfishes does not seem to be a problem. They will accept a variety of meaty aquarium foods, especially chopped shrimp and chopped fishes. They normally feed on the bottom in typical catfish fashion.

Hemipimelodus papillifer

Arius "leptaspis"

Arius n. sp. #1

Arius graeffei

Brustarius nox

Hemipimelodus velutinus

Arius solidus

636

Plate #425

Arius stirlingi

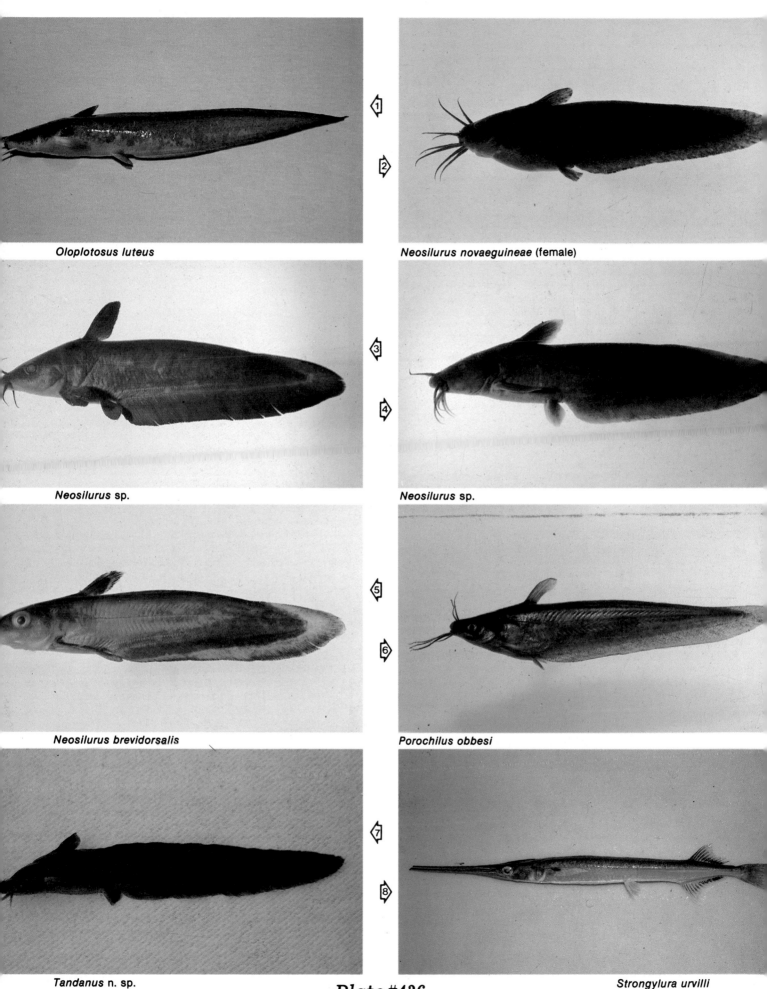

Oloplotosus luteus

Neosilurus novaeguineae (female)

Neosilurus sp.

Neosilurus sp.

Neosilurus brevidorsalis

Porochilus obbesi

Tandanus n. sp.

Strongylura urvilli

Plate #426

637

Oloplotosus luteus Gomon & Roberts • Orange-whiskered Catfish

RANGE: Known only from the highlands of the Fly River, New Guinea.
HABITS: This is a catfish of moderate to swift waters where the bottom consists of variable-sized rocks and cobbles.
WATER CONDITIONS: Not critical. Being from swift-flowing currents means that the water should be clean, clear, and well aerated. Normal temperatures should prevail.
SIZE: Attains a length of about 14 cm.
FOOD REQUIREMENTS: Will accept a variety of aquarium foods such as chopped shrimp and fishes.

Neosilurus sp. • Tandans (two species?)

RANGE: Papua New Guinea, one from the Bensbach River (# 3) and one from near Bewani (# 4).
HABITS: Like the other species of tandans, these two species are bottom-fishes that grub around searching for food. The dorsal fin spine is stiff and strong and may be poisonous. As possibly new species, nothing much is known about their habits.
WATER CONDITIONS: Not critical. Efficient filtration is necessary, and a relatively high level of aeration is recommended.
SIZE: Not known, but should be in the neighborhood of 7-10 cm.
FOOD REQUIREMENTS: Chopped fishes and shrimp suit the tandans quite well. They are able to search them out once they fall to the bottom by using their senses of smell and their barbels.

Neosilurus brevidorsalis (Guenther) • Short-finned Catfish

RANGE: Southern rivers of New Guinea.
HABITS: Apparently restricted to freshwater rivers. A typically bottom-living catfish that grubs in the bottom material for food.
WATER CONDITIONS: Not critical. A good filtration system should be in use as this species tends to stir up the bottom mulm, causing turbid conditions.
SIZE: Attains a length of about 20 cm.
FOOD REQUIREMENTS: Carnivorous; will feed on meaty aquarium foods such as chopped fishes and chopped shrimp.

Tandanus n. sp. • False-spine Tandan

RANGE: Australia.
HABITS: A typical catfish that grubs among the bottom material for good things to eat. Most likely prepares a hollow nest in which to deposit the eggs. Male tandans usually guard the eggs until hatching or even a short time thereafter.
WATER CONDITIONS: Not critical. Can thrive under most normal aquarium conditions.
SIZE: At least 10 cm.
FOOD REQUIREMENTS: Will accept a wide variety of aquarium foods. Make sure that they fall to the bottom where the catfish can most easily dispose of them.

Neosilurus novaeguinea • New Guinea Tandan

RANGE: Western New Guinea (Irian Jaya).
HABITS: Like a typical catfish, it grubs about in the bottom with its barbels, seeking out bits of food.
WATER CONDITIONS: Not critical. Sufficient filtration is necessary. Temperatures for a normal community tank are sufficient.
SIZE: Attains a length of about 7 or 8 cm.
FOOD REQUIREMENTS: Meaty foods that fall to the bottom are best for this catfish.

Porochilus obbesi Weber • Obbes's Catfish

RANGE: Northern Territory of Australia and part of New Guinea.
HABITS: A bottom-dwelling catfish that grubs in the bottom for bits of food. Cannot be trusted with very small fishes.
WATER CONDITIONS: Not critical. Sufficient filtration is required for keeping the tank clean with a fish that stirs up the bottom.
SIZE: Attains a length of at least 8 cm.
FOOD REQUIREMENTS: A carnivorous species that will accept aquarium foods that find their way to the bottom of the tank. Chopped fishes and shrimp are ideal.

Strongylura urvilli (Valenciennes) • D'Urville's Long Tom

RANGE: East Indies and New Guinea.
HABITS: Usually seen in brackish or fresh waters. A surface fish with sharp teeth. This species is not to be trusted with smaller fishes. May aggregate with others of the same species. An excellent jumper. Needs plenty of room.
WATER CONDITIONS: Not critical. Does well in both fresh and brackish water at normal aquarium temperatures.
SIZE: Attains a length of over 40 cm.
FOOD REQUIREMENTS: Small fishes will soon disappear from their tank; will take other foods from or near the surface.

Zenarchopterus dunckeri Mohr • Duncker's River
Garfish

RANGE: Northern shores of New Guinea.
HABITS: Occurs mainly in salt water, but also enters harbors and rivers, where they swim at the surface. This species, like most other *Zenarchopterus*, has a midlateral silvery stripe. Sometimes there is a broad band of dark spots below it. A livebearer.
WATER CONDITIONS: Not critical. Normal temperatures are suitable.
SIZE: Attains a length of about 18 cm.

Zenarchopterus robertsi Collette • Roberts's Garfish

RANGE: Eastern New Guinea (Kumasi River).
HABITS: A livebearer that spends most of its time at or near the surface. It is generally peaceful, but small fishes will be eaten if the opportunity arises.
WATER CONDITIONS: Seems to prefer slightly hard water with a pH a little above neutral. Temperatures can be in the normal range for tropical fishes. In nature the fish is found in clear, fairly swift-flowing streams around logs and debris.
SIZE: Attains a length of at least 13 cm.

NEW GUINEA RAINBOWFISHES

Rainbowfishes were once known basically by a single species or even a mixed bag of species all under the single common name "Australian Rainbowfish," which probably was, or at least included, *Melanotaenia maccullochi*. Recently, however, due to the work of Dr. Gerald R. Allen rainbowfishes have taken on a new meaning and are gaining in popularity as new and different species are presented to the aquarist. Much of the recent popularity is due to the spectacular Red Rainbowfish, *Glossolepis incisus*, with *Melanotaenia herbertax-elrodi* and *M. boesemani* coming up fast in popularity.

Some of the popularity is due to the fact that these simply are nice, peaceful, hardy fishes that are easily spawned in captivity. A tank of about 80 liters capacity can easily house three or four breeding-size rainbowfishes comfortably. The water type is not critical, as rainbowfishes can tolerate a wide range of conditions but seem to do best at temperatures between 22 and 24°C and a pH of about 7. A water hardness around 100-150 ppm is recommended. *Iriatherina* species like the water a bit more on the acid side, as do some *Pseudomugil* species. The tank should be well planted. *Vallisneria*, *Ceratopsis*, and *Fontinalis* are recommended by Dr. Allen. The beauty of these fishes can best be seen when they receive an hour or two of direct sunlight each day. Artificial lighting can make up the difference to keep the plants growing well. The rainbowfishes will eat a variety of aquarium foods. Live foods should be offered on a regular basis (brine shrimp, mosquito larvae, *Drosophila,* and even ants).

The male usually initiates courtship, which consists of chasing, displaying, and intensification of coloration. When ready, the female will accept the male's advances by swimming into a dense plant thicket; the male follows. With the pair side by side the eggs are expelled into the plants, becoming attached there by thread-like filaments. Spawning continues sporadically for a two-week period, with only a few eggs deposited each day. Hatching occurs in about a week to 12 days. Parents can be removed after a week of spawning as they tend to eat the eggs or newly hatched fry. *Iriatherina*, *Pseudomugil*, and *Popondetta* are not prone to this fry-eating habit. Growth is rapid, and sexual maturity is reached before the end of the first year. Small species have a life span of about two to three years, the larger rainbows about four to eight.

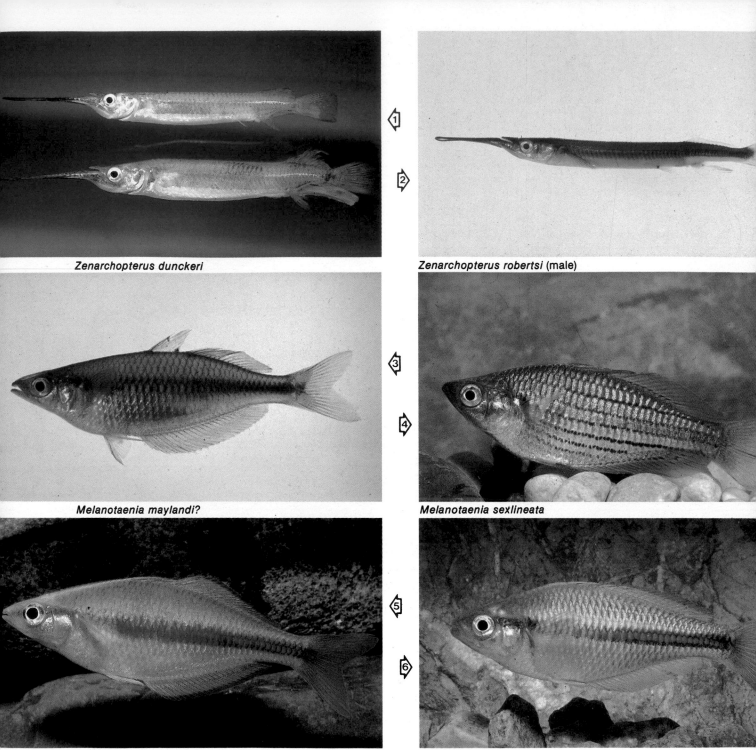

Zenarchopterus dunckeri

Zenarchopterus robertsi (male)

Melanotaenia maylandi?

Melanotaenia sexlineata

Melanotaenia oktediensis

Melanotaenia monticola

Plate #427

Melanotaenia maccullochi (male upper)

Melanotaenia goldiei

Melanotaenia goldiei (male upper)

Melanotaenia goldiei (female)

Melanotaenia herbertaxelrodi (male)

Melanotaenia herbertaxelrodi (female)

Plate #428

641

Melanotaenia monticola (male upper)

Melanotaenia papuae

Habitat of M. sexlineata and M. goldiei

Habitat of M. parkinsoni

Melanotaenia parkinsoni

Melanotaenia parkinsoni

Plate #429

642

Melanotaenia parkinsoni (female)

Melanotaenia parkinsoni (male)

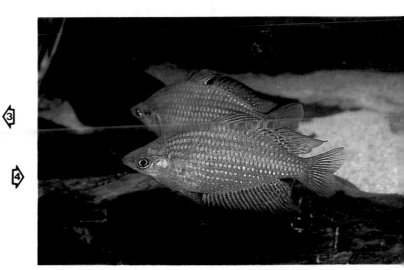

Melanotaenia pimaensis (female)

Melanotaenia splendida rubrostriata

Melanotaenia affinis (male upper)

Plate #430

Melanotaenia affinis (male)

643

Melanotaenia affinis (male)

Melanotaenia boesemani

Chilatherina bulolo

Chilatherina campsi (male)

Chilatherina campsi (male)

Chilatherina campsi (female)

Plate #431

644

Chilatherina crassispinosa (male upper fish)

Habitat of Chilatherina fasciata

Chilatherina fasciata (male upper)

Chilatherina fasciata (male)

Chilatherina axelrodi

Plate #432

Chilatherina lorentzi (female)

645

Glossolepis maculosus (male above)

Habitat of Glossolepis multisquamatus

Glossolepis multisquamatus (male)

Glossolepis multisquamatus (female)

Glossolepis wanamensis

Glossolepis incisus

Plate #433

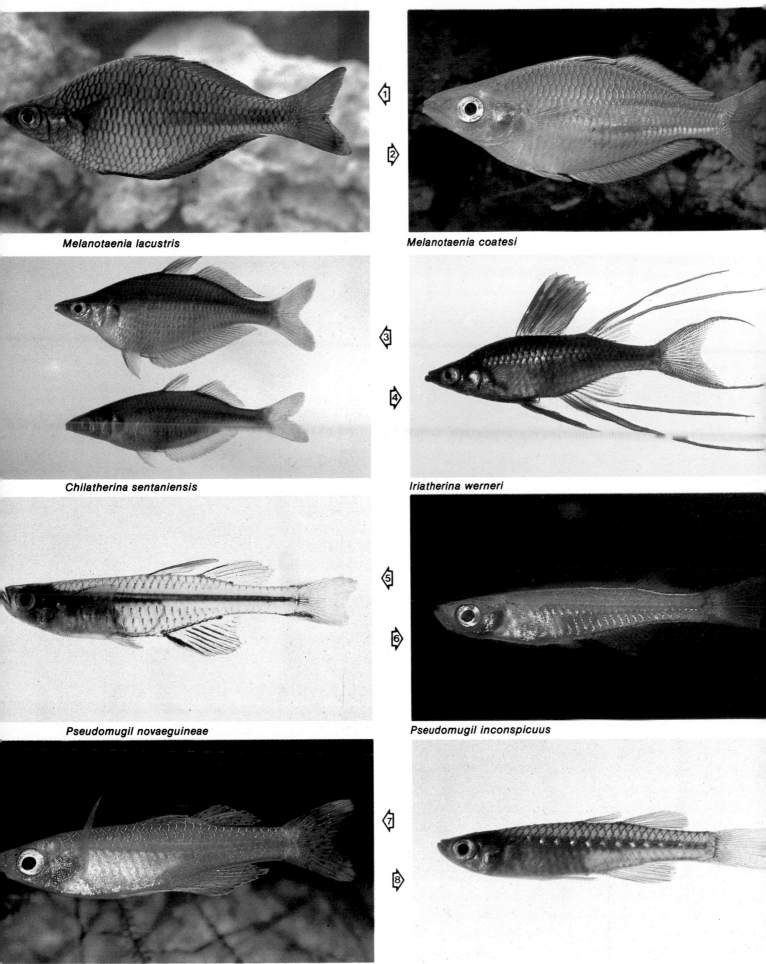

Melanotaenia lacustris

Melanotaenia coatesi

Chilatherina sentaniensis

Iriatherina werneri

Pseudomugil novaeguineae

Pseudomugil inconspicuus

Pseudomugil sp.

Pseudomugil tenellus

Plate #434

647

Pseudomugil paludicola

Iriatherina werneri

Popondetta connieae

Popondetta connieae

Popondetta furcata

Habitat of Popondetta connieae

Plate #435

648

Craterocephalus lacustris

Craterocephalus randi

Craterocephalus n. sp.

Craterocephalus sp.

Craterocephalus n. sp.

Mugil cephalus

Valamugil buchanani

Liza vaigiensis

Plate #436

649

Craterocephalus lacustris Trewavas • Lake Kutubu Hardyhead

RANGE: Apparently restricted to Lake Kutubu in New Guinea.

HABITS: A strictly freshwater species that usually is found along the perimeter of the lake near the surface. Sheds small, slightly adhesive, demersal eggs. Colors of the spawning pair may become stronger at that time.

WATER CONDITIONS: Not critical. Does best in pure fresh water but is tolerant of salt. Temperatures of 23-28°C are acceptable.

SIZE: Attains a length of about 13 or 14 cm.

FOOD REQUIREMENTS: Feeds mainly on insects and small crustaceans. Small live foods are best, but it will accept other aquarium foods in time.

Craterocephalus randi Nichols & Raven • Kubuna River Hardyhead

RANGE: At least the Kubuna and Fly Rivers of New Guinea, possibly also northern Australia.

HABITS: Occurs in swift-flowing riffles as well as deep pools. Spawns by shedding tiny eggs that adhere to vegetation, rocks, etc.

WATER CONDITIONS: Not critical. Normal temperatures for aquaria are recommended.

SIZE: Attains a length of about 3 cm.

FOOD REQUIREMENTS: In nature feeds on aquatic insect larvae, filamentous algae, and bits of higher aquatic plants. A balanced diet including vegetable matter should therefore be offered.

Craterocephalus spp. • Hardyheads

Several species of *Craterocephalus* have been collected in New Guinea that have not as yet been identified. These may actually turn out to be new species. They behave in much the same manner as other species of the genus and are often found in small, lively schools. Spawning consists of shedding small adhesive eggs that adhere to objects on the bottom. Food consists of insects (they are beneficial in that they destroy a large number of mosquito larvae) and small crustaceans. Most of the species are no more than 8 cm long.

Mugil cephalus Linnaeus • Striped Mullet

RANGE: Throughout the subtropical and tropical waters of the world in fresh water, brackish water, and pure ocean water.

HABITS: This fish is found in a very wide range of habitats from very deep marine waters to shallow ponds, streams, and rivers that are completely fresh but under tidal influence.

WATER CONDITIONS: Warmer waters and lots of room. Does well in large circular tropical aquaria with either fresh, brackish or salt water. Thrives at temperatures over 20°C.

SIZE: May reach 60 cm, but usually found at half that size.

FOOD REQUIREMENTS: A plankton feeder. Eats brine shrimp when small.

Valamugil buchanani (Bleeker) • Buchanan's Mullet

RANGE: Abundant and widespread in the warmer waters of the Indo-West Pacific region.

HABITS: Inhabits shallow coastal waters, the young usually entering estuaries or penetrating into pure fresh water.

WATER CONDITIONS: Does well in pure fresh to brackish and even marine waters. Temperatures should be in the normal range for tropical species.

SIZE: Attains a length of about 40 cm.

FOOD REQUIREMENTS: Generally feed on fine algae and slime on the bottom mud. Should receive vegetable matter in an aquarium along with other aquarium foods.

Liza vaigiensis (Quoy & Gaimard) • Diamond-scale Mullet

RANGE: Widely distributed in the Indo-West Pacific.

HABITS: A coastal fish in which the young enter estuaries and even move up into pure fresh water. The pectoral fins are black in the juveniles but are yellow-margined in adults.

WATER CONDITIONS: Does well in fresh or brackish water aquaria. Normal aquarium temperatures for tropical species are adequate.

SIZE: Reaches a length of about 45 cm.

FOOD REQUIREMENTS: Feeds on fine algae and bottom slime in nature. In an aquarium it will take some substitutes but should also receive algae or other vegetable matter.

Doryichthys retzi (Bleeker) • Ragged-tail Pipefish

RANGE: East Indies and Philippines to New Guinea, the Bismarck Archipelago, and New Caledonia.
HABITS: This is an estuarine species that commonly enters fresh water. Females deposit eggs in the male's brood pouch. After incubation the male will "give birth" to the young pipefishes. Some of the caudal rays are apparently extended, giving rise to the common name.
WATER CONDITIONS: Does well in brackish or fresh water at temperatures between 23 and 27°C.
SIZE: Attains a length of about 11.5 cm.
FOOD REQUIREMENTS: Should be offered small live foods such as baby brine shrimp or even baby guppies, depending upon the size of the pipefish.

Oostethus brachyurus (Bleeker) • Red-line Pipefish

RANGE: Widespread in the Indo-Pacific.
HABITS: The female deposits eggs in the "brood pouch" of the male, who incubates them until they hatch. In this species the brood pouch is not developed but is reduced to a pair of lateral bony plates that serve to hold the eggs in place.
WATER CONDITIONS: An inhabitant of river mouths and estuaries, so it can tolerate fresh to brackish conditions. Normal aquarium temperatures are sufficient.
SIZE: Attains a length of up to 26 cm.
FOOD REQUIREMENTS: Live foods such as newly hatched brine shrimp are usually necessary to keep pipefishes for any length of time. Baby guppies may also be accepted.

Hippichthys spicifer (Rueppell) • Black-barred Freshwater Pipefish

RANGE: Indo-Pacific.
HABITS: A peaceful fish that should not be kept with aggressive feeders. The female places her eggs in the male's brood pouch and he "gives birth" to the young.
WATER CONDITIONS: Usually found in brackish or fresh water and may be common in the lower reaches of rivers. Can tolerate salt in the water. Temperatures should be in the normal range for tropical species.
SIZE: Attains a length of 17 cm.
FOOD REQUIREMENTS: Usually a bit finicky about feeding. Best results are obtained with live foods, especially brine shrimp.

Toxotes jaculator (Pallas) • Archer Fish

RANGE: India, Burma, Malaysia, Philippines, East Indies and Thailand.
HABITS: Usually peaceful, but individual specimens can be aggressive; not a good community fish unless kept with other fishes liking slightly brackish water.
WATER CONDITIONS: Water should be slightly salty; tank should be large. Temperature 23 to 29°C.
SIZE: Over 15 cm, but always sold at a much smaller size.
FOOD REQUIREMENTS: Best food is live insects which the fish captures for itself, but it will accept meaty substitutes; some hobbyists claim that it will accept dry food, but this depends on the individual fish.

Toxotes lorentzi Weber • Primitive Archerfish

RANGE: Northern Territory of Australia and New Guinea.
HABITS: Like other archerfishes, this species will shoot insects out of the overhanging vegetation by using droplets of water propelled with deadly accuracy. The scales are smaller than in the other species.
WATER CONDITIONS: Fresh to slightly brackish water is acceptable. Normal water temperatures are proper.
SIZE: Attains a length of about 14 cm.
FOOD REQUIREMENTS: Will accept a variety of aquarium foods. Insects and insect larvae are, of course, preferred.

Toxotes chatareus (Hamilton-Buchanan) • Seven-spotted Archer Fish

RANGE: India to the New Hebrides (including the Indo-Australian Archipelago, Thailand, Vietnam, Philippines, New Guinea and northern and northeastern Australia).
HABITS: Peaceful to slightly aggressive; best kept with other brackish water fishes.
WATER CONDITIONS: Although pure fresh or pure salt water can be tolerated, brackish water is best. Temperature 22 to 28°C.
SIZE: A maximum size of about 20 cm is attained; usually smaller in aquaria.
FOOD REQUIREMENTS: Live foods, especially insects, are best; other foods, even hamburger meat, are also accepted.

Doryichthys retzi

Doryichthys retzi

Oostethus brachyurus

Oostethus brachyurus

Hippichthys spicifer

Toxotes lorentzi

Toxotes jaculator

Toxotes chatareus

Plate #437

Ambassis reticulata

Ambassis miops

Ambassis interrupta

Ambassis near reticulata

Ambassis buruensis

Parambassis gulliveri

Parambassis confinis

Parambassis near confinis

Plate #438

653

Ambassis reticulata Weber & De Beaufort • Reticulated Perchlet

RANGE: Southern Papua. If this is a synonym of *A. macleayi* as is suspected, it actually occurs from New Guinea to Australia.
HABITS: A freshwater glassfish.
WATER CONDITIONS: Not critical. Can take salt added to the water.
SIZE: About 8-9 cm.
FOOD REQUIREMENTS: Takes most small live foods.

Ambassis miops Guenther • Flag-tailed Glassfish

RANGE: Much of the southern Pacific, including small islands.
HABITS: A bay and estuarine species that penetrates freshwater.
WATER CONDITIONS: Prefers brackish water or fresh water with sizable additions of salt.
SIZE: Reaches at least 10 cm in length.
FOOD REQUIREMENTS: Takes most small invertebrates and small fish fry.

Ambassis interruptus Bleeker • Long-spined Glassfish

RANGE: Andaman Islands, East Indies, the Philippine Islands, New Guinea, and Australia.
HABITS: Seems to prefer brackish mangrove estuaries. Will enter freshwater streams, but ventures no more than about 20 kilometers from the sea.
WATER CONDITIONS: Should be kept in brackish water or water with at least some salt content. Normal aquarium temperatures are acceptable.
SIZE: Attains a length of over 10 cm.
FOOD REQUIREMENTS: Small invertebrates. Brine shrimp, daphnia, cyclops, and bloodworms (chironomid larvae) are best, but other foods are accepted.

Ambassis buruensis Bleeker • Buru Glassfish

RANGE: Found over a very wide range from Southeast Asia to the Pacific Islands.
HABITS: A coastal and estuarine species that also occurs in pure fresh water.
WATER CONDITIONS: Not critical.
SIZE: About 8 cm long.
FOOD REQUIREMENTS: Although it will adapt to prepared foods, it prefers small living foods of all types.

Parambassis gulliveri (Castelnau) • Giant Perchlet, Giant Glassfish

RANGE: Southern New Guinea and northern Australia.
HABITS: Usually occurs in relatively large freshwater rivers that have high turbidity levels. Probably spawns in the summer months. Largest of the glassfishes and probably will outgrow many smaller tanks quickly. Also called *Ambassis gulliveri*.
WATER CONDITIONS: Not critical. Does well under most aquarium conditions.
SIZE: Reaches a length of at least 28 cm.
FOOD REQUIREMENTS: Feeds on small invertebrates. Will accept the usual aquarium live foods and some of the prepared foods.

Parambassis confinis Weber • Papuan Perchlet

RANGE: Irian Jaya and the Sepik River.
HABITS: A species of freshwater rivers and lakes.
WATER CONDITIONS: Warm water is about the only requirement.
SIZE: Over 10 cm long.
FOOD REQUIREMENTS: Like other glassfishes, it will take most small live foods.

Denariusa bandata (Whitley) • Penny Fish

RANGE: Occurs in rivers along the coast of northern Australia.

HABITS: Commonly found in fairly large schools after the wet season, usually in areas where there is heavy weed growth or even in swampy areas. Often eaten by birds (herons, terns, cormorants).

WATER CONDITIONS: Tolerant of most conditions. Although a freshwater species, it can tolerate a good deal of salt in its water.

SIZE: Attains a length of 4.5 to 5 cm.

FOOD REQUIREMENTS: Will accept a variety of aquarium foods, especially live foods.

Tetracentrum apogonoides Macleay • Four-spined Perchlet

RANGE: Southern Papua.

HABITS: A species of freshwater rivers that grows to a rather large size for a glassfish. Easily recognized by the presence of four stout anal spines (most glassfishes have only three).

WATER CONDITIONS: Found in freshwater rivers. Warm, oxygenated water the only requirement.

SIZE: To at least 18 cm.

FOOD REQUIREMENTS: Will take almost all live foods of suitable size.

Xenambassis honessi Schultz • Honess's Perchlet

RANGE: Found near Buna, Papua.

HABITS: Poorly known, but a species of freshwater coastal streams.

WATER CONDITIONS: Uncertain, but can probably tolerate some salt.

SIZE: Only about 8 cm long.

FOOD REQUIREMENTS: Small invertebrates.

Xenambassis simoni Schultz • Simon's Perchlet

RANGE: Known only from near Buna, Papua.

HABITS: An obscure species from freshwater coastal streams.

WATER CONDITIONS: Not known with certainty.

SIZE: About 11 cm long.

FOOD REQUIREMENTS: Takes most small invertebrates, especially insects.

Lates calcarifer (Bloch) • Silver Barramundi; Giant Perch

RANGE: Found in the tropical coastal rivers of Australia and from China to the Persian Gulf.

HABITS: Live most of their early lives in fresh water but move downstream into estuarine waters during spring to late summer to spawn. Large numbers of floating eggs are spawned; the fry hatch out quickly and have absorbed their yolk sacs in about five days.

WATER CONDITIONS: The young do best in fresh water, although they can tolerate the addition of salt to the aquarium water. Temperatures of 27° to 28°C are recommended.

SIZE: Grows quite large, with individuals of close to 2 meters and almost 60 kilos known.

FOOD REQUIREMENTS: Young feed on aquatic insects, small crustaceans, small fishes, and plant material; older giant perch feed mostly on larger fishes and crustaceans.

Kurtus gulliveri Castelnau • Nursery Fish

RANGE: Northern Australia and New Guinea.

HABITS: The male incubates the eggs on a hook that develops on his head.

WATER CONDITIONS: Lives equally well in fresh and brackish waters. Probably hard, alkaline water is preferred. Can survive low oxygen conditions.

SIZE: Attains a length of 63 cm.

FOOD REQUIREMENTS: Requires a well balanced diet, perhaps heavy on shrimp or other meaty foods such as live fishes.

Kuhlia rupestris (Lacepede) • Jungle Perch; Rock Flagtail

RANGE: A fairly common species in torrential rivers of northern Queensland, Australia, but also found from East Africa to the Tuamotu Archipelago in pools and mountain torrents.

HABITS: Freely moves back and forth from marine to fresh water. Possibly spawns in brackish water.

WATER CONDITIONS: Not critical. Does equally well in fresh and salt water. Temperatures 21°C to 26°C suitable.

SIZE: Attains a length of over 50 cm.

FOOD REQUIREMENTS: Feeds mainly on crustaceans but will also take other items, including figs that fall into the water.

Kuhlia marginata (Cuvier) • Spotted Flagtail

RANGE: Widely distributed in the central and western Pacific from Tahiti to the East Indies and Japan to New Guinea.

HABITS: Commonly found in brackish and freshwater environments. An active and hardy fish.

WATER CONDITIONS: Not critical. Does well under a variety of conditions. Normal temperatures should be acceptable.

SIZE: Attains a length of about 21 to 22 cm.

FOOD REQUIREMENTS: Not a fussy eater. Will accept a variety of aquarium foods.

Denariusa bandata

Tetracentrum apogonoides

Xenambassis honessi

Xenambassis simoni

Lates calcarifer

Kurtus gulliveri

Kuhlia rupestris

Kuhlia marginata

Plate #439

656

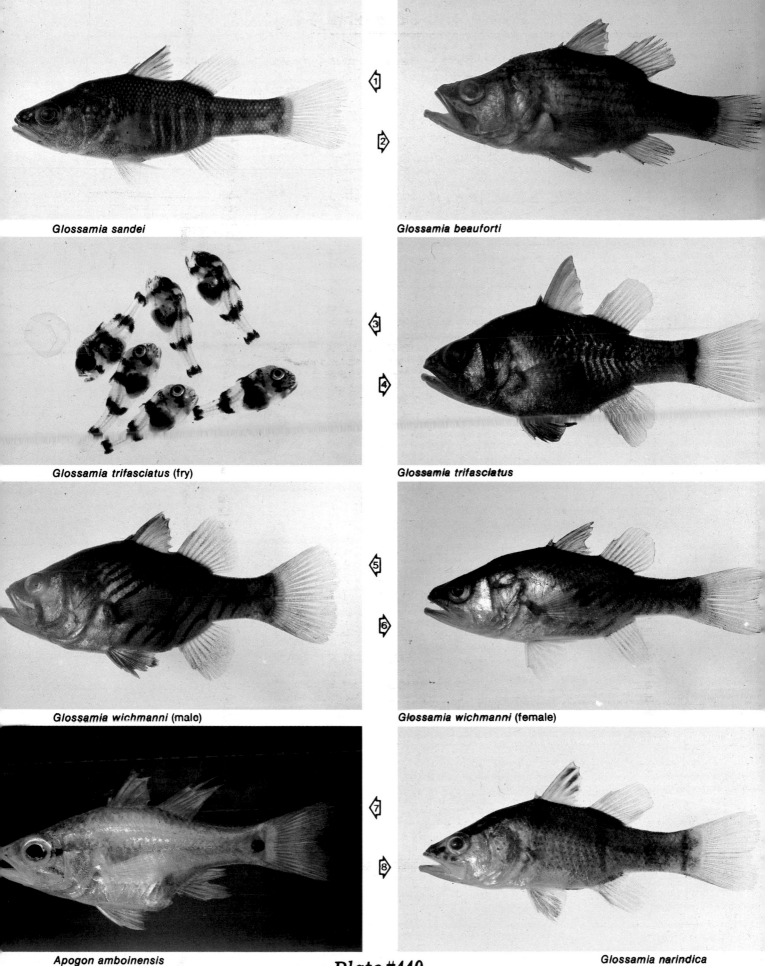

Glossamia sandei

Glossamia beauforti

Glossamia trifasciatus (fry)

Glossamia trifasciatus

Glossamia wichmanni (male)

Glossamia wichmanni (female)

Apogon amboinensis

Glossamia narindica

Plate #440

657

Glossamia sandei (Weber) • Giant Cardinalfish

RANGE: Central and southern New Guinea.
HABITS: Most likely a mouthbrooder, as are many cardinal-fish species in both marine and fresh water. Not to be trusted with fishes that it can swallow.
WATER CONDITIONS: A freshwater cardinalfish of tropical rivers. The water chemistry is not critical and the temperatures should be in the normal range for tropical species.
SIZE: According to Weber, its describer, this species grows to more than 23 cm, making it the largest cardinalfish.
FOOD REQUIREMENTS: Will accept a variety of meaty foods and will dispatch any small fishes that are placed in the aquarium.

Glossamia trifasciata (Weber) • Three-banded Cardinalfish

RANGE: Known only from the rivers of central-southern New Guinea.
HABITS: A freshwater species that is also a mouthbrooder. The three bands that are the basis of both the scientific and common names can readily be seen in the fry in our photo. In the adult they are more obscure.
WATER CONDITIONS: Not critical. A freshwater species that does well in temperatures between 23 and 28°C.
SIZE: Attains a length of about 13 or 14 cm.
FOOD REQUIREMENTS: Accepts chopped fish, chopped shrimp, and other meaty aquarium foods.

Glossamia wichmanni (Weber) • Wichmann's Cardinalfish

RANGE: Northern New Guinea.
HABITS: A mouthbrooder that apparently will spawn year-around if conditions are right. This species has been divided into two subspecies (*A. w. wichmanni, A. w. gjellerupi*) on the basis of number of scales in a lateral series.
WATER CONDITIONS: A freshwater species that will do fairly well under normal aquarium conditions.
SIZE: Attains a length of between 18 and 22 cm.
FOOD REQUIREMENTS: Will accept normal aquarium foods, especially meaty types, along with live fishes.

Apogon amboinensis Bleeker • Ambon Cardinalfish

RANGE: A wide-ranging species distributed in the tropical Indian Ocean and the western Pacific from southern Japan to New Guinea.
HABITS: This is more of a brackish water species in New Guinea, although it does enter fresh water. It is a mouthbrooder.
WATER CONDITIONS: Lives well in both fresh and brackish water. Temperatures between 23 and 28°C are suitable.
SIZE: Attains a length of about 10 cm.
FOOD REQUIREMENTS: Does well on chopped fish, chopped shrimp, frozen foods, and an occasional live fish.

Glossamia beauforti (Weber) • Beaufort's Cardinalfish

RANGE: New Guinea and the Aru Islands.
HABITS: A striking fish with a number of horizontal lines crossing the body. However, it sometimes turns quite dark, obscuring these lines. A mouthbrooder that lives exclusively in fresh water.
WATER CONDITIONS: Not critical. Should be given temperatures in the normal range (about 23-28°C) for tropical species.
SIZE: Attains a length of about 19 cm.
FOOD REQUIREMENTS: Will accept a variety of meaty foods normally available for aquarium fishes. Small fishes are also taken.

Glossamia narindica Roberts • Nose-spot Cardinalfish

RANGE: Known only from the Middle Fly River of New Guinea.
HABITS: A mouthbrooder that apparently spawns year-around with interruptions due only to temporarily un-favorable conditions. This species was described quite recently (1978). Not to be trusted with fishes that are small enough for it to swallow.
WATER CONDITIONS: Not critical. A freshwater tropical species.
SIZE: Attains a length of about 13 cm.
FOOD REQUIREMENTS: This is a piscivore in nature but will accept a variety of meaty foods in the aquarium. Small live fishes of course would be the most natural food.

Pingalla lorentzi (Weber) • Lorentz River Grunter

RANGE: Central portion of southern New Guinea and possibly the Jardine River in Australia.

HABITS: A fairly hardy species that is not very aggressive. Like other species in this family, it makes grunting noises at times.

WATER CONDITIONS: Not critical. A tropical species, so temperatures should be between 23 and 28°C.

SIZE: Attains a length of at least 6-7 cm.

FOOD REQUIREMENTS: Will accept a variety of aquarium foods. Some vegetable matter should be included in its diet.

Hephaestus lineatus • Lined Grunter

RANGE: Apparently known only from Irian Jaya in New Guinea.

HABITS: Generally carnivorous and should not be trusted with fishes much smaller than itself. Fairly active and nicely patterned.

WATER CONDITIONS: Not critical. Does well in standard aquarium setups at normal temperatures.

SIZE: Attains a length of at least 10 cm.

FOOD REQUIREMENTS: Not a fussy eater. Will accept a variety of aquarium foods.

Hephaestus adamsoni (Trewavas) • Adamson's Grunter

RANGE: Known from Lake Kutubu in New Guinea, some 3,000 feet above sea level.

HABITS: Typical of the grunters. An active fish that does well under normal aquarium conditions. Known also as *Therapon adamsoni* and *Madigania adamsoni*.

WATER CONDITIONS: Not critical. Temperatures between 20 and 23°C are proper.

SIZE: Attains a length of about 21-22 cm.

FOOD REQUIREMENTS: Will dine on small fishes as well as any small pieces of shrimp or fish. Will accept frozen aquarium foods.

Terapon sp. • Plain-tailed Flagtail

RANGE: New Guinea. This seemingly undescribed species is very similar superficially to *Hephaestus lineatus* but can be immediately separated by the much higher dorsal spines.

HABITS: Typically found in coastal streams.

WATER CONDITIONS: Unknown, but can probably survive well in most conditions.

SIZE: To about 10 cm.

FOOD REQUIREMENTS: Insects, insect larvae, small crustaceans, smaller fishes; vegetable matter should be offered.

Leiopotherapon affinis (Mees & Kailola) • Fly River Grunter

RANGE: Known only from the Upper, Middle, and Lower Fly and Morehead Rivers, New Guinea. There is a possibility that it is the same species as *Amniataba percoides* of Australia.

HABITS: Somewhat aggressive and active. Not to be trusted with fishes much smaller than itself.

WATER CONDITIONS: Not critical. Normal aquarium temperatures will suffice.

SIZE: Attains a length of at least 10 cm.

FOOD REQUIREMENTS: Eats a number of aquarium foods. Beefheart is said to be a good conditioning food.

Pingalla lorentzi

Leiopotherapon affinis

Hephaestus lineatus (38mm)

Hephaestus lineatus (100mm)

Hephaestus adamsoni

Hephaestus near adamsoni

Terapon sp.

Hephaestus near lineatus

Plate #441

Mogurnda adspersa

Tateurndina ocellicauda

Mogurnda n. sp. #3

Mogurnda n. sp. #4

Mogurnda n. sp.

Mogurnda variegata

Mogurnda sp.

Mogurnda n. sp. #1

Plate #442

NEW GUINEA GOBIES

Of the literally thousands of species of gobies, well over 75% are marine fishes found from shallow muddy estuaries to the white coral sands of tropical reefs. There are a great number of species that have penetrated into freshwater realms in the tropics, however, and freshwater gobies are not uncommon in Central and South America, Africa, and Southeast Asia. However, they probably reach their peak of variety in New Guinea and Australia. Here there are relatively few other freshwater fishes with which to compete for food and living space, and the broad ecological tolerances inherent in gobies have allowed many different types to find homes in the shallow streams and small rivers of these areas.

Unfortunately, few of the New Guinea gobies are imported on a regular basis, although two or three have found what seem to be permanent homes in the aquarium hobby. The numerous species of *Glossogobius* and *Oxyeleotris* are usually just brownish fishes, but they are common and easy to keep in the aquarium. The really exotic types of gobies such as the metallic *Stiphodon*, the high-finned *Sicyopterus*, and the big-mouthed *Butis* are rarities in the aquarium and often come from niches too specialized to allow duplication in the aquarium.

The species of *Mogurnda* and *Tateurndina* are exceptions to the usual rule of inavailability of New Guinea gobies. Because of their bright spawning colors and ease of spawning in the aquarium, they have caught on at least temporarily in the hobby, especially in Europe. *Tateurndina ocellicauda* is now spawned regularly and is seen fairly often in petshops. Its spawning habits were covered in detail in the April, 1983, issue of *Tropical Fish Hobbyist* and illustrated in numerous color photos. Although so far only the Australian *Mogurnda mogurnda* is common in the hobby, the several New Guinea species of *Mogurnda* are very much like it in general appearance and behavior and almost certainly spawn the same way; spawning of *Mogurnda mogurnda* was covered in the June, 1984, issue of *Tropical Fish Hobbyist*.

Ophieleotris aporos

Oxyeleotris sp.

Oxyeleotris sp.

Oxyeleotris sp.

Oxyeleotris sp.

Oxyeleotris herwerdinii

Mogurnda sp.

Ophiocara porocephala

Plate #443

663

Butis amboinensis

Eleotris sp.

Hypseleotris cyprinoides

Gobiomorphus n. sp.

Glossogobius n. sp. #13

Glossogobius celebius

Glossogobius sp.

Glossogobius n. sp. #16

Plate #444

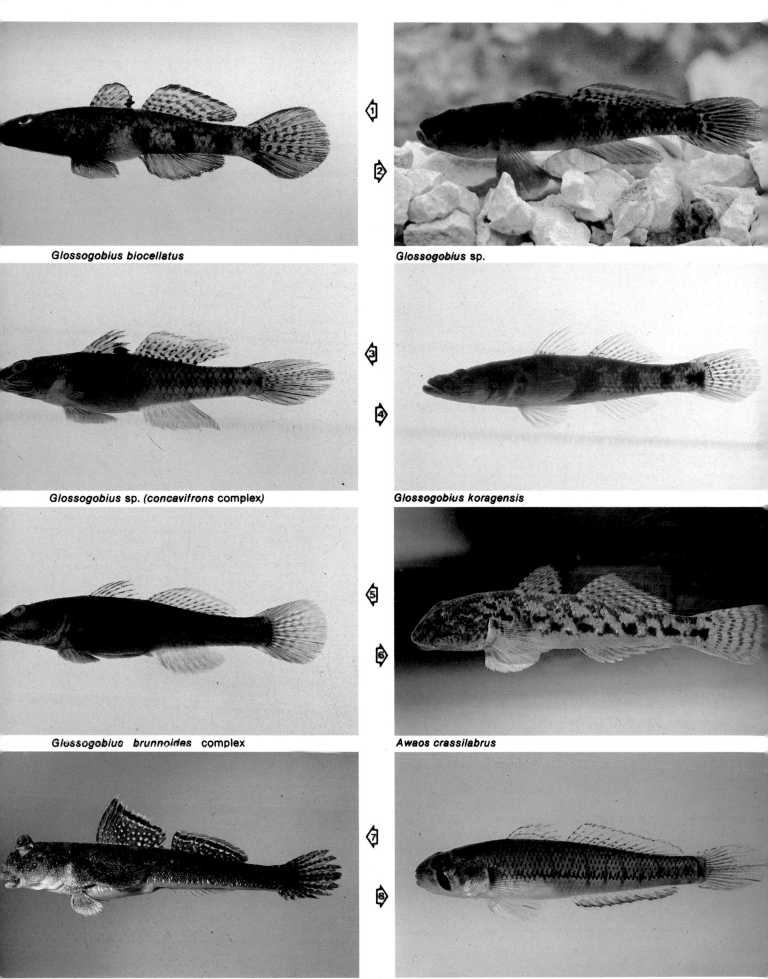

Glossogobius biocellatus

Glossogobius sp.

Glossogobius sp. *(concavifrons* complex)

Glossogobius koragensis

Glossogobius *brunnoides* complex

Awaos crassilabrus

Periophthalmus vulgaris

Stenogobius genivittatus

Plate #445

665

Belobranchus belobranchus

Stiphodon elegans

Sicyopterus cyanocephalus

Sicyopterus zosterophorus

Sicyopterus longifilis

Redigobius bikolanus

Plate #446

666

Lates calcarifer

Anguilla reinhardti

Anguilla bicolor

Ophisternon candidum

Zenarchopterus dispar

Hippichthys spicifer

Plate #447

Anguilla reinhardti Steindachner • Long-finned Eel

RANGE: Eastern coast of Australia as well as New Caledonia and Lord Howe Island.
HABITS: Spawns in the ocean, producing pelagic eggs. The young eels (elvers) return to fresh water and after several years make their own spawning run to the sea.
WATER CONDITIONS: Elvers can be kept in fresh, brackish or salt water. The tank must be carefully covered to prevent them from getting out.
SIZE: Large adults may grow to almost a meter in length but usually are much smaller. Elvers of about 30 cm or so are usually the ones kept in aquaria.
FOOD REQUIREMENTS: These are carnivorous fish and can be fed small fishes, pieces of fish and shrimp, and other meaty foods.

Lates calcarifer
See Plate #463

Ophisternon candidum (Mees) • Blind Freshwater Eel

RANGE: Found only in the dark, subterranean waters of North West Cape, Western Australia.
HABITS: The most obvious character of this eel is that it is eyeless. Its living color is white (the specimen seen here is preserved) as in most cave-dwelling species. Despite its lack of eyes, it gets around quite well and is able to find its food without much ado.
WATER CONDITIONS: Probably would prefer water on the alkaline side with temperatures in the range of 23-27°C. The aquarium should be dimly lighted.
SIZE: Attains a length of about 37 cm.
FOOD REQUIREMENTS: Will accept a variety of meaty foods, especially those that give off an odor for it to home in on.

Anguilla bicolor
See Plate #424

Zenarchopterus dispar (Cuvier & Valenciennes) • Spoon-fin Garfish

RANGE: From Queensland in Australia to the East Indies.
HABITS: Occurs in marine environments as well as the still waters of mangrove creeks and rivers. Often seen in small shoals at the surface. A livebearer, the male with a modified anal fin.
WATER CONDITIONS: Not critical. Normal aquarium conditions will suffice.
SIZE: Attains a length of about 15 cm.
FOOD REQUIREMENTS: Generally eats insects and small crustaceans. Live foods are probably necessary in the aquarium, at least at first.

Hippichthys spicifer
See Plate #437

Galaxias cleaveri • Mud Galaxias, Tasmanian Mudfish

RANGE: Restricted to swampy environments of coastal Tasmania.

HABITS: Little is known about the habits of this species. It probably spawns in late winter. Captured when drains are being cleaned and may even be dug out of the mud or from under logs.

WATER CONDITIONS: Probably should be kept in slightly acid water at cool temperatures.

SIZE: Attains a length of about 12 cm.

FOOD REQUIREMENTS: Feeds on insects and material obtained from the detritus. Will accept some live and prepared aquarium foods.

Galaxias fuscus • Jellybean Jollytail

RANGE: Known from at least Victoria, Australia.

HABITS: Found in freshwater streams in the colder regions of Australia. A colorful species as can be seen in the accompanying photo. Does well in captivity.

WATER CONDITIONS: Water should be slightly acid and relatively cool (unheated tanks).

SIZE: Attains a length of about 6 cm.

FOOD REQUIREMENTS: Feeds on insects and small crustaceans. Aquarium foods are accepted.

Galaxias nigrostriata Shipway • Striped Galaxias

RANGE: Found only in the southwestern section of Australia.

HABITS: Apparently spawns in peaty water. A pretty species with black stripes bordering an orange, yellow, or white ground color.

WATER CONDITIONS: Fairly hardy but does best in acid water. The use of peat is recommended. Should be placed only in unheated aquaria.

SIZE: A small species of 5-7 cm.

FOOD REQUIREMENTS: Feeds on invertebrates such as small crustaceans and insects and their larvae. Will accept a number of live aquarium foods and eventually some of the prepared foods as well.

Scleropages jardini
See Plate #424

Tandanus sp.
See Plate #453

Galaxias cleaveri

Galaxias fuscus

Galaxias nigrostriata

Galaxias nigrostriata

Scleropages jardini

Tandanus n. sp.

Plate #448

670

Galaxias auratus

Galaxias brevipinnis

Galaxias fontanis

Galaxias fontanis

Galaxias maculatus

Galaxias maculatus

Galaxias johnstoni

Galaxias olidus

Plate #449

671

Galaxias auratus Johnston • Golden Galaxias

RANGE: Occurs only in Lakes Sorell and Crescent and associated rivers in Tasmania.
HABITS: Spawns in the southern winter or spring. A nice aquarium fish because of its golden color.
WATER CONDITIONS: Purely fresh water. A cool-water fish that is eaten by trout.
SIZE: Normally 14 cm, but could grow as large as 24 cm.
FOOD REQUIREMENTS: Feeds on small aquatic insects and crustaceans. Live aquarium foods are acceptable.

Galaxias fontanis Fulton • Swan Galaxias

RANGE: Known only from the upper reaches of the Swan River in Tasmania.
HABITS: Occurs in shallow, rocky, spring-fed streams. Probably spawns during the warm mouths. The entire life is lived in fresh water.
WATER CONDITIONS: Not critical. A cool-water species and should not be placed in a heated aquarium.
SIZE: Usually about 7 cm, but can grow to 9 cm or more.
FOOD REQUIREMENTS: Probably feeds on aquatic insects and crustaceans in the wild. Will accept living aquarium foods and may be coaxed onto prepared foods as well.

Galaxias maculatus (Jenyns) • Common Jollytail

RANGE: Coastal streams of southern and southeastern Australia, Tasmania, New Zealand, the Chatham Islands, Patagonian South America, and the Falkland Islands.
HABITS: Small schools occur in quiet or slowly flowing streams and rivers and at lake margins. Spawning occurs during a full or new moon in autumn after a downstream migration. Several thousand eggs scattered in vegetation are left high and dry until high spring tides cover them again (2 weeks) and they hatch. The larvae spend winter in the sea.
WATER CONDITIONS: A cool-water species that needs an unheated tank.
SIZE: Usually 10 cm, but may grow to almost twice that length.
FOOD REQUIREMENTS: Aquatic and terrestrial insects are its natural foods. Does well on chironomid larvae (bloodworms).

Galaxias johnstoni Scott • Clarence Galaxias

RANGE: Occurs only in the Clarence Lagoon, its tributaries, and the upper Clarence River in Tasmania.
HABITS: An uncommon species that probably is solitary and secretive. Probably bottom-living in both still and moving waters.
WATER CONDITIONS: Strictly fresh water. A cool-water species requiring an unheated tank.
SIZE: Attains a length of up to 10 cm, but usually smaller.
FOOD REQUIREMENTS: Most likely feeds on aquatic insects and small crustaceans as well as other benthic invertebrates. Aquarium fare is accepted, especially live foods.

Galaxias brevipinnis Guenther • Climbing Galaxias

RANGE: Inland lakes of Tasmania and coastal drainages of Australia from Sydney to Adelaide as well as New Zealand and the Chatham, Auckland, and Campbell Islands.
HABITS: Occurs in small rocky streams as well as lakes. A secretive solitary species commonly hiding among the rocks. Some larvae are thought to go to sea on hatching, returning when 4-5 cm long.
WATER CONDITIONS: A cool-water species to be kept in an unheated aquarium.
SIZE: Usually about 16 cm, but can get much larger.
FOOD REQUIREMENTS: Feeds on benthic invertebrates. Aquarium foods, especially live foods, are acceptable.

Galaxias olidus Guenther • Mountain Galaxias

RANGE: Eastern Australia at moderate to high elevations.
HABITS: Occurs in small, loose schools in pools and runs as well as solitary individuals around the rocks of the stream margins. Spawning occurs in the spring (no migration to the sea).
WATER CONDITIONS: Prefers clean, clear, cool waters. Easy to keep.
SIZE: Commonly seen at 6 or 7 cm but can grow to twice that length.
FOOD REQUIREMENTS: Feeds on a variety of insects and other small invertebrates. Aquarium substitutes accepted.

Galaxias occidentalis

Galaxias occidentalis

Galaxias parvus

Galaxias pedderensis

Galaxias rostratus

Galaxias truttaceus

Galaxias tanycephalus

Galaxias tanycephalus

Plate #450

Galaxias occidentalis • Westralian Jollytail

RANGE: Occurs only in the extreme southwestern corner of Australia.
HABITS: Not a very common species and very little is known about it. May be found only in some of the rivers north of Perth and south and west of that city.
WATER CONDITIONS: Not critical. Should be housed in an unheated aquarium.
SIZE: Attains a length of about 12-15 cm.
FOOD REQUIREMENTS: Small aquatic insects and crustaceans. Will accept live aquarium foods such as daphnia, cyclops, mosquito larvae, and chironomid larvae.

Galaxias parvus Frankenberg • Dwarf Galaxias

RANGE: Endemic to southwestern Tasmania.
HABITS: Likes the quiet waters of swamps, backwaters, pools and lake margins where there are rocks and abundant vegetation. A spring spawner in which there is no migration to the sea.
WATER CONDITIONS: Not critical. A cool-water species that can only be housed in an unheated tank.
SIZE: A small species of about 7 cm (can grow to 9 cm).
FOOD REQUIREMENTS: Easy to keep and feed. Accepts a variety of aquarium fare, but live foods should be included.

Galaxias pedderensis Frankenberg • Pedder Galaxias

RANGE: Occurs only in Lake Pedder and associated streams in Tasmania.
HABITS: Hides among the rocks along the shores of the lake and the streams. Apparently there is no seaward migration.
WATER CONDITIONS: Not critical, but should only be housed in an unheated tank.
SIZE: Attains a length of 11 cm.
FOOD REQUIREMENTS: Feeds on aquatic invertebrates, especially insects. Will accept aquarium foods, preferably live.

Galaxias rostratus Klunzinger • Murray Jollytail

RANGE: Restricted to the Murray-Darling River system of Australia. Locally abundant.
HABITS: Prefers the quiet waters of lakes, lagoons, and backwaters. Usually seen in midwater schools. Several thousand demersal eggs are scattered randomly at temperatures between 9 and 14°C. They hatch in about 9 days.
WATER CONDITIONS: A cool-water species (note spawning temperatures) that requires an unheated tank.
SIZE: Seldom exceeds about 10 cm.
FOOD REQUIREMENTS: Feeds on a variety of aquatic insects and crustaceans. Aquarium foods are acceptable.

Galaxias truttaceus (Valenciennes) • Spotted Mountain Trout

RANGE: Coastal drainages of southern Victoria, Australia, islands of the Bass Strait, and Tasmania; also found in Western Australia.
HABITS: A fall or early winter spawner whose larvae make a seaward migration. Juveniles return during spring when they are about 5 cm long. Found along the margins of rivers and streams where there is abundant cover and little water movement. Also found under cover on the lake bottoms.
WATER CONDITIONS: A cool-water species requiring an unheated tank.
SIZE: Usually seen at a size of 12 to 14 cm but does get as large as 20 cm.
FOOD REQUIREMENTS: Feeds mostly on insects, both aquatic and terrestrial. Chironomid larvae are an excellent food along with mosquito larvae when available.

Galaxias tanycephalus Fulton • Saddled Galaxias

RANGE: A rare species known only from Arthurs Lake and Woods Lake in Tasmania.
HABITS: Occurs around boulders of man-made groins and apparently shuns the weed beds near these groins. Apparently no migration to the sea.
WATER CONDITIONS: Must have a cool-water aquarium.
SIZE: About 7 cm, but can grow as large as 11 cm.
FOOD REQUIREMENTS: Small aquatic insects and crustaceans are acceptable.

Galaxias maculatus
See Plate #449

Galaxias tanycephalus
See Plate #450

Galaxiella munda • Swan Galaxias

RANGE: This species is known only from just north of Perth to about Albany in southwestern Australia.
HABITS: This is a relatively newly discovered species and little is known about its habits. It is expected to behave much like other species of the genus.
WATER CONDITIONS: Not critical, but should be housed in an unheated aquarium.

Galaxias truttaceus
See Plate #450

SIZE: Probably reaches a length of about 6 or 7 cm.
FOOD REQUIREMENTS: Feeds on small aquatic insects and crustaceans. Similar aquarium foods are accepted.

Paragalaxias mesotes McDowall & Fulton • Arthurs Paragalaxias

RANGE: Only in the central plateau of Tasmania in Arthurs Lake, Woods Lake, and the Lake River below Woods Lake.
HABITS: Seems to prefer to hide among rocks and boulders rather than among vegetation along the shores of the lakes. No seaward migration.
WATER CONDITIONS: A cool-water species that must be kept in an unheated aquarium.
SIZE: Attains a length of a little over 7 cm.
FOOD REQUIREMENTS: Feeds on crustaceans and insects. Aquarium foods, especially live brine shrimp, daphnia, and chironomid larvae, accepted.

Lepidogalaxias salamandroides Mees • Long-finned Galaxias

RANGE: Found only in extreme southwestern Australia.
HABITS: Mating involves internal fertilization after little or no courtship. A week after copulation the ovipositor appears and some 100-150 eggs are laid. The adults usually die shortly after reproducing. Young fish may burrow into the mud bottom for a period of estivation when their pools dry up. Easy prey to fungal infections.
WATER CONDITIONS: The pH should be very low, at least below 6 and possibly even to 4.5. A cool-water species for which the temperature should not exceed 20°C, preferably 12-15°C.
SIZE: Attains a maximum length of 6-7 cm, normally smaller, with females larger than the males.
FOOD REQUIREMENTS: Will accept only live foods.

675

Galaxias maculatus

Galaxias tanycephalus

Galaxias truttaceus

Galaxiella munda

Paragalaxias mesotes

Lepidogalaxias salamandroides

Plate #451

676

Galaxiella pusilla

Galaxiella pusilla

Paragalaxias dissimilis

Paragalaxias dissimilis

Paragalaxias eleotroides

Paragalaxias eleotroides

Paragalaxias julianus

Paragalaxias mesotes

Plate #452

Galaxiella pusilla (Mack) • Eastern Pygmy Galaxias, Dwarf Galaxias

RANGE: Southeastern Australia and Tasmania.
HABITS: Spawns in late winter to early spring, the ripe females courted by 2 to 3 males. A pair will choose the surface of a rock or underside of a leaf, where eggs are laid individually and then ignored. 150-200 eggs per female are laid over a 2-3 week period.
WATER CONDITIONS: A thickly planted aquarium with a slightly acid pH and gentle aeration is recommended. Temperatures should be on the low side as this fish spawns at 16-21°C.
SIZE: A tiny species with 3 cm males and 4 cm females.
FOOD REQUIREMENTS: Live foods are preferred, particularly mosquito larvae, brine shrimp, and small cladoceran crustaceans.

Paragalaxias dissimilis (Regan) • Shannon Paragalaxias

RANGE: Known only from the Central Plateau of Tasmania.
HABITS: Possibly a nocturnal species hiding by day under rocks, vegetation, or other debris and coming up into midwater to feed at night. Will remain in midwater in aquaria when not frightened. No seaward migration.
WATER CONDITIONS: A cool-water species that requires an unheated tank.
SIZE: About 5 cm, but will grow to 7.5 cm.
FOOD REQUIREMENTS: Small midwater crustaceans and aquatic insects. Prefers live foods in aquaria but may be coaxed onto prepared foods.

Paragalaxias eleotroides McDowall & Fulton • Great Lake Darter Galaxias

RANGE: Known only from Great Lake (where it is common) and Shannon Lagoon on the Central Plateau of Tasmania.
HABITS: Hides among the vegetation, rocks, and debris of the lake floor. A bottom fish that will sit propped up on its pectoral fins and scoot about like a goby or darter. No seaward migration.
WATER CONDITIONS: A cool-water species requiring an unheated tank.
SIZE: Attains a length of 4-6 cm.
FOOD REQUIREMENTS: Feeds on aquatic insects and crustaceans. Will accept aquarium foods, especially if alive.

Paragalaxias julianus McDowall & Fulton • Julian Paragalaxias

RANGE: Found only on the high altitude Central Plateau of Tasmania.
HABITS: Common under the cover of rocks, vegetation, and debris on lake bottoms. Little else is known, but there is no apparent seaward migration.
WATER CONDITIONS: A cool-water species that requires unheated tanks.
SIZE: Attains a length of over 9 cm (one of the largest species of the genus).
FOOD REQUIREMENTS: Feeds on aquatic insects and crustaceans. Will accept aquarium fare.

Paragalaxias mesotes
See Plate #451

Neosilurus ater (Perugia) • Black Catfish, Narrow-fronted Tandan, Butter Jew

RANGE: Northern Australia and New Guinea.
HABITS: Has been known under at least three generic names, *Tandanus*, *Neosilurus*, and *Lambertichthys*. Lives on the bottom where it grubs for bits of food. Probably builds a nest for spawning that is guarded by the male.
WATER CONDITIONS: Not critical. A tropical species, so temperatures should be in the normal range for other tropical fishes.
SIZE: May grow to as much as 50 cm.
FOOD REQUIREMENTS: Will accept a variety of foods including small live fishes.

Neosilurus hyrtlii Steindachner • Hyrtl's Tandan

RANGE: Occurs only in the river systems of Queensland, Australia.
HABITS: A bottom-living catfish that grubs along the bottom for food.
WATER CONDITIONS: Not critical. A good filtration system is usually necessary to accommodate the material stirred up by the catfish.
SIZE: Attains a length of at least 40 cm.
FOOD REQUIREMENTS: Carnivorous. Accepts meaty food and live fishes.

Porochilus rendahli • Rendahl's Tandan

RANGE: Australia.
HABITS: Not known for certain. Normally grubs in the bottom material for its food and should be fed accordingly. Some species of tandan are egg-scatterers over gravel in streams where the water is swift-flowing.
WATER CONDITIONS: Not critical. Normal pH and temperatures should apply.
SIZE: Attains a length of about 15 to 20 cm.
FOOD REQUIREMENTS: Accepts a variety of foods that fall to the bottom of the aquarium. Not a fussy eater.

Tandanus bostocki Whitley • Cobbler

RANGE: Found only in rivers of southwestern Australia.
HABITS: A bottom-dwelling catfish that tends to stir up the bottom material. Good filtration is necessary. Said to build nests and that the male guards the eggs and young.
WATER CONDITIONS: Not critical. Temperatures should be on the low side (unheated tank).
SIZE: Attains a length of at least 40-50 cm.
FOOD REQUIREMENTS: Carnivorous. Frozen and fresh chopped fishes and shrimp can be offered along with small live fishes.

Tandanus tandanus Mitchell • Dewfish

RANGE: Endemic to eastern Australian rivers.
HABITS: Creates a saucer-shaped depression in which to lay the eggs. The eggs, about 3.2 mm in diameter, hatch in about a week. In another two weeks the young are 15 mm long and resemble their parents.
WATER CONDITIONS: Not critical.
SIZE: Reaches a length of almost a meter and a weight of about 7 kilos.
FOOD REQUIREMENTS: Feeds in the wild on shellfish and shrimp. In aquaria will accept most frozen foods including chopped meat and dead fishes. Feeds from the bottom as do most catfishes.

Neosilurus ater

Neosilurus ater

Neosilurus hyrtlii

Neosilurus hyrtlii

Neosilurus hyrtlii

Porochilus rendahli

Tandanus bostocki

Tandanus tandanus

Plate #453

680

Scleropages leichardti

Arius berneyi

Arius leptaspis

Neosilurus ater

Neosilurus ater

Neosilurus sp. aff. ater

Plate #454

681

Scleropages leichardti Guenther • Spotted Barramundi

RANGE: Fitzroy River system of Queensland, Australia. Has been introduced elsewhere in Queensland.

HABITS: A buccal incubator. Some 70-200 10-mm eggs are carried in the mouth at one time. Spawning may occur when water temperatures rise above 20°C.

WATER CONDITIONS: Not critical.

SIZE: Reaches a length of almost a meter.

FOOD REQUIREMENTS: Normally feeds at the surface on insects. Will also feed on small fishes, crayfishes, and even frogs. In an aquarium most meaty foods and small live fishes are accepted.

Arius berneyi Whitley • Berney's Catfish

RANGE: Found only in northern and northeastern Australia.

HABITS: Paternal mouthbrooders; that is, males carry the eggs in their mouths during the incubation period of about two weeks. Also called *Hexanematichthys berneyi*. The species was named after the Australian naturalist F.L. Berney.

WATER CONDITIONS: Equally at home in fresh or marine water.

SIZE: Attains a length of up to 20 cm.

FOOD REQUIREMENTS: A carnivorous species that will accept meaty foods and live fishes.

Arius leptaspis (Bleeker) • Salmon Catfish

RANGE: Rivers of coastal Australia and New Guinea.

HABITS: Males incubate some 100-300 eggs in the mouth. The eggs, about 14 mm in diameter, hatch in approximately two weeks, during which period the males do not feed. Also known as *Hexanematichthys leptaspis*.

WATER CONDITIONS: Occurs in pure fresh water to full marine water. Larger individuals are sensitive to colder waters.

SIZE: A mouthbrooding male weighed in at 1.6 kilos. Grows to at least 50 cm.

FOOD REQUIREMENTS: Will accept a wide variety of foods, including small fishes.

Neosilurus ater
See Plate #453

Neosilurus hyrtlii
See Plate #453

Porochilus obbesi
See Plate #426

Pseudomugil mellis Allen & Ivantsoff • Honey Blue-eye

RANGE: Found only in southern Queensland, Australia.
HABITS: Spawns easily in aquaria supplied with Java moss or a similar spawning medium. Eggs placed there in hatch in about 18 hours, the fry feeding on infusoria or fine powdered food. They attain sexual maturity at the end of one year.
WATER CONDITIONS: The water should be acid (pH 4.4 to 5.8) and the temperature on the high side (25°C to 33°C). Their natural water is tea colored and there is dense vegetation.
SIZE: Reaches a maximum size of about 30 mm, most only 25 mm.
FOOD REQUIREMENTS: Feeds on insects and small crustaceans (newly hatched brine shrimp for example), as well as chopped liver and spinach.

Tandanus tandanus
See Plate #453

Ambassis agrammus agrammus Guenther • Sailfin Perchlet

RANGE: Northern Australia and New Guinea.
HABITS: Relatively peaceful, but males may squabble a bit. Most are schooling fishes, and it is best that several be kept together. A fairly efficient mosquito control fish.
WATER CONDITIONS: Not critical. Extremes should be avoided. Can stand a bit of salt in their water.
SIZE: Attains a length of 7 cm.
FOOD REQUIREMENTS: Mosquito larvae, daphnia, and other such live foods are best, but it eventually will accept prepared aquarium foods.

Craterocephalus stercusmuscarum (Guenther) •
Fly-specked Hardyhead

RANGE: Common in northern and northeastern Australian river systems.
HABITS: An excellent and sought-after aquarium species. Swims near the surface and is effective in mosquito control. Said to "leap-frog" over objects floating in its path, so an aquarium cover is necessary.
WATER CONDITIONS: Not critical. Temperature should be about 23°-26°C.
SIZE: Reaches a length of 7.5 cm.
FOOD REQUIREMENTS: Will accept prepared or even dried foods that can be taken near the surface or that float. Of course would prefer small floating insects and larvae.

Neosilurus hyrtlii

Porochilus obbesi

Tandanus tandanus

Pseudomugil mellis

Croterocephalus stercusmuscarum

Ambassis agrammus

Plate #455

Lepidogalaxias salamandroides

Nematalosa erebi

Scleropages jardini

Scleropages leichardti

Retropinna semoni

Retropinna semoni

Anodontoglanis dahli

Neosilurus brevidorsalis

Plate #456

Lepidogalaxias salamandroides
See Plate #451

Scleropages jardini
See Plate #424

Scleropages leichardti
See Plate #454

Nematalosa erebi (Guenther) • Bony Bream

RANGE: Rivers of Australia.
HABITS: Spawns in the Australian spring and summer months. A schooling fish.
WATER CONDITIONS: Not critical, but should have plentiful aeration.
SIZE: Attains a length of about 40 cm.
FOOD REQUIREMENTS: In the wild it feeds on vegetable matter (algae and aquatic plants), insects, and organic material filtered from the ingestion of mud. Aquarium foods should contain vegetable matter. Chironomid larvae and mosquito larvae are also very good.

Retropinna semoni (Weber) • Australian Smelt

RANGE: Southeastern Australia.
HABITS: Active surface schooling fish that help eradicate mosquito larvae. The coloration is such that the fish are almost invisible against a sandy background.
WATER CONDITIONS: Lives in both fresh and salt water. Prefers cooler water temperatures than the northern Australian tropical species.
SIZE: Normally 5 to 6 cm, rarely to twice that size.
FOOD REQUIREMENTS: Mosquito larvae, various worms, and even dry food.

Anodontoglanis dahli (Rendahl) • Toothless Catfish
RANGE: Restricted to northern Australia. Relatively rare.
HABITS: Builds saucer-shaped nests in sand or gravel bottom. Will breed in small ponds. The flesh is orange-colored and considered excellent.
WATER CONDITIONS: Not critical.
SIZE: To at least 15 cm.
FOOD REQUIREMENTS: Bottom feeders that will eat almost anything that is available. Although the mouth is toothless, there are "teeth" in the gullet.

Neosilurus brevidorsalis
See Plate #426

Neosilurus sp.
See Plate #453

Melanotaenia splendida fluviatilis (Castelnau) • Crimson-spotted Rainbowfish

RANGE: Coastal section of southern Queensland and northern New South Wales.
HABITS: Relatively peaceful and suitable for a community aquarium. This subspecies has been considered as a distinct species by some authors. It inhabits a variety of environments including streams, lakes, ponds, and reservoirs but seems to prefer clear water with minimal flow.
WATER CONDITIONS: Not critical. A hardy species that can live within a pH range of 5.3-7.5 and a temperature range of 18 to 28°C.
SIZE: Males grow to about 9 cm but are normally only 7 cm; females grow to about 6.5 cm.
FOOD REQUIREMENTS: Prefers live foods but will accept other aquarium foods as well.

Rhadinocentrus ornatus Regan • Southern Soft-spined Rainbowfish

RANGE: Southern Queensland and northern New South Wales Australia.
HABITS: Active mid-water swimmers; peaceful.
WATER CONDITIONS: Neutral to slightly alkaline water to which a little bit of salt has been added. Temperature should range from about 22 to 26°C.
SIZE: Attains a length of about 8 cm.
FOOD REQUIREMENTS: Will readily accept most common aquarium foods, but for best conditioning should have some live foods.

Pseudomugil mellis
See Plate #455

Strongylura kreffti (Guenther) • Long Tom

RANGE: Northern and northeastern Australia and New Guinea.
HABITS: These are surface fish capable of not only leaping from the water, but they engage in "tail-walking" along the surface. This is an efficient predator so it cannot be kept with smaller fishes. Sometimes seen in small schools or aggregations.
WATER CONDITIONS: Not critical. Can tolerate some salt in the water.
SIZE: Reaches a length of about 65 cm.
FOOD REQUIREMENTS: Does best on small fishes that swim near the surface. Will accept shrimp and other meaty food if it remains in the upper water levels.

Melanotaenia trifasciata (Rendahl) • Banded Rainbowfish

RANGE: Restricted to the Northern Territory and Cape York Peninsula of Australia.
HABITS: This species spawns daily, releasing 30-50 eggs per spawning. The eggs hatch in about a week, yielding tiny fry that need the smallest of foods (infusoria or egg yolk infusion).
WATER CONDITIONS: Needs clean, fresh water with a pH of 7.5 and a hardness of 50-200 ppm. Trouble occurs if the pH drops below 6.8. The temperature should be on the high side, 24-30°C.
SIZE: Attains a maximum size of 9-10 cm.
FOOD REQUIREMENTS: An avid consumer of duckweed, green algae, and other vegetable matter. Mosquito larvae, daphnia, brine shrimp, and other live foods preferred, but will take frozen and prepared foods.

Pseudomugil signifer Kner • Southern Blue-eye

RANGE: Australian states of Queensland and New South Wales.
HABITS: A peaceful, active fish.
WATER CONDITIONS: Prefers alkaline, slightly hard water but is adaptable to life in water of different composition. Best temperature range 22 to 26°C.
SIZE: To about 6 cm for males.
FOOD REQUIREMENTS: Accepts all standard aquarium foods except large, chunky prepared foods.

Pseudomugil gertrudae Weber • Gertrude's Blue-eye

RANGE: New Guinea and Aru Islands to Queensland, Australia.
HABITS: A peaceful, active species.
WATER CONDITIONS: Not critical, but prefers hard alkaline water, perhaps with some salt added. The best temperature range is 20 to 26°C.
SIZE: A small species rarely exceeding 2.5 cm in length.
FOOD REQUIREMENTS: Does well on live foods such as mosquito larvae, tubificid worms, etc.

Neosilurus sp.

Strongylura kreffti

Melanotaenia splendida fluviatilis

Melanotaenia trifasciatus

Rhadinocentrus ornatus

Pseudomugil signifer

Pseudomugil mellis

Pseudomugil gertrudae

Plate #457

688

Cairnsichthys rhombosomoides

Rhadinocentrus ornatus

Iriatherina werneri

Pseudomugil tenellus

Pseudomugil signifer

Pseudomugil signifer

Plate #458

689

Cairnsichthys rhombosomoides (Nichols & Raven) •
Cairns Rainbowfish

RANGE: Inhabits only a small area in the vicinity of Cairns, Queensland, Australia.

HABITS: A relatively short-lived species (maximum about 3 years) that is somewhat delicate to handle. With sufficient water from their natural habitat they may make it to your aquarium safely and are relatively easy to care for from then on. Males have yellow margins on the dorsal and anal fins.

WATER CONDITIONS: Once acclimated to captivity, this species can be cared for in the same manner as the rainbowfishes. A pH that is neutral to slightly alkaline and a temperature of 22-24°C should suffice.

SIZE: Males grow to about 7 cm, females to 6.5 cm.

FOOD REQUIREMENTS: It is best to start with live foods such as brine shrimp, daphnia, and chironomid larvae. Other aquarium foods can be added in time.

Rhadinocentrus ornatus
See Plate #457

Iriatherina werneri Meinken • Featherfin Rainbow

RANGE: West Irian (on island of New Guinea). Queensland

HABITS: Peaceful and active.

WATER CONDITIONS: pH and hardness are not critical, as long as extremes are avoided. Temperature 24 to 27°C.

SIZE: To about 4 cm.

FOOD REQUIREMENTS: Accepts most standard aquarium foods, but only in small sizes.

Pseudomugil tenellus Taylor • Delicate Blue-eye

RANGE: This small species is known only from the East Alligator River system of the Northern Territory, Australia.

HABITS: A typical habitat would be a marshy pond or quiet backwater with mud or gravel bottoms and abundant vegetation. The water may be green with suspended algae, and water lilies float on the surface.

WATER CONDITIONS: The water can be neutral to slightly acid and the temperature a bit on the warm side (28-35°C in nature).

SIZE: Reaches a length of only about 2.6 cm.

FOOD REQUIREMENTS: Should be fed the finest of live foods (newly hatched brine shrimp is good).

Pseudomugil signifer
See Plate #457

Melanotaenia eachamensis Allen & Cross • Lake Eacham Rainbowfish

RANGE: Known only from Lake Eacham on the Atherton Tableland in Queensland.

HABITS: A lake-dwelling species of rainbowfish that prefers the clear, shallow water along the shoreline. Relatively peaceful, making a suitable community tank fish. A well planted tank is recommended.

WATER CONDITIONS: Not critical. A pH of about neutral and a temperature between 23 and 27°C suits them very well. A 20-25% water change every month or so is recommended.

SIZE: Attains a length of about 5-6 cm.

FOOD REQUIREMENTS: Accepts a variety of aquarium foods but should receive some live foods regularly for best results.

Melanotaenia nigrans (Richardson) • Dark Australian Rainbow

RANGE: Northeastern Australia as far south as Sydney.

HABITS: Peaceful and very hardy; prefers to be kept in small groups.

WATER CONDITIONS: Neutral to slightly alkaline water to which a small amount of salt has been added. Temperature 19 to 24°C.

SIZE: To 10 cm.

FOOD REQUIREMENTS: Easily fed; accepts prepared foods as readily as live or frozen foods.

Melanotaenia splendida

This species has been broken up into a number of subspecies, some of which have been known as full species at one time or another. Five of the subspecies (australis, inornata, tatei, fluviatilis, and splendida) occur in Australia, with a sixth (rubrostriata) in southern New Guinea. They are most easily distinguished by their point of origin.

Melanotaenia gracilis Allen • Slender Rainbowfish

RANGE: This species is restricted to the Drysdale and King Edward River systems in the extreme northern portion of Western Australia.

HABITS: Prefers large watercourses and isolated rocky pools. The water flow is usually minimal. A peaceful fish suitable for community tanks.

WATER CONDITIONS: A neutral pH with temperatures between 22 and 24°C is best. The tank should be heavily planted and regular water changes should be made. Some sunlight on the tank is beneficial.

SIZE: Males reach a length of about 7.5 cm, females 6.5 cm.

FOOD REQUIREMENTS: Small live foods are preferred, but it will accept a variety of other foods commonly used for aquarium fishes.

Melanotaenia splendida inornata (Castelnau) • Checkered Rainbowfish

RANGE: Generally streams flowing into the Gulf of Carpentaria in Northern Territory, Australia, but also an island or two in the Torres Straits.

HABITS: A peaceful species suitable for a community tank. Easily spawned in a well planted tank. A couple of hours of sunlight on the tank are beneficial.

WATER CONDITIONS: A neutral pH with temperatures between 22 and 24°C is acceptable. Regular water changes are recommended.

SIZE: Males reach a length of about 10 cm, females 8.5-9.0 cm.

FOOD REQUIREMENTS: Eats a variety of aquarium foods. Live foods should be offered on a regular basis.

Melanotaenia eachamensis (male)

Melanotaenia gracilis (male)

Melanotaenia nigrans (male)

Melanotaenia splendida inornata

Melanotaenia splendida

Melanotaenia splendida inornata (female upper)

Plate #459

692

Melanotaenia nigrans (male upper)

Melanotaenia splendida australis (male)

Habitat of *M. splendida australis*

Habitat of *M. splendida fluviatilis* and *Pseudomugil signifer*

Habitat of *M. splendida inornata*

Plate #460

Habitat of *M. splendida inornata*

Melanotaenia nigrans
See Plate #459

Melanotaenia splendida australis (Castelnau) •
Western Australian Rainbowfish

RANGE: Found in northwestern Australia.

HABITS: Found in rivers, lakes, smaller streams, swamps and marshy lagoons where the water flow is minimal. They occur at or near the surface of deeper pools in stream habitats where there is vegetation or log debris. In lake habitats they are found around the shallow margins.

WATER CONDITIONS: Not critical. A pH range of 6.5-7.8 and a temperature range of 25-32°C occur in their natural habitat. Periodic water changes (20-25% every month or so) are recommended. Some sunlight is beneficial.

SIZE: Males reach 9 cm, females about 7.5-8.0 cm.

FOOD REQUIREMENTS: Normal aquarium foods are accepted, but there is a preference for live foods.

Melanotaenia splendida splendida (Peters) • Eastern
Australian Rainbowfish

RANGE: This species occurs in river systems east of the
Great Dividing Range of Queensland.

HABITS: A very variable species, each stream seeming to
have a different strain. Prefers small streams but also
occurs in lakes and reservoirs. The water in the habitat
varies from clear to turbid and there may or may not be
vegetative cover.

WATER CONDITIONS: Occurs in nature in water temperatures from 20-29°C and a pH range from 6.4-7.2. A 20-25%
water change should be made every month or so.

SIZE: Males grow to 11 cm, females to about 10 cm.

FOOD REQUIREMENTS: Small live foods are preferred, but
it will accept other frozen and prepared foods as well.

Melanotaenia trifasciata
See Plate #457

Melanotaenia splendida splendida (males)

Melanotaenia splendida splendida (male)

Melanotaenia splendida splendida (female upper)

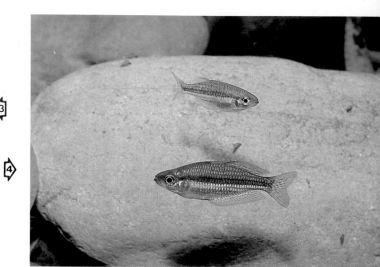

Melanotaenia splendida splendida (male lower fish)

Melanotaenia trifasciata (male)

Melanotaenia trifasciata (male)

Plate #461

Craterocephalus cuneiceps

Craterocephalus marjoriae

Craterocephalus randi

Craterocephalus stercusmuscarum fulvus

Craterocephalus stercusmuscarum

Craterocephalus stercusmuscarum

Craterocephalus sp.

Craterocephalus n. sp.

Plate #462

697

Craterocephalus cuneiceps • Deep Hardyhead

RANGE: Found only in western Australia between 20°S and 30°S latitudes.
HABITS: A poorly known species that probably behaves like other species of the genus.
WATER CONDITIONS: Not critical. Will tolerate some salt in their water. The best temperatures are on the lower side of the normal range for aquaria.
SIZE: Attains a length of about 7 to 8 cm.
FOOD REQUIREMENTS: Does well on live aquarium foods. Known as a destroyer of mosquito larvae.

Craterocephalus marjoriae Whitley • Marjorie's Freshwater Hardyhead

RANGE: Known only from the coastal streams of Queensland, New South Wales, Northern Territory, and northwestern Australia.
HABITS: A schooling species inhabiting shallow waters where there is a sandy substrate. During the breeding season the color changes to a bright canary yellow.
WATER CONDITIONS: Not critical. Easy to keep under normal aquarium conditions.
SIZE: Attains a length of up to 8 cm.
FOOD REQUIREMENTS: Accepts a variety of aquarium foods, even dried foods.

Craterocephalus spp. • Hardyheads

Hardyheads of the genus *Craterocephalus* make relatively good aquarium fishes. They often like to school and are said to lay tiny adhesive eggs of pinhead size. None of them grow very large (between 8 and 10 cm maximum). They feed on small aquatic animals and are inveterate mosquito eaters. Several of the species are quite colorful, especially when in breeding colors.

Quirichthys stramineus Whitley • Strawman; Blackmast

RANGE: River systems of northern Australia.
HABITS: With external teeth on its lips the strawman is able to scrape the surface of plants and other submerged objects. It has even been reported to nibble on wader's legs. Peaceful and hardy and makes an excellent aquarium fish.
WATER CONDITIONS: Not critical. A neutral pH and water temperature around 23° to 26°C are recommended. Addition of salt to the water is possible.
SIZE: Attains a length of about 7 cm.
FOOD REQUIREMENTS: Will accept a variety of aquarium foods as long as they are small. Will also scrape plant leaves for food.

Ophisternon sp. • Single-gilled Eel

These eels make unusual aquarium inhabitants and are usually kept only by aquarists looking for something different. They are usually hardy but seem to be able to escape from aquaria quite easily through even the most minute space. A cover is therefore highly recommended.

Priopidichthys sp. • Plain-head Perchlet

RANGE: Coastal areas of New Guinea.
HABITS: The species of this genus are often found in fully marine situations and also commonly penetrate estuaries and tidal rivers. Relatives of this possibly undescribed species range from the Indian Ocean to the Pacific Islands.
WATER CONDITIONS: Hard water with salt added is preferable.
SIZE: Reaches at least 10 cm in length.
FOOD REQUIREMENTS: Predaceous on smaller crustaceans and fishes.

Ambassis agrammus agassizi Steindachner • Olive Glassfish, Olive Perch

RANGE: Northwestern, northern, and eastern Australia, with the exception of Northern Territory (range of *A. agrammus agrammus*).
HABITS: Will breed in aquaria. In nature this species is usually found among aquatic vegetation. Very abundant.
WATER CONDITIONS: Not critical. A freshwater fish that could tolerate some salt in its water if necessary. Normal aquarium temperatures should prevail.
SIZE: Attains a length of at least 7 cm.
FOOD REQUIREMENTS: Small invertebrates are eaten in nature. Live aquarium foods are acceptable (brine shrimp, daphnia, bloodworms, mosquito larvae, etc.).

Ophisternon gutturale (Richardson) • One-gilled Eel

RANGE: Northern Australia near river mouths.
HABITS: This estuarine eel commonly and regularly enters fresh waters. It has no paired fins, no scales, minute eyes, and a single gill opening located on the lower surface of the throat.
WATER CONDITIONS: Lives well in fresh, brackish or even full salt water.
SIZE: Grows to more than 60 cm.
FOOD REQUIREMENTS: Feeds on small invertebrates and fishes. Will accept a variety of prepared and frozen aquarium foods.

Lates calcarifer
See Plate #439

Quirichthys stramineus

Ophisternon gutturale

Ophisternon sp.

Lates calcarifer

Priopidichthys

Ambassis agrammus agassizi

Ambassis agrammus agassizi

Ambassis agrammus agassizi

Plate #463

Ambassis agrammus

Ambassis agrammus

Ambassis agrammus

Ambassis agrammus

Ambassis agrammus

Ambassis elongatus

Ambassis interruptus

Ambassis interruptus

Plate #464

701

Ambassis agrammus
See Plate #455

Ambassis elongatus
See Plate #465

Ambassis interruptus
See Plate #438

Ambassis elongatus (Castelnau) • Yellowfin Glassfish

RANGE: Gulf of Carpentaria drainage of northern Queensland, Australia.

HABITS: Occurs in freshwater streams that frequently have moderate to high turbidity levels. Often occurs in schools.

WATER CONDITIONS: Not critical. Normal aquarium temperature ranges are sufficient.

SIZE: Attains a length of at least 4-5 cm.

FOOD REQUIREMENTS: Small invertebrates are eaten in the natural environment. Aquarium foods, especially live foods, are acceptable.

Ambassis commersoni Cuvier & Valenciennes • Commerson's Glassfish

RANGE: A wide-ranging species that is found from the western Indian Ocean to the Fiji Islands. Its range includes the Philippines and Australia.

HABITS: This is an estuarine species that will ascend rivers into pure fresh water.

WATER CONDITIONS: Does well in pure fresh water as well as brackish water. Normal temperature ranges are acceptable.

SIZE: Attains a length of at least 10 cm.

FOOD REQUIREMENTS: Feeds on small invertebrates. Does well on live aquarium foods. Will accept prepared and frozen foods if coaxed.

Ambassis macleayi Castelnau • Reticulated Glassfish

RANGE: Northern Australia and south-central New Guinea.

HABITS: This species is most usually seen in the heavily vegetated peripheries of swamps and margins of rivers.

WATER CONDITIONS: Prefers pure fresh water in a well planted aquarium. Normal temperatures are sufficient.

SIZE: Grows to about 8 cm.

FOOD REQUIREMENTS: Feeds on small invertebrates. Live aquarium foods such as cyclops, daphnia, brine shrimp, etc. are accepted along with some prepared foods.

Ambassis marianus Guenther • Mary River Glassfish

RANGE: Eastern Australia (Queensland and New South Wales).

HABITS: Occurs in brackish mangrove estuaries, tidal creeks, and the lower reaches of freshwater streams.

WATER CONDITIONS: Occurs naturally in brackish water, so the water should have at least some salt content. Temperatures should be in the normal aquarium range.

SIZE: Attains a length of about 8 cm.

FOOD REQUIREMENTS: Prefers small invertebrates. Brine shrimp, cyclops, daphnia, bloodworms, and other small live foods are best.

Parambassis gulliveri
See Plate #438

Ambassis elongatus

Ambassis elongatus

Ambassis commersoni

Ambassis macleayi

Ambassis macleayi

Ambassis macleayi

Ambassis marianus

Ambassis gulliveri

Plate #465

704

Craterocephalus dalhousiensis

Ambassis macleayi

Parambassis gulliveri

Parambassis gulliveri

Nannoperca n. sp.

Nannatherina bostocki

Leiopotherapon macrolepis

Amphitherapon caudovittata

Plate #466

Craterocephalus dalhousiensis • Dalhousie Hardyhead

RANGE: Known only from east-central Australia.
HABITS: Lays tiny eggs that adhere to submerged objects during the summer months. The sexes are distinguishable on the basis of external shape.
WATER CONDITIONS: Not critical. Can tolerate some salt in the water. A pH slightly on the alkaline side and temperatures between 23 and 27°C are recommended.
SIZE: May attain a length of about 8 cm.
FOOD REQUIREMENTS: Feeds on snails and plant material in nature. Will accept a variety of aquarium foods but should also receive some vegetable matter as well.

Ambassis macleayi
See Plate #465

Parambassis gulliveri
See Plate #438

Nannoperca n. sp. • Golden Pygmy Perch

This new species of Pygmy Perch comes from Australia, probably along the eastern portion of the continent. The small fishes of this genus make excellent aquarium fishes and have been spawned in captivity. The eggs are shed while the parents are swimming and then sink to the bottom, where they adhere slightly. Hatching occurs in about 2-3 days.

Nannatherina bostocki • Shy Mountain Perch

RANGE: Australia.
HABITS: A fish of rivers and cool lakes. Adapts well to aquaria and can probably be bred in captivity.
WATER CONDITIONS: Hard, alkaline water that is relatively cool (20°C) should be tried.
SIZE: Reaches at least 3 cm.
FOOD REQUIREMENTS: Small lives foods of all types are accepted.

Leiopotherapon macrolepis • Kimberley Spangled Perch

RANGE: The northwestern Kimberley region of Western Australia.
HABITS: Maturity is reached at a small size (just over 11 cm). Probably spawns at night, releasing a large number of demersal non-adhesive eggs. Hatching occurs in about two days.
WATER CONDITIONS: Not critical. A hardy species that can adapt to most aquarium conditions.
SIZE: Probably does not grow to much more than 12 or so centimeters.
FOOD REQUIREMENTS: Will accept a variety of aquarium foods, but prefers live foods.

Amphitherapon caudavittatas (Richardson) • Yellowtail Grunter, Flagtail Grunter
RANGE: Western Australia, Northern Territory, Queensland, and New Guinea.
HABITS: Lives equally well in marine and brackish water and enters freshwater estuaries. Not to be trusted with very small fishes.
WATER CONDITIONS: Not critical. Normal aquarium temperatures are adequate.
SIZE: Attains a length of about 25 to 26 cm.
FOOD REQUIREMENTS: Feeds on small invertebrates and fishes. Does well on most aquarium foods.

Ambassis agrammus agassizi
See Plate #463

Denariusa bandata
See Plate #439

Bostockia porosa (Castelnau) • Nightfish

RANGE: Southwestern Australia.
HABITS: This rather drab-looking fish has not become much of a favorite with aquarists. Not only is it not colorful, but it also is nocturnal and not seen very often.
WATER CONDITIONS: Not critical. Since this species is found in temperate Australia it should be placed only in a cool water tank.
SIZE: Attains a length of about 15 cm.
FOOD REQUIREMENTS: Will accept a variety of aquarium foods including small fishes. Remember to feed in dim light or at night.

Macquaria ambiguus (Richardson) • Golden Perch; Yellowbelly

Bidyanus bidyanus (Mitchell) • Silver Perch

RANGE: Eastern Australia.
HABITS: Spawning is induced by a rise in the water level in its natural habitat. It moves upstream when temperatures exceed 23°C to shed up to a half million semi-buoyant eggs. Hatching time is about 30 hours, and the yolk sac is absorbed in about five days. May spawn at 18 cm (2 years old). A schooling fish.
WATER CONDITIONS: Not critical. Can tolerate temperatures from 2° to 37°C (but only for short periods of time at either extreme).
SIZE: Reaches a length of over 60 cm.
FOOD REQUIREMENTS: Feeds on a wide variety of material including aquatic insects, crustaceans, molluscs, plant material, and even plankton. Will accept a variety of aquarium foods.

RANGE: Eastern Australia in sluggish, sometimes turbid, inland rivers.
HABITS: Spawning occurs with a combined rise in water level and a rise in temperature to more than 23°C. Adults appear to move upstream to spawn up to a million eggs that are released into the currents. In about a day and a half hatching occurs, yielding 3.2 mm fry. Females are generally larger than males. May be golden, blackish, or dark above with a yellow belly.
WATER CONDITIONS: Not critical. Will survive under crowded conditions in nature, but this is not recommended in aquaria.
SIZE: Females about 29 cm, males closer to 20-23 cm.
FOOD REQUIREMENTS: Feeds on fishes, crustaceans, molluscs, and other small animals. Will lie in ambush in shady or weedy places waiting for prey animals to pass by. Will accept a wide variety of aquarium foods including feeder fishes.

Ambassis agrammus agassizi

Denariusa bandata

Bostockia porosa

Bidyanus bidyanus

Bidyanus bidyanus

Macquaria ambigua

Plate #467

708

Macquaria australasica

Macquaria colonorum

Maccullochella macquariensis

Maccullochella macquariensis

Maccullochella peeli

Amniataba percoides

Plate #468

709

Macquaria australasica (Cuvier & Valenciennes) •
Macquarie Perch

RANGE: Southeastern Australia, mainly in the cool higher
altitude reaches of the Murray-Darling River systems.
HABITS: Spawning occurs at about three years of age (at
30 cm). Large numbers of eggs are shed in spring or
early summer in shallow, fast-flowing streams. The eggs
are adhesive and become attached to the gravel of the
bottom.
WATER CONDITIONS: Needs clean, clear, cool water that is
highly oxygenated.
SIZE: Attains a length of about 43 cm.
FOOD REQUIREMENTS: Most of the diet in nature consists of
insects or insect larvae. Will accept suitably sized
aquarium foods.

Maccullochella macquariensis (Cuvier & Valenciennes)
Trout Cod

RANGE: Apparently restricted to the Murray River drainage system in southeastern Australia.
HABITS: Spawns (like many of its relatives) with a rise in
water level due to storm runoff and a rise in water
temperature to about 21°C. Close to and possibly the
same species as *M. peeli,* the Murray cod. Said to mature
earlier than the Murray cod.
WATER CONDITIONS: Not critical.
SIZE: To more than 50 cm.
FOOD REQUIREMENTS: Feeds mainly on crustaceans but
also takes molluscs and fishes. Aquarium fare is generally accepted.

Maccullochella peeli Mitchell • Murray Cod

RANGE: Endemic to rivers of eastern Australia.
HABITS: Unlike its close relative the trout cod, the Murray
cod does not seem to need a rise in water level to spawn
(although it helps) but it does need a temperature rise to
20°C or more. More than 20,000 adhesive eggs can be produced. Hatching occurs in 1-2 weeks. The Murray cod has
a marbled pattern and projecting longer jaw; the trout
cod is spotted and has an overhanging upper jaw.
WATER CONDITIONS: Not critical.
SIZE: Attains a length of up to 2 meters. First spawns at
about 50 cm.
FOOD REQUIREMENTS: The greatest part of the diet is
crustaceans, but molluscs and small fishes are also included. Aquarium specimens will accept a variety of
foods. Reported to eat mice in nature if available.

Macquaria colonorum (Guenther) • Estuary Perch

RANGE: Formerly restricted to southern and eastern
Australia (including Tasmania) but may have been introduced into Western Australia and as far as Fiji.
HABITS: Spawns after a downstream migration to estuaries
in late winter or early spring. Small pelagic eggs are produced. The young estuarine perch have dark blotching at
the anterior of the dorsal, anal, and pelvic fins. A second
form, called *novemaculeatus,* is sometimes accepted.
WATER CONDITIONS: Not critical. Does best in the cooler
temperature ranges.
SIZE: Attains a length of about 50-60 cm.
FOOD REQUIREMENTS: A carnivorous species that will accept a variety of meaty aquarium foods.

Amniataba percoides (Guenther) • Black-striped Grunter

RANGE: Rivers of Australia.
HABITS: An aggressive and active fish that cannot be kept
with fishes much smaller than itself.
WATER CONDITIONS: Not critical.
SIZE: Attains a length of about 15 cm.
FOOD REQUIREMENTS: Will accept most live or frozen foods,
especially small feeder fishes.

Maccullochella macquariensis
See Plate #468

Maccullochella peeli
See Plate #468

Amniataba percoides
See Plate #468

Hephaestus fuliginosus (Macleay) • Sooty Grunter

RANGE: River drainages of north and northeastern Australia. Relatively common.
HABITS: Spawning occurs during the summer months (wet season), with tens of thousands of non-adhesive demersal eggs shed that apparently fall into the crevices of the gravel. The fry hatch out in about 42 hours and have absorbed their yolk sac in another 96 hours.
WATER CONDITIONS: Not critical, but the water temperature should not fall below 12°C.
SIZE: Attains a length of 38 cm.
FOOD REQUIREMENTS: Feeds on a variety of items in nature including insects, worms crustaceans, frogs, plant roots, and palm berries that fall into the water.

Hephaestus carbo (Ogilby & McCulloch) • Coal Grunter

RANGE: Found only in northern Australia. Occurrence is very patchy and they are not abundant.
HABITS: Prefers clear, moving water with sandy bottoms. The Coal Grunter first spawns when about 13 cm long. Several thousand adhesive, demersal eggs are shed.
WATER CONDITIONS: Needs clean, clear, well-oxygenated water. The temperature should at least be above 15°C.
SIZE: Attains a length of 18-19 cm.
FOOD REQUIREMENTS: Shrimp and other crustaceans form most of the diet. In aquaria most frozen foods (including shrimp) can be fed.

Hephaestus jenkinsi (Whitley) • Jenkins's Grunter

RANGE: Northwestern Australia.
HABITS: Occupies a variety of waters from clear to turbid and sluggish to swiftly flowing. May also be found over different bottom types including sand, mud, and rocks. Some individuals develop thick fleshy lips such as seen in some fishes of the family Cichlidae.
WATER CONDITIONS: Not critical. Will fare well in most normal aquarium conditions.
SIZE: Attains a length of about 15 cm.
FOOD REQUIREMENTS: Will accept a variety of aquarium foods.

Maccullochella macquariensis

Maccullochella peeli

Amniataba percoides

Hephaestus fuliginosus

Hephaestus carbo

Hephaestus carbo

Hephaestus jenkinsi

Hephaestus jenkinsi

Plate #469

712

Hephaestus carbo

Hephaestus fuliginosus

Leiopotherapon unicolor

Pingalla midgleyi

Scortum barcoo

Syncomistes butleri

Plate #470

713

Hephaestus carbo
See Plate #469

Hephaestus fuliginosus
See Plate #469

Leiopotherapon unicolor (Guenther) • Jewel Perch; Spangled Grunter

RANGE: Widely distributed in Australian river systems. Also found in small pools, isolated billabongs, etc.

HABITS: The jewel perch matures at a small size, and even small fish can produce more than 20,000 eggs (older fish may produce up to 100,000 eggs). Spawning occurs at night once the temperature exceeds 20°C. Hatching occurs in about 50 hours. Also called *Madigania unicolor*.

WATER CONDITIONS: Not critical. Can withstand a wide temperature range (7° to 37°C), but fungal infections may occur at long exposure to temperatures below 10°C.

SIZE: Attains a length of 24 cm.

FOOD REQUIREMENTS: Feeds on small invertebrates such as crustaceans, molluscs, and aquatic insects, as well as plant material. Should be offered a balanced diet including plant material.

Pingalla midgleyi Allen & Merrick • Black-blotch Grunter

RANGE: Apparently restricted to the Katherine and Alligator River systems, Northern Territory, Australia.

WATER CONDITIONS: Not critical. In nature found over sand and rocky bottoms, pH 7-6.2. Fairly hardy and will do well under most normal aquarium conditions. Temperatures should be between 23 and 28°C.

SIZE: Attains a length of 6-15 cm.

FOOD REQUIREMENTS: Feeds primarily on benthic algae. Must be given a good portion of vegetable material in its diet.

Scortum barcoo (McCulloch & Waite) • Barcoo Grunter

RANGE: Occurs only in east-central Australia.

HABITS: Typical of species of *Scortum,* there will be black spots or blotches on the sides at times. These vary considerably in position, size, and number, even on the same fish. In dim aquarium light the Barcoo Grunter becomes silvery in color and the spots tend to disappear. Spawning assumedly occurs after the summer flooding.

WATER CONDITIONS: Not critical.

SIZE: Attains a length of over 30 cm; females mature at 25 cm.

FOOD REQUIREMENTS: Will accept a variety of prepared and frozen aquarium foods.

Syncomistes butleri Vari • Butler's Grunter

RANGE: Western Australia from the Bow to the South Alligator Rivers.

HABITS: Occurs in lagoons, streams and rivers in a variety of conditions. Water movement was slow to rapid and clarity was clear to turbid. Occurred over a variety of bottoms.

WATER CONDITIONS: Not critical. Normal aquarium conditions only are needed.

SIZE: Attains a length of at least 12 cm.

FOOD REQUIREMENTS: Apparently adapted to feeding on filamentous algae. Must give a diet of greens including filamentous algae if possible.

Hephaestus welchi (McCulloch & Waite) • Welch's
Grunter

RANGE: Found only in east-central Australian rivers in sluggish, turbid areas where there are high salt concentra-
tions.
HABITS: Females mature at about 28 cm and may produce up
to 100,000 eggs per spawning. Eggs are semi-buoyant and
non-adhesive, hatching after some 30 hours in the
downstream currents. The yolk sac is absorbed after
about five days.
WATER CONDITIONS: Not critical. Temperatures in the
range of 21° to 25°C are adequate.
SIZE: Attains a length of 35 cm or more.
FOOD REQUIREMENTS: Small fishes and crustaceans are its
basic diet, and these items can be fed in aquaria. Welch's
Grunter will accept other aquarium fare, including
various worms, as well.

Leiopotherapon aheneus Mees • Western Australian
Grunter

RANGE: Known only from the Ashburton and Fortesque
Rivers in Western Australia.
HABITS: The habitat of the Western Australian Grunter is
permanently running water from springs. Juveniles are
reported to have indistinct vertical bands on their sides.
WATER CONDITIONS: Not critical. Should have sufficient
aeration. Temperatures can be on the cool side.
SIZE: Grows to a length of 12 cm, making it one of the smaller
species of grunter and more suitable for aquaria.
FOOD REQUIREMENTS: Feeds on crustaceans and small
fishes. Accepts a variety of aquarium foods, both love
and prepared.

Pingalla lorentzi
See Plate #441

Pingalla midgleyi
See Plate #470

Leiopotherapon
See Plate #470

Pingalla gilberti Whitley • Gilbert's Grunter

RANGE: Found only in the Gilbert, Norman, and Flinders
Rivers, Cape York Peninsula, northern Australia.
HABITS: Similar to that of other grunters. Named for John
Gilbert, naturalist with Leichhardt's expedition, who was
speared by the natives. The Gilbert River was also named
after him.
WATER CONDITIONS: Not critical. Temperatures from 21°C
to 27°C are suitable.
SIZE: Attains a length of about 9 or 10 cm.
FOOD REQUIREMENTS: Accepts a variety of aquarium foods
both live and prepared, but a large vegetable content—
especially filamentous algae—should be included.

Syncommistes butleri
See Plate #470

Hephaestus welchi

Leiopotherapon unicolor

Leiopotherapon aheneus

Leiopotherapon aheneus

Pingalla lorentzi

Pingalla gilberti

Pingalla midgleyi

Syncomistes butleri

Plate #471

716

Syncomistes kimberleyensis

Syncomistes trigonicus

①
②

Edelia vittata

Edelia vittata (male)

③
④

Nannatherina balstoni

Nannatherina australis

⑤
⑥

Nannatherina obscura

Nannoperca oxleyana

⑦
⑧

Plate #472

Syncomistes kimberleyensis Vari • Kimberley Grunter

RANGE: Known only from the Bow River in the Kimberley region of Australia.
HABITS: Little known. Found in an isolated pool over a sand and rock bottom where the water was green and murky.
WATER CONDITIONS: Probably will live well under normal aquarium conditions.
SIZE: Only juveniles of up to 36 mm known.
FOOD REQUIREMENTS: Feeds mainly on filamentous algae. Aquarium specimens should be offered a high vegetable content in their diet.

Syncomistes trigonicus Vari • Triangle Grunter

RANGE: Northwestern Australia, principally the Roe, Prince Regent, and Drysdale River drainages.
HABITS: Occurs in fresh water where it is clear or slightly murky and over a variety of bottom types.
WATER CONDITIONS: Should live well under normal aquarium conditions.
SIZE: Attains a length of at least 13 cm.
FOOD REQUIREMENTS: Its normal diet is filamentous algae. As an herbivore it should receive the bulk of its diet as vegetable matter.

Edelia vittata Castelnau • Westralian Pygmy Perch

RANGE: Endemic to the fresh waters of the southwestern corner of Australia.
HABITS: Has a lifespan of about five years. Some 40 to 50 eggs are laid separately by each female. The Westralian pygmy perch matures in its first year at about 3 cm.
WATER CONDITIONS: Not critical. Comes from a cool water area, so the tank should be kept no higher than room temperature.
SIZE: A small species growing to about 7 or 7.5 cm.
FOOD REQUIREMENTS: Most of its diet consists of insects and insect larvae. To these can be added small-sized aquarium foods both living and frozen.

Nannatherina balstoni (Regan) • Balston's Perchlet

RANGE: Apparently endemic to rivers in the Albany area of southwestern Australia.
HABITS: Although first thought to be a kind of hardyhead (Atherinidae), this species was eventually placed in the Kuhliidae. Said to do well as an aquarium fish.
WATER CONDITIONS: Not critical. This species comes from the cooler latitudes of Australia and should be kept in an unheated tank.
SIZE: Attains a length of only about 7.5 cm.
FOOD REQUIREMENTS: Will accept a variety of aquarium foods.

Nannatherina australis Guenther • Southern Australia Pygmy Perch

RANGE: Endemic to the southeastern portion of Australia including Tasmania.
HABITS: The fins of the male (excepting the pectorals) turn bright red before spawning. Scatters demersal eggs randomly while swimming. The eggs are slightly adhesive and hatch in about three days. Makes an excellent aquarium fish.
WATER CONDITIONS: Not critical. Will spawn at temperatures in the range of 16° to 21°C. Should be maintained at relatively cool temperatures.
SIZE: Attains a length of from 6 to 8 cm.
FOOD REQUIREMENTS: Feeds on insects and insect larvae, small crustaceans, and various prepared aquarium foods.

Nannatherina obscura (Klunzinger) • Yarra Pygmy Perch

RANGE: Known only from Victoria in southern Australia.
HABITS: Similar to the Westralian Pygmy Perch. A very suitable aquarium fish that will breed in captivity. Scatters slightly adhesive (?) eggs randomly.
WATER CONDITIONS: Not critical. Can tolerate lower water temperatures as it comes from a cool temperate area.
SIZE: Length apparently does not exceed 7 cm.
FOOD REQUIREMENTS: Will accept small live foods and some frozen and prepared foods. Be sure to offer a balanced diet.

Nannoperca oxleyana Whitley • Oxleyan Pygmy Perch

RANGE: Coastal waters of southern Queensland and northern New South Wales in Australia. Said to be common in many freshwater dune lakes.
HABITS: A peaceful aquarium fish that is readily spawned. Apparently an egg scatterer.
WATER CONDITIONS: Not critical. Normal temperature range of 21° to 26°C is sufficient.
SIZE: Attains a length of about 7 cm.
FOOD REQUIREMENTS: Will accept a wide variety of live and frozen foods suitable for aquarium fishes.

Edelia vittata
See Plate #472

◁1

2▷

Nannatherina australis
See Plate #472

Nannoperca oxleyana
See Plate #472

◁3

4▷

Toxotes chatareus
See Plate #437

Toxotes oligolepis Bleeker • Few-scaled Archerfish

RANGE: Molucca Islands, Irian Jaya, and Western Australia.
HABITS: Like other archerfishes, this species will spit drops of water at insects in order to knock them into the water so they can be eaten. This is a rare species looking like the banded pattern of *T. jaculator*. It differs by having 5 dorsal fin spines versus 4 for *jaculator*. Peaceful.
WATER CONDITIONS: Not critical. Will thrive in fresh, salt, or brackish water. Temperatures should be around 23-28°C.
SIZE: To 12-13 cm.
FOOD REQUIREMENTS: Small bits of chopped fish and shrimp and a variety of insects including small flies are taken.

Toxotes lorentzi Weber • Primitive Archerfish

RANGE: Northern Territory of Australia and New Guinea.
HABITS: Like other archerfishes, this species will shoot insects out of the overhanging vegetation by using droplets of water propelled with deadly accuracy. The scales are smaller than in the other species.
WATER CONDITIONS: Fresh to slightly brackish water is acceptable. Normal water temperatures are proper.
SIZE: Attains a length of about 14 cm.
FOOD REQUIREMENTS: Will accept a variety of aquarium foods. Insects and insect larvae are, of course, preferred.

Edelia vittata (female)

Nannatherina australis

Nannoperca oxleyana

Toxotes chatareus

Toxotes oligolepis

Toxotes lorentzi

Plate #473

720

Glossamia aprion

Glossamia aprion

Glossamia aprion

Toxotes chatareus

Toxotes oligolepis

Gadopsis marmoratus

Gadopsis marmoratus

Gadopsis marmoratus

Plate #474

Glossamia aprion (Richardson) • Queensland
Mouthbrooder; Mouth Almighty

RANGE: Occurs in river drainages of northern and eastern
Australia and Papua New Guinea.
HABITS: Spawning occurs when temperatures rise beyond
22°C. The eggs are laid in a ball that possibly is
enveloped in a thin membrane. The male picks up the
eggs in his mouth and broods them for about two weeks
(until hatching), apparently without feeding during this
time. May be subdivided into two subspecies: *G. a.*
aprion and *G. a. gilli.*
WATER CONDITIONS: Not critical. Water temperatures of
from 21° to 26°C are suitable.
SIZE: Attains a length of about 17 or 18 cm.
FOOD REQUIREMENTS: Feeds well on small feeder fishes (or
any other small fishes available to it in the aquarium)
and other live foods. Reported to shun dead or non-
moving food.

Toxotes chatareus
See Plate #437

Toxotes oligolepis
See Plate #473

Gadopsis marmoratus (Richardson) • River Blackfish;
Slippery

RANGE: Southeastern Australia, including Tasmania.
HABITS: This mostly nocturnal species lays a few (less than
500) large (about 4 mm diameter) eggs. Eggs were seen
attached to the inside of hollow logs. Adults have been
tamed enough to take food from a person's hand.
WATER CONDITIONS: Not critical. A cool-water species that
requires generally lower temperatures than the tropical
species.
SIZE: Usually seen less than 30 cm long, but attains lengths
of more than twice that.
FOOD REQUIREMENTS: Insects and insect larvae when
small, adding crustaceans, worms, molluscs, and small
fishes to their diet as they grow.

Glossogobius aureus Akihito & Meguro • Golden Goby

RANGE: Tropical western Pacific.
HABITS: A bottom-living species occurring mostly in brackish water.
WATER CONDITIONS: This species is best kept in a brackish water tank. Normal aquarium temperatures are acceptable.
SIZE: Attains a length of over 10 cm.
FOOD REQUIREMENTS: Will accept a variety of aquarium foods, preferably live.

Glossogobius near *celebius* (Valenciennes) •
Reticulated Goby

RANGE: At least in New Guinea (almost the entire island) and northern Australia. *G. celebius* also occurs in the Celebes and other islands near New Guinea. The Australia version of this fish is often called *G. concavifrons*, usually considered to be a synonym of *G. celebius*.
HABITS: Found in both highland and lowland rivers, streams, and lakes. Also in estuarine situations. Very adaptable.
WATER CONDITIONS: Not critical as long as warm and well-oxygenated. Will tolerate salt added to the water but does not need it.
SIZE: Reaches almost 10 cm in length.
FOOD REQUIREMENTS: Prefers insects in all forms, but will adapt to prepared foods.

Mogurnda adspersa (Castelnau) • Purple-spotted Gudgeon

RANGE: Queensland and New South Wales, Australia.
HABITS: Prefers slow-flowing waters with a good supply of weeds and where there are solid objects on which to spawn. They spawn in the warmer months (temperatures 20-34°C) after an elaborate courtship. About 280-1,300 transparent eggs that have an adhesive disc are produced. Males guard. Hatching is in 3 days to a week, and feeding commences in about another week. Males develop nuchal humps.
WATER CONDITIONS: Not critical. Fairly hardy and easy to keep. Will breed in aquaria.
SIZE: Attains a length of 12 cm (more commonly 7 cm).
FOOD REQUIREMENTS: A variety of invertebrates are eaten, particularly insect larvae and worms. Also feeds on small fishes. Aquarium fare is readily accepted.

Mogurnda mogurnda (Richardson) • Purple-striped Gudgeon

RANGE: Most of tropical Australia.
HABITS: Not well known. Most available information probably actually pertains to *M. adspersa*, from which this species differs primarily in scale counts. Occurs in rivers as well as muddy waters.
WATER CONDITIONS: Not critical. Does well under normal aquarium conditions.
SIZE: Normally about 10 cm long, but can grow to over 17 cm.
FOOD REQUIREMENTS: Feeds on small invertebrates. Will accept a variety of aquarium foods.

Hypseleotris aureus • Golden Gudgeon

RANGE: Discovered in the Murchison River, Western Australia.
HABITS: Males are more colorful than females. Small eggs are attached to objects on the bottom and guarded by the male.
WATER CONDITIONS: Not critical. A fairly hardy fish that can be kept under normal aquarium conditions.
SIZE: Attains a length of at least 6 cm.
FOOD REQUIREMENTS: Accepts a wide variety of aquarium foods including prepared foods.

Glossogobius aureus

Glossogobius aureus

Glossogobius near celebius

Glossogobius near celebius

Mogurnda adspersa

Mogurnda mogurnda

Mogurnda near adspera

Hypseleotris aureus

Plate #475

724

Gadopsis marmoratus

Chlamydogobius eremius

Mogurnda adspersa

Mogurnda mogurnda

Hypseleotris galii

Hypseleotris near galli

Plate #476

Chlamydogobius eremius (Zietz) • Desert Goby

RANGE: Central part of Australia to southern part of Northern Territory. Apparently restricted to the Lake Eyre drainage.
HABITS: Inhabits pools and streams associated with artesian springs and bores. Spawns from November to March (southern summer). About 150-250 eggs are produced by each female. The male has a broader head than the female and its genital papilla is long and slender; that of the female is short and stubby.
WATER CONDITIONS: Not critical. This goby exists under all sorts of adverse conditions including sudden changes in salinity and temperature. If the oxygen content drops it can utilize aerial respiration.
SIZE: Reaches a length of about 6 cm.
FOOD REQUIREMENTS: Omnivorous, feeding on filamentous algae, small insects and crustaceans, and detritus. Easy to feed in aquaria.

Gadopsis marmoratus
See Plate #474

Mogurnda adspersa
See Plate #475

Mogurnda mogurnda
See Plate #475

Hypseleotris galii (Ogilby) • Fire-tailed Gudgeon

RANGE: Common in coastal streams of Queensland and New South Wales, Australia.
HABITS: Males fan and guard the eggs until they hatch some 4-5 days later. Males develop nuchal humps and have longer posterior dorsal and anal fin rays. Breeding males also turn dark, the reddish orange of the fins becoming stronger.
WATER CONDITIONS: Purely fresh water. Does well in aquaria that are well planted. Otherwise no particular conditions are necessary.
SIZE: Males grow to 5.5 cm, females to only 4 cm.
FOOD REQUIREMENTS: Feeds on small aquatic invertebrates but accepts a variety of aquarium foods, preferably alive.

Hypseleotris near *galli*
See Plate #476

Gobiomorphus coxi (Krefft) • Cox's Gudgeon

RANGE: Apparently restricted to rivers of New South Wales, especially the southern portion.

HABITS: Seems to prefer more swiftly flowing waters, even rapids. Apparently able to climb out of water over obstructions. A substrate spawner (on rocks) with the male guarding the nest and fanning the eggs. The eggs hatch in a few days.

WATER CONDITIONS: Does not tolerate salt in the water as well as do some of the other gobies. Prefers well oxygenated water. Does best in aquaria kept at room temperature.

SIZE: Normally attains a length of 15 cm, occasionally to 19 cm.

FOOD REQUIREMENTS: Feeds on small aquatic insects. In the aquarium mosquito larvae and chironomic larvae are best bets.

Philypnodon n. sp. • Dwarf Flathead Gudgeon

RANGE: Southern Queensland, New South Wales, Victoria and South Australia.

HABITS: Found in quiet areas over rocks, muddy bottoms and weedy areas. Inhabits estuarine waters to pure fresh water. Males have larger mouths, more bulbous heads, and larger pelvic fins. They also turn very dark when spawning

WATER CONDITIONS: Not critical. Will live in fresh and brackish waters.

SIZE: Usually 4 cm but may grow a little larger.

FOOD REQUIREMENTS: Accepts a variety of living and prepared aquarium foods.

Megalops cyprinoides (Broussonet) • Oxeye Herring, Indo-Pacific Tarpon

RANGE: Widespread in the tropical Indo-Pacific from East Africa to Tahiti. Occurs in all Australian seas.

HABITS: A marine species in which young individuals (between 20 and 50 cm) are found in freshwater situations. Spawning takes place in the warm months in shallow waters or estuaries, producing a leptocephalus-like larva.

WATER CONDITIONS: Young specimens suitable for aquaria can be kept in fresh or brackish water.

SIZE: Grows to more than 150 cm.

FOOD REQUIREMENTS: Adults eat fishes and crustaceans; the young will also feed on insects and their larvae.

Notesthes robusta (Guenther) • Bullrout

RANGE: Queensland and New South Wales, Australia.

HABITS: A bottom-dwelling species that should not be kept with fishes it can swallow.

WATER CONDITIONS: Tolerant of a wide range of water conditions. Will even live in brackish water.

SIZE: Attains a length of about 30 cm, but more commonly is 15 to 20 cm long

FOOD REQUIREMENTS: Will accept many different foods, including small shrimp, worms and fishes.

Hypseleotris "midgleyi"

Gobiomorphus coxi

Gobiomorphus near coxi

Philypnodon n. sp.

Megalops cyprinoides

Notesthes robusta (juvenile)

Plate #477

728

Geotria australis (larva)

Atherinosoma microstoma

Atherinason esox

Hippichthys heptagonus

Notesthes robustus

Notesthes robustus

Lutjanus russelli

Gerres filamentosus

Plate #478

729

Geotria australis Gray • Pouched Lamprey

RANGE: Southeastern and Western Australia, Tasmania, New Zealand, and Patagonian South America.

HABITS: Undergoes a complicated life cycle from a larval *ammocoete* stage through a *macrophthalmis* stage, then the *velasia* stage, and finally to the adult. Ammocoetes are filter-feeders; adults die after spawning.

WATER CONDITIONS: Depending upon the stage, either salt-water or pure fresh. Not normally kept in home aquaria.

SIZE: Ammocoete 10 cm; macrophthalmia 8-10 cm; velasia 35-67 cm; adults may shrink a bit from the *velasia* stage.

FOOD REQUIREMENTS: Varies with stage.

Atherinason esox • Tasmanian Hardyhead

RANGE: Tasmania, Australia.

HABITS: A small species found in cool Tasmanian coastal waters. Generally a surface fish, often traveling in small schools. Peaceful but not very colorful, being somewhat translucent with a silvery lateral band.

WATER CONDITIONS: Not critical. Probably does best with a small amount of salt added to the aquarium. A cool-water fish that should not be placed in a heated aquarium.

SIZE: Attains a length of about 7 or so cm.

FOOD REQUIREMENTS: Does best on small live foods, particularly crustaceans and small insects.

Notesthes robustus
See Plate #477

Lutjanus russelli (Bleeker) • Moses Perch, Russell's Snapper

RANGE: Indo-West Pacific region including Japan and Australia.

HABITS: Primarily a marine fish, but enters estuaries where the water has very little salt content. Called "Moses perch" because of the black spots or "St. Peter's finger-marks," although the true fish of the legend is a species of *Tilapia*.

WATER CONDITIONS: This fish can be treated as a marine fish or can be kept in a lower salinity brackish situation.

SIZE: Attains a length of over 50 cm.

FOOD REQUIREMENTS: A carnivorous species that will eat small fishes and crustaceans. Frozen foods are also accepted.

Atherinosoma microstoma (Guenther) • Smallmouthed Hardyhead

RANGE: Abundant along the southeastern coast of Australia, including Tasmania.

HABITS: Not much is known. Possibly a continual breeder. Whether the lateral stripe becoming pinkish to red or the eye becoming the same color is sexual in nature is not known.

WATER CONDITIONS: Apparently a delicate fish that is hard to keep under any conditions.

SIZE: To 7 cm in New South Wales, but reaches 9 cm in Tasmania.

FOOD REQUIREMENTS: Feeds on small crustaceans and aquatic insects.

Hippichthys heptagonus Bleeker • Heptagonal Pipefish

RANGE: East Indies to New Guinea and possibly west to Sri Lanka.

HABITS: Occurs in full sea water to brackish water of estuaries and fresh water of streams and brooks. The male incubates the eggs in a brood pouch until they hatch.

WATER CONDITIONS: Not critical. Will exist in most types of water from salt to fresh. Normal temperatures of 23-28°C are suitable.

SIZE: Attains a length of about 14 cm.

FOOD REQUIREMENTS: Needs small live foods such as newly hatched brine shrimp.

Notesthes robustus
See Plate #477

Gerres filamentosus Cuvier • Spotted Silverbelly

RANGE: Widely distributed in the western Pacific and Indian Oceans.

HABITS: Occurs in shallow coastal waters, bays, and river mouths, ascending to fresh water.

WATER CONDITIONS: Not critical. This species is probably best maintained in a brackish water aquarium or even in pure salt water. Normal aquarium temperatures are sufficient.

SIZE: Attains a length of at least 25 cm.

FOOD REQUIREMENTS: Feeds on small invertebrates that live in the sand. These are obtained with their very protrusible mouths. Aquarium foods are generally accepted, but some individuals may not take to them.

Kuhlia rupestris
See Plate #439

Lutjanus argentimaculatus (Bonnaterre) • Mangrove Jack; River Roman

RANGE: Widespread over the entire Indo-Pacific area including the Red Sea. In Australia it is found in the northern and eastern coastal areas.
HABITS: Commonly found around mangroves in tidal areas but does move well upstream into pure fresh water. Spawns in estuaries, where it scatters large numbers of pelagic eggs. Only small individuals are generally kept in aquaria.
WATER CONDITIONS: Does well in fresh, brackish, or marine aquaria. Temperatures should be between 21°C and 26°C.
SIZE: Can attain a length of up to a meter.
FOOD REQUIREMENTS: A carnivorous species feeding on fishes, crustaceans, etc. Will accept most meaty aquarium foods.

Pseudophrites urvillii (Cuvier & Valenciennes) • Congolli

RANGE: Freshwater streams and estuaries of southern and southeastern Australia and Tasmania.
HABITS: Does not seem to be concerned about whether it is living in fresh or salt water or what type of habitat it is in as it may be found in a wide variety of either. Nothing is known about the spawning habits.
WATER CONDITIONS: Primarily a marine species but lives as well in brackish or pure fresh water. A cool water species.
SIZE: Normally 15 to 20 cm, but grows to 30 cm.
FOOD REQUIREMENTS: Eats a wide variety of foods including worms, crustaceans, and insects and their larvae. May also include some plant material as well.

Butis butis (Buchanan) • Bony-snouted Gudgeon

RANGE: Tropical western Pacific Ocean, including the tropical coasts of Australia.
HABITS: Commonly occurs in brackish estuaries but also extends up coastal rivers into pure fresh water. Prefers slow-moving waters. Can be sexed using genital papillae: female's is short and fat with a few small, fine flaps at tip; male's is thinner and flat and with fine scalloped flaps at tip.
WATER CONDITIONS: Not critical. Can be kept in fresh, brackish or pure marine water with ease.
SIZE: Normally less than 10 cm, but can reach as much as 15 cm in length.
FOOD REQUIREMENTS: Small fishes and crustaceans can be fed in aquaria. It will accept other foods as well.

Ophieleotris aporos (Bleeker) • Snakehead Gudgeon

RANGE: Northern Australia and New Guinea.
HABITS: Spends most of its time on the bottom. Tankmates must be large enough to take care of themselves as this fish will regard anything small enough to eat as potential food.
WATER CONDITIONS: Not critical. Clear, clean, well-aerated water is recommended. Temperatures between 21° and 26°C are suitable.
SIZE: Reaches a length of about 30 cm.
FOOD REQUIREMENTS: This carnivorous species will eat live fishes as well as most other meaty foods offered.

Brachirus salinarum Ogilby • Salt-pan Sole

RANGE: Occurs only in the area of Australia surrounding the Gulf of Carpentaria. Not widespread.
HABITS: Not well known. Probably similar to that of the other species of *Brachirus*. Typically fresh water.
WATER CONDITIONS: Not critical. Normal aquarium conditions should be acceptable.
SIZE: Attains a length of about 14 cm.
FOOD REQUIREMENTS: Will accept a variety of aquarium foods. These should sink to the bottom where the sole can get to them.

Kuhlia rupestris

Lutjanus argentimaculatus

Pseudophrites urvilli

Butis butis

Ophieleotris aporos

Brachirus salinarum

Plate #479

732

Mugilogobius n. sp.

Periophthalmus regius

Arenigobius bifrenatus

Kurtus gulliveri

Caranx papuensis

Acanthopagrus australis

Chelonodon patoca

Chelonodon patoca

Plate #480

733

Mugilogobius n. sp. • Wanmorr Goby

RANGE: Eastern Australia.
HABITS: Most of the species of this genus of rather non-descript gobies are found in bays and estuaries, penetrating fresh water on occasion.
WATER CONDITIONS: Alkaline, warm water with salt added should be tried.
SIZE: 2-4 cm.
FOOD REQUIREMENTS: Will take both small live foods and vegetable matter as will most gobies.

Arenigobius bifrenatus (Kner) • Bridled Goby

RANGE: From Western Australia along the southern coast of the continent to New South Wales and Tasmania.
HABITS: This is a relatively common species in the sea grass beds as well as in fresh water a couple of kilometers or so from river mouths. It is a bottom-living species and somewhat aggressive.
WATER CONDITIONS: Not critical, living equally well in fresh brackish, or pure salt water. Does best in cooler water aquaria.
SIZE: Attains a length of about 20 cm or more.
FOOD REQUIREMENTS: Will accept a variety of aquarium foods, especially live foods.

Caranx papuensis Alleyne & Macleay • Papuan Trevally

RANGE: This species ranges from Papua New Guinea to northern Queensland.
HABITS: The Papuan trevally may be a synonym of *C. sansun* according to some authors. The young fish are the ones entering brackish waters of harbors and estuaries, the adults keeping to more open waters. This fish is not to be trusted with fishes small enough to swallow. It is very active.
WATER CONDITIONS: The addition of at least some salt to the water is advisable. Normal conditions for a brackish water aquarium are suitable.
SIZE: Attains a length of about 80 cm.
FOOD REQUIREMENTS: Small fishes plus a variety of meaty foods will be sufficient for the Papuan trevally.

Chelonodon patoca (Hamilton-Buchanan) • Milk-spotted Puffer

RANGE: India to China and Southeast Asia, south to the East Indies and northern Australia.
HABITS: The color pattern is very good camouflage when seen against the bottom of a river. Normally taken in clear flowing water with no plants, but seems to like *Vallisneria* in the aquarium. Not a good community fish as it is an inveterate fin-nipper.
WATER CONDITIONS: A usually estuarine species, so salt may be provided in the aquarium water.
SIZE: To 30 cm.
FOOD REQUIREMENTS: Prefers fresh fish (will eat small live fishes in aquaria) or hermit crabs. Will accept dry and frozen foods.

Periophthalmus regius (Whitley) • Royal Mudskipper

RANGE: This specimen was collected in the Daintree River in Queensland, Australia. This species may be a synonym of a wider ranging species.
HABITS: Mudskippers are known for their habit of skipping across mud flats, usually in estuarine situations. They can remain out of water for quite some time as long as they remain moist. Aquarists usually provide them with a "dry" resting place out of the water.
WATER CONDITIONS: Hardy fish that do well in fresh, brackish or full marine water. Temperatures should be in the range of 23-28°C.
SIZE: Attains a length of about 15-16 cm.
FOOD REQUIREMENTS: Prefers small invertebrates including insects. Will take a variety of aquarium foods as substitutes.

Kurtus gulliveri
See Plate #439

Acanthopagrus australis (Guenther) • Australian Bream

RANGE: Creeks, rivers, estuaries, and coastal waters of central and southern Queensland.
HABITS: There is a spawning migration during midwinter toward waters in the vicinity of ocean beaches. Colors vary depending upon locality, with lighter individuals inhabiting the clear ocean waters and darker ones in the more muddy estuarine areas.
WATER CONDITIONS: Not critical. Does well in a variety of water conditions. Temperatures should be between 23 and 27°C.
SIZE: The average size seems to be about half a kilo, although fishing records have much larger individuals (even up to 4 kilos).
FOOD REQUIREMENTS: Feeds on a wide variety of crustaceans, fishes and even young oyster spat. It will accept similar foods in the aquarium.

Scatophagus argus (Gmelin) • Spotted Scat

RANGE: Tropical Indo-Pacific region along the coasts.
HABITS: Peaceful toward other fishes, but will graze on aquatic plants right down to the roots.
WATER CONDITIONS: Fairly hard, alkaline water with a teaspoon of salt per four liters of water added. Temperature 23 to 26°C.
SIZE: To 33 cm in their home waters; about half that in captivity.
FOOD REQUIREMENTS: Live foods of all kinds, with the addition of vegetable substances like lettuce or spinach leaves; will also eat frozen foods.

Neoceratodus forsteri (Krefft) • Australian Lungfish

RANGE: Endemic to eastern Australia. Found originally only in the Burnett and Mary Rivers, but may have been introduced into more southerly rivers of Queensland as well.
HABITS: A primitive lungfish whose fossil ancestors go back some 400 million years. It normally breathes by means of its gills, but it also has a functional lung and can utilize air from the surface. It can live for several days out of water if kept damp. Spawning occurs in spring during the night in shallow water. The eggs are adhesive and stick to aquatic plants.
WATER CONDITIONS: Very tolerant of water conditions. Does best at normal aquarium temperatures.
SIZE: Attains a length of over 150 cm.
FOOD REQUIREMENTS: Feeds on a variety of foods including tadpoles and adult frogs, earthworms, frozen and pellet foods, and even some vegetable material.

Exyrias puntang (Bleeker) • Silver-spotted Goby

RANGE: Western Pacific Ocean from Japan to New Caledonia and westward to the Andaman Islands.
HABITS: Occurs in coastal and brackish waters. A bottom-living species.
WATER CONDITIONS: Not critical. Can tolerate some salt in the water. Normal aquarium temperatures should prevail.
SIZE: Attains a length of about 16 cm.
FOOD REQUIREMENTS: Feeds on small invertebrates. Will accept a variety of aquarium foods including prepared and frozen items.

Awaous crassilabrus
See Plate #445

Favonogobius suppositus (Sauvage) • Southwestern Australian Goby

RANGE: Western Australia.
HABITS: A not very active bottom-living species. Members of the genus are said to lay their eggs among rocks.
WATER CONDITIONS: Not critical. The aquarium should be maintained at room temperature.
SIZE: Attains a length of about 9 cm.
FOOD REQUIREMENTS: Feeds on small invertebrates. Will accept most aquarium foods that reach the bottom levels where it lives.

Favonogobius tamarensis (Johnston) • Tamar River Goby

RANGE: Restricted to southern and southeastern Australia, including Tasmania.
HABITS: Seems to prefer the quiet waters of estuaries and coastal lakes where the bottom is usually covered with silt or mud. Breeds in the spring. Males have larger mouths, more bulbous cheeks, and the posterior dorsal and anal fin rays are more elongate than in females.
WATER CONDITIONS: Not critical. Equally at home in fresh, brackish, or salt water.
SIZE: Attains a length of about 11 cm.
FOOD REQUIREMENTS: Will accept a wide variety of aquarium foods.

Scatophagus argus

Neoceratodus forsteri

Neoceratodus forsteri

Awaous crassilabrus

Exyrias puntang

Favonogobius suppositus

Favonogobius tamarensis

Plate #481

736

INDEX

Aba Aba 395,396
aberrans, Procatopus 452
abramis, Astyanax 163,164
Abramis brama 78,79
Acanthodoras cataphractus 210
Acanthodoras spinosissimus 210
acanthogaster, Mylossoma 138,139
acanthomias, Synodontis 417
Acanthopagrus australis 733,734
Acanthophthalmus anguillaris 555,556
Acanthophthalmus javanicus 555,556
Acanthophthalmus kuhli 555,556
Acanthophthalmus myersi 555,556
Acanthophthalmus semicinctus 555,556
Acanthophthalmus shelfordi 557,558
Acanthopsis choirorhynchus 565,566
Acanthorhodeus asmussi 90,91
Acara compressus 358
Acara crassispinis 358
Acara hyposticta 358
Acarichthys 335,354
Acarichthys geayi 354
Acarichthys heckelii 354
Acaronia 335,345
Acaronia nassa 345
Acaropsis 334
Acestrorhynchus falcatus 149,150
Acestrorhynchus falcirostris 149,150
Acestrorhynchus heterolepis 149,150
Acestrorhynchus isalinae 151,152
Acheilognathus cyanostigma 99
Acheilognathus lanceolata 99
Acheilognathus limbata 99
Acheilognathus longipinnis 101
Acheilognathus moriokae 99
Acheilognathus rhombea 99
Acheilognathus tabira 99
Achirus lineatus 384,385
Acipenser ruthenus 78,79
Acipenser transmontanus 17
acipenserinus, Hemiodontichthys 264
aculeatus, Gasterosteus 30,31
acus, Farlowella 260
acuticeps, Etheostoma 56
acuticeps, Geophagus 356
acutidens, Micralestes 399,400
acutirostre, Ctenopoma 541,542
acutus, Corydoras 228,246
adamsoni, Hephaestus 659,660
Adamson's Grunter 659,660
adloffi, Cynolebias 267,268
adolfoi, Corydoras 237
adspersa, Mogurnda 661,662,725,726
adspersa, Mogurnda near 723,724
aeneus, Corydoras 229,236,248,249
Aequidens 327,334,341,342,343,344
Aequidens awani 343
Aequidens caeruleopunctatus 342
Aequidens curviceps 341

Aequidens dorsigerus 341,343
Aequidens duopunctatus 344
Aequidens gold saum 342
Aequidens itanyi 342,343
Aequidens mariae 344
Aequidens maroni 343
Aequidens portalegrensis 327,341
Aequidens pulcher 342
Aequidens rivulatus 342
Aequidens species 343,344
Aequidens tetramerus 344
Aequidens thayeri 343
Aequidens vittata 344
Aequidens species 343,344
aequifasciata, Symphysodon 368,370,371
aequipinnatus, Danio 574
aethiopicus, Propterus 387,388
afer, Papyrocranus 391,392
affinis, Bryconops 167,168
affinis, Distichodus 403,404
affinis, Gambusia 6
affinis, Heterandia 6
affinis, Leiopotherapon, 659,660
affinis, Melanotaenia 643,644
affinis, Otocinclus 260
affinis, Parodon 128,129
afra, Cynotilapia 480
African Bullhead Catfish 425,426
African Butterfly Cichlid 537,538
African Characidium 405,406
African Featherfin 391,392,397,398
African Flathead Catfish 413,414
African Freshwater Pipefish 547,548
African Glass Catfish 409,410
African Killifishes 434
African Knife Fish 391,392
African Kuhli 411,412
African Lungfish 387,388
African Moon Tetra 401,402
African Mudfish 391,392
African Pike 397,398
African Pike Characin 405,406
African Region 386
African Rift Valley 454
African Shoulder-spot Catfish 409,410
African Spotted Catfish 413,414
African Whale 391,392
African Whiptail Catfish 411,412
afro-fischeri, Synodontis 413,414
Agamyxis pectinifrons 209
agassizi, Apistogramma 348,349
agassizi, Corydoras 245
Ageneiosidae 211
Ageneiosus 211,214
Ageneiosus caucanus 214
Agila Rivulus 271,272
agilae, Rivulus 271,272
agilis, Rasbora 570
Agmus lyriformis 205
Agnes' Tetra 167,168

elegans, Rasbora 571
elegans, Steatogenys 201
elegans, Stiphodon 666
elegansXbualanum, Aphyosemion 441
Eleotris species 664
eleotroides, Paragalaxias 677,678
elephas, Gnathonemus 393,394
ellipsifer, Mastacembalus 548
Elodea 226
Elongate Hemichromis 539,540
Elongate Piranha 145,146
elongatus, Ambassis 701,702,703,704
elongatus, Hemichromis 539,540
elongatus, Lamprologus 513,519
elongatus, Pseudotropheus 472
elongatus, Serrasalmus 145,146
Emerald Betta 615,616
Emerald Shiner 22,23
Emperor Tetra 161,162
endlicheri, Polypterus 390
engystoma, Mormyrops 395,396
Enneacampus ansorgii 547,548
Enneacanthus chaetodon 30,31
Enneacanthus gloriosus 30,31
Enneacanthus obesus 30,31
Entomocorus benjamini 212
Entre Rios Pearl Fish 267,268
Epalzeorhynchus kalopterus 589
Epalzeorhynchus siamensis 589
Epiplatys 434,448,449,450,451
Epiplatys annulatus 448
Epiplatys barmoiensis 451
Epiplatys bifasciatus 451
Epiplatys chevalieri 448
Epiplatys dageti 449
Epiplatys duboisi 449
Epiplatys fasciolatus 451
Epiplatys grahami 450
Epiplatys huberi 448
Epiplatys macrostigma 450
Epiplatys njalaensis 450
Epiplatys roloffi 450
Epiplatys sexfasciatus 449
Epiplatys spilargyreius 451
Epiplatys spilargyreiusXfasciolatus 451
eques, Corydoras 232
eques, Gouldiella 217
eques, Nannostomus 112,113
erebi, Nematalosa 685,686
eremius, Chlamydogobius 725,726
Eretmodus 454,492
Eretmodus cyanostictus 492
erhardti, Corydoras 243
Erimyzon sucetta 24,25
Erpetoichthys calabaricus 387,388,390
erythrodon, Spathodus 492
erythrogaster, Phoxinus 22,23
erythrophthalmus, Scardineus 90,91
erythrops, Stethoprion 157,158
erythrostigma, Hyphessobrycon 179,180

erythrotaenia, Mastacembalus 627,628
erythrozonus, Hemigrammus 181,182
erythrurus, Aphyocharax 155,156
erythrurus, Chalceus 151,152
erythrurus, Labeo 587
Esomus danricus 569
Esomus metallicus 569
Esox americanus 20,21
esox, Atherina 729,730
Esox lucius 20,21
Esox niger 20,21
espei, Nannostomus 110,111
Estuary Perch 709,710
Etheostoma 44-73
Etheostoma acuticeps 56
Etheostoma aquali 55
Etheostoma asprigene 62
Etheostoma atripinne 51,71
Etheostoma australe 65
Etheostoma baileyi 49
Etheostoma barbouri 68
Etheostoma barrenensis 48
Etheostoma bellum 58
Etheostoma blennioides gutselli 47
Etheostoma blennioides newmani 47
Etheostoma blennioides pholidotum 47
Etheostoma blennius blennius 46
Etheostoma blennius sequatchiense 47
Etheostoma boschungi 60
Etheostoma caeruleum caeruleum 63
Etheostoma caeruleum subspecies 63
Etheostoma camurum 57
Etheostoma chlorobranchium 57
Etheostoma chlorosomum 54
Etheostoma cinereum 45
Etheostoma collettei 62
Etheostoma collis 70
Etheostoma coosae 52
Etheostoma cragini 60
Etheostoma davisoni 55
Etheostoma ditrema 61
Etheostoma duryi 52
Etheostoma edwini 59
Etheostoma etnieri 52
Etheostoma euzonum 44
Etheostoma euzonum euzonum 44
Etheostoma exile 69
Etheostoma flabellare 67
Etheostoma fonticola 71
Etheostoma fricksium 59
Etheostoma fusiforme 70
Etheostoma gracile 69
Etheostoma grahami 65
Etheostoma histrio 48
Etheostoma hopkinsi 65
Etheostoma inscriptum 46
Etheostoma jessiae 52
Etheostoma jordani 58
Etheostoma juliae 55
Etheostoma kanawhae 45

Lined Citharinid 403,404
Lineofortis, Curimata 134,135
lineopunctata, Curimata 132,133,195,196
lini, Hemigrammocypris 576
linni, Haplochromis 467
Lionhead Cichlid 527,528
Lionhead Cichlid II 527,528
Liosomadoras 211,214
Liosomadoras oncinus 214
Lithogenes 234
Lithoxus 235
littorale, Hoplosternum 227
livingstoni, Haplochromis 467
livingstonii, Pseudotropheus 473,474
Liza vaigiensis 649,650
Loach 94
Lobochilotes labiatus 507
loennbergi, Aphyosemion 436
lohachata, Botia 557,558
loisae, Bryconamericus 161,162
lombardoi, Pseudotropheus 474
Longeared Sunfish 32,33
Longfinned African Tetra 399,400
Long-finned Eel 667
Long-finned Galaxias 675,676,677,678
Longfinned Glass 153,154
Long-finned Spottail 321,322
Long-jawed Catfish 425,426
Long-nosed Black Ghost 203,204
Long-nosed Distichodus 405,406
Long-nosed Loach 565,566
Long-spined Glassfish 653,654
Long Tom 687,688
longibarbis, Dianema 225
longifilis, Parailia 409,410
longifillis, Sicyopterus 666
longimanum, Etheostoma 54
longimanus, Cichlasoma 335
longimanus, Haplochromis 459
longior, Astyanax 165
longipinnis, Acheilognathus 101
longipinnis, Brycinus 399,400
longipinnis, Pterolebias 273,274
longirostris, Mormyrus 395,396
longirostris, Synodontis 416
Longnose Sucker 24,25
Lophiobagrus cyclurus 425,426
lorentzi, Pingalla 659,660,715,716
lorentzi, Toxotes 651,652,719,720,721,722
Lorentz River Grunter 659,660
lorentzi, Chilatherina 645
loretoensis, Hyphessobrycon 173,174
Loreto Tetra 173,174
Loricaria 235,240,248
Loricariichthys 235,239,240
Loricariidae 224,234
Loricariids 240
Loricariinae 235
lorteti, Carinotetraodon 629,630
lourensi, Nothobranchius 445,447

Lowland Snubnose 49
loxozonus, Corydoras 236
Lucania 26,27,435
Lucania goodei 26,27
lucida, Ammocrypta 73
lucioperca, Stizostedion 96,97
Luciosoma 568,575
Luciosoma bleekeri 575
Luciosoma setigerum 575
Luciosoma species 575
lucius, Esox 20,21
lucius, Ptychocheilus 22,23
luelingi, Apistogramma 350
lujae, Aphyosemion 440
luna, Myleus 140,141
lusosso, Distichodus 405,406
luteovinctum, Etheostoma 63
luteus, Opoplotosus 637,638
Lutjanus argentimaculatus 731,732
Lutjanus russelli 729,730
lutrensis, Notropis 22,23
lyriformis, Agmus 205
Maccullochella macquariensis 709,710,711,712
Maccullochella peeli 709,710,711,712
maccullochi, Melanotaenia 639,641
macleayi, Ambassis 703,704,705,706
macmasteri, Apistogramma 350
Macquaria ambiguus 707,708
Macquaria australasica 709,710
Macquaria colonorum 709,710
Macquarie Perch 709,710
macquariensis, Maccullochella 709,710,711,712
macracantha, Botia 557,558
macrocephala, Percina 36
macrochirus, Lepomis 32,33
macrognathus, Haplochromis 520
Macrognathus siamensis 627,628
macrolepida, Percina 42
macrolepidota, Hampala 586
macrolepidotus, Chalceus 153,154
Macrolepidotus Groupee 397,398
Macrolepidotus Silver 397,398
macrolepis, Curimatopsis 134,135,136,137
macrolepis, Heterocharax 149,150
macrolepis, Leiopotherapon 705,706
macrolepis, Phanagoniates 155,156
macrolepis, Zacco 576
macrophthalmus, Aplocheilichthys 453
macrophthalmus, Rhamphochromis 485
Macropodus concolor 619,620
Macropodus opercularis 619,620
macrops, Barbodes 429
macrops, Callochromis 488,508
macropterus, Callophysus 216
macropterus, Centrarchus 30,31
macropterus, Corydoras 233
macrostigma, Epiplatys 450
macrostigma, Synodontis 423
macrostoma, Betta 613,614,615,616
macrostoma, Haplochromis 460

morletii, Botia 559,560,561
Mormyrops boulengeri 395,396
Mormyrops engystoma 395,396
Mormyrus longirostris 395,396
Morulius 567,588
Morulius chrysophekadion 588
Moses Perch 729,730
Mosquitofishes 317,318
mossambicus, Clarias 407,408
mossambicus, Sarotherodon 523,526
motaguense, Cichlasoma 329
motoro, Potamotrygon 105
Mottled Catfish 425,426
Mottled Ctenopoma 543,544
Mottled Loach 563,564
Mottled Sculpin 74,75
Mountain Galaxias 671,672
Mountain Mullet 74,75
Mountain Minnow Tetra 155,156
Mousetail Knife Fish 203,204
Mouth Almighty 721,722
Mouth-brooding Betta 615,616
Mudskipper 545,546,609,610
muelleri, Sternarchorhamphus 200
Mugil cephalus 74,75
Mugilogobius valigouva 609,610
Mugilogobius new species 733,734
Mullet-headed Goby 609,610
multicolor, Pseudocrenilabrus 521,522
multifasciatus, Hemigrammocharax 405,406
multifasciatus, Lamprologus 515
multipunctatus, Synodontis 417
multiradiatus, Pterygoplichthys 260
multispinis, Ctenopoma 541,542
multispinosa, Herotilapia 340
multisquamatus, Glossolepis 646
Mummichog 26,27
munda, Galaxiella 675,676
Murray Cod 709,710
Murray Jollytail 673,674
mustax, Lamprologus 514,515
mustelinus, Heptapterus 217
Myers Gaucho 265,266
Myers Hillstream Loach 565,566
myersi, Acanthophthalmus 555,556
myersi, Aplocheilichthys 453
myersi, Carnegiella 136,137
myersi, Pseudogastromyzon 565,566
myersi, Rasbora 572
Myleus argenteus 140,141
Myleus luna 140,141
Myleus micans 140,141
Myleus pacu 140,141
Myleus rubripinnis 140,141
Myleus schomburgki 140,141
Myleus ternetzi 140,141
Mylossoma acanthogaster 138,139
Mylossoma aureum 138,139
Mylossoma duriventre 138,139
Mylossoma paraguayensis 138,139

Mystus micracanthus 593,594
Mystus vittatus 593,594
namaycush, Salvelinus 18,19
nana, Hasemania 187,188
Nandus 601,602
Nandus nandus 601,602
nandus, Nandus 601,602
nanensis, Barilius 576
Nannacara 334,347
Nannacara anomala 347
Nannaethiops unitaeniatus 403,404
Nannatherina australis 717,718,719,720
Nannatherina balstoni 717,718
Nannatherina bostocki 705,706
Nannatherina obscura 717,718
Nannocharax fasciatus 405,406
Nannoperca oxleyana 717,718,719,720
Nannoperca species 705,706
Nannostomus beckfordi 110,111
Nannostomus bifasciatus 112,113
Nannostomus eques 112,113
Nannostomus espei 110,111
Nannostomus harrisoni 110,111
Nannostomus marginatus 112,113
Nannostomus trifasciatus 112,113
Nannostomus unifasciatus 112,113
Nanochromis dimidiatus 529,530
Nanochromis parilius 529,530
Nanochromis splendens 529,530
nanum, Ctenopoma 543,544
nanus, Corydoras 233,243,244
narcissus, Corydoras 237
narindica, Glossamia 657,658
naritus, Chonerhinus 549,550
Narrow Hatchetfish 153,154
Narrow-lined African Tetra 397,398
naryani, Puntius 577
Nase Nosefish 88,89,90,91
nassa, Acaronia 345
nasus, Chondrostoma 88,89,90,91
nasuta, Percina 36
nasutus, Ophthalmochromis 519
nattereri, Corydoras 241
nattereri, Serrasalmus 145,146
ndianum, Aphyosemion 441
Neetroplus 326,340
Neetroplus nematopus 340
Nemacheilus barbatulus 93,94
Nemacheilus barbatulus toni 93,94
Nemacheilus botia 563,564
Nemacheilus kessleri 93
Nemacheilus=Noemacheilus 563,564
Nematalosa erebi 685,686
Nematalosa papuensis 633,634
Nematobrycon Gery 161,162
Nematobrycon lacortei 159,160
Nematobrycon palmeri 161,162
nematopus, Neetroplus 340
Neoceratodus forsteri 735,736
Neolebias ansorgii 403,404

Plain-tailed Astyanax 163,164
Plain-tailed Flagtail 659,660
Plataplochilus cabindae 453
Plataxoides dumerilii 6
Plataxoides leopoldi 6
Platies 296
platorhynchus, Scaphirhynchus 17
Platy variatus 303,304
platychir, Amphilius 411,412
Platydoras armatulus 210
Platydoras costatus 210
Platypoecilus 296
platypus, Zacco 576
Platystacus cotylephorus 205
Platystomatichthys sturio 219
Platytropius siamensis 595,596
playfairii, Pachypanchax 448
Plecostominae 234
Plecostomus 234,235
pleuromaculatus, Lamprologus 517
pleurops, Synodontis 421
pleurospilus, Callochromis 508
pleurotaenia, Puntius 580
podestemone, Etheostoma 54
Poecilia caucana 315,316
Poecilia latipinna 313,314
Poecilia latipunctata 315,316
Poecilia melanogaster 315,316
Poecilia ornata 317,318
Poecilia sphenops 315,316
Poecilia velifera 313,314
Poecilia reticulata 281
Poecilocharax weitzmani 108,109
poecilus, Microglanis 220
Poll, Dr. Max 415
polli, Lethrinops 485
polli, Tropheus 498
Pollimyrus castelnaui 393,394
Pollimyrus nigripinnis 393,394
polyacanthus, Monocirrhus 203,204
Polycentrus schomburgki 203,204
polydon, Hemibrycon 159,160
polylepis, Tylochromis 521,522
polyodon, Petrochromis 493
Polyodon spathula 17
Polypterus 390
Polypterus bichir 390
Polypterus congicus 387,388,389,390
Polypterus delhezi 389,390
Polypterus endlicheri 390
Polypterus lapradii 390
Polypterus ornatipinnis 389,390
Polypterus palmas 389,390
Polypterus retropinnis 390
Polypterus senegalus 389,390
Polypterus weeksii 390
polystictus, Corydoras 241
polystigma, Haplochromis 467
polystigma, Synodontis 423
polyuranodon, Gymnothorax 633,634

Pomoxis nigromaculatus 32,33
Pond Goby 607,608
pongoense, Parodon 128,129
popenoi, Cichlasoma 333
Popondetta 639,648
Popondetta connieae 648
Popondetta furcata 648
Poptella orbicularis 159,160
porocephala, Ophiocara 663,664
Porochilus obbesi 683,684
Porochilus rendahli 679,680
porosa, Bostockia 707,708
porosus, Cynolebias 277,278
portalegrensis, Aequidens 327,341
Potamorrhaphis guineensis 384,385
Potamotrygon humboldtii 105
Potamotrygon laticeps 105
Potamotrygon magdalenae 105
Potamotrygon motoro 105
Potamotrygon reticulatus 105
pottsi, Etheostoma 65
Pouched Lamprey 729,730
Pretty Chalcinus 153,154
Priapella intermedia 319,320
Priapichthys chocoensis 319,320
Primitive Archerfish 651,652,719,720,721,722
Prionobrama filigera 153,154
prionocanthus, Barbodes 429
Priopidichthys species 699,700
Pristella 191,192
Pristella maxillaris 191,192
Pristigaster cayana 384,385
Pristolepis fasciatus 601,602
Probarbus julienni 576
Procatopus 434
Procatopus aberrans 452
Procatopus Fire Tail 452
Procatopus gracilis 452
Procatopus nototaenia 452
Procatopus similis 452
Prochilodus nigricans 132,133
Prochilodus ortonianus 132,133
prochilus, Lamprologus 517
proeliare, Etheostoma 70,71
profundicola, Lamprologus 519
Pronek,Neal 9
Propterus aethiopicus 387,388
Propterus annectens 387,388
Propterus dolloi 387,388
Proterorhinus marmoratus 96,97
Pseudacanthicus leopardus 257
Pseudauchenipterus 211,214
Pseudauchenipterus nodosus 214
Pseudepapterus 211,213
Pseudepapterus hasemani 213
Pseudoancistrus 234
Pseudobagrus fulvidraco 96,97
Pseudobarilius, Chela 569
Pseudochalceus kyburzi 161,162
Pseudocorynopoma doriae 157,158

Pseudocorynopoma riisei 157,158
Pseudocrenilabrus multicolor 521,522
Pseudocrenilabrus philander 521,522
Pseudodoras holdeni 207,208
Pseudodoras niger 207,208
Pseudogastromyzon myersi 565,566
Pseudomugil 639,647,648,683,684,687,688,689,690
Pseudomugil inconspicuus 647
Pseudomugil mellis 683,684
Pseudomugil novaeguineae 647
Pseudomugil paludicola 648
Pseudomugil signifer 687,688,689,690
Pseudomugil species 647
Pseudomugil tenellus 647,689,690
Pseudophrites urvillii 731,732
Pseudopimelodus albomarginatus 220
Pseudopimelodus nigricauda 220
Pseudoplatystoma fasciatum 220
Pseudoscaphirhynchus kaufmani 78,79
Pseudosphromenus cupanus 619,620
Pseudotropheus aurora 471
Pseudotropheus brevis 472
Pseudotropheus crabro 471
Pseudotropheus eduardi 473
Pseudotropheus elegans 472
Pseudotropheus elongatus 472
Pseudotropheus lanisticola 473
Pseudotropheus livingstonii 473,474
Pseudotropheus lombardoi 474
Pseudotropheus microstoma 471
Pseudotropheus novemfasciatus 469
Pseudotropheus species 471,472,473
Pseudotropheus tropheops 455,469,470,471,473
Pseudotropheus zebra 474,475,476
Pseudotropheus species 471,472,473
psittacum, Cichlasoma 339
Pterolebias longipinnis 273,274
Pterolebias peruensis 273,274
Pterolebias zonatus 273,274
Pterophyllum 6,230,326,327,335,360,363
Pterophyllum altum 6
Pterophyllum dumerilii 360,363
Pterophyllum eimekei 6
Pterophyllum scalare 360,363
Pterygoplichthys 234,239,255,260
Pterygoplichthys gibbiceps 255
Pterygoplichthys multiradiatus 260
Pterygoplichthys sp. 257
Ptychocheilus lucius 22,23
pucallpaensis, Apistogrammoides 347
puellus, Puntius 432
puerzli, Aphyosemion 441
pugnax, Betta 615,616
pulcher, Aequidens 342
pulcher, Corydoras 244
pulcher, Hemigrammus 183,184
pulcher, Pelvicachromis 533,534
pulcher, Synodontis 422
pumilus, Trichopsis 613,614
Pumpkinseed Sunfish 32,33

punctatus, Chilodus 130,131
punctatus, Ictalurus 24,25
punctatus, Rivulus 277,278,280
punctifer, Synodontis 423
punctulata, Crenicara 346
punctulatum, Etheostoma 60
punctulatus, Micropterus 32,33
punctulatus, Synodontis 422
pungo, Tilapia 524
puntang, Exyrias 735,736
Puntius 427,429,432,567,577,578,579,580,581
Puntius amphibius 580
Puntius conchonius 578
Puntius dorsalis 580
Puntius filamentosus 577
Puntius jae 429
Puntius lineatus 584
Puntius naryani 577
Puntius nigrofasciatus 579
Puntius Odessa Barb 577
Puntius pleurotaenia 580
Puntius puellus 432
Puntius sachsi 579
Puntius semifasciolatus 579
Puntius somphongsi 581
Puntius sylvaticus 432
Puntius ticto 578
Puntius woehlerti 432
Purple-spotted Gudgeon 723,724
Purple-striped Gudgeon 723,724
pusilla, Galaxiella 677,678
pusillus, Dermogenys 553,554
pygmaea, Umbra 20,21
pygmaeus, Corydoras 233
Pygmy Gourami 613,614
Pygmy Hatchetfish 136,137
Pygmy Killifish 26,27
pyropunctata, Rachovia 275,276
Pyrrhulina brevis 112,113
quadrifasciatus, Datnioides 605,606
quadrifiliis, Tetranematichthys 212
Queensland Mouthbrooder 721,722
Quintana atrizona 315,316
Quirichthys stramineus 699,700
rabauti, Corydoras 237
Racer Tetra 159,160
Rachovia brevis 275,276
Rachovia hummelincki 275,276
Rachovia maculipinnis 275,276
Rachovia pyropunctata 275,276
rachovii, Nothobranchius 446
Rachoviscus crassiceps 153,154
radiatus, Barbodes 432
radiosum, Etheostoma 61
rafinesquei, Etheostoma 48
Ragged tail Pipefish 651,652
Rainbow Gudgeon 90,91
Rainbow Tetra 159,160
ramirezi, Apistogramma 330
ramirezi, Microgeophagus 330,354

rancureli, Aplocheilichthys 453
randi, Craterocephalus 649,650,697
ranga, Chanda 603,604
Rasbora agilis 570
Rasbora borapetensis 570
Rasbora brittani 570
Rasbora caudimaculata 572
Rasbora cephalotaenia 568
Rasbora daniconius 568
Rasbora einthoveni 572
Rasbora elegans 571
Rasbora heteromorpha 568,571,592
Rasbora heteromorpha spawning 590,592
Rasbora kalochroma 573
Rasbora maculata 570
Rasbora meinkeni 571
Rasbora myersi 572
Rasbora nondescript 573
Rasbora pauciperforata 570
Rasbora Pike 573
Rasbora somphongsi 572
Rasbora species 573
Rasbora sumatrana 571
Rasbora trilineata 572
Rasbora urophthalma 570
Rasbora vaterifloris 570
Rasborichthys altior 573
rathbuni,Aphyocharax 155,156
Rathbun's Tetra 155,156
Razorback Sucker 24,25
Red-bellied Freshwater Pipefish 599,600
Red-bellied Pacu 138,139
Red-bellied Piranha 145,146
Red-bellied Puffer 629,630
Red-belly, Doryichthys 599,600
Redfin Pickerel 20,21
Red-finned Distichodus 405,406
Red-finned Hemigrammus 187,188
Red-finned Pacu 138,139
Red-finned Tetra 159,160
Red-flecked Rivulus 271,272
Redhook Metynnis 140,141
Red-line Pipefish 651,652
Red Megalamphodus 191,192
Redneck Goby 607,608
Red Shiner 22,23
Red Snakehead 603,604
Red Snubnose 49
red-spot, Astyanax 165
Red-spot Spot-finned Killie 275,276
Red-tailed Flag Tetra 175,176
Red-tailed Goodeid 323,324
Red-topped Tetra 167,168
Redogobius bikolanus 666
Reganella 235
regani, Julidochromis 489
Reganochromis calliurus 497
Regan's Bishop 317,318
regius, Periophthalmus 733,734
reinhardti, Anguilla 667

Rendahl's Tandan 679,680
rendahli, Porochilus 679,680
rendalli, Tilapia 525
rerio, Brachydanio 575
reticulata, Ambassis 653,654
Reticulated Glassfish 703,704
Reticulated Goby 723,724
Reticulated Perchlet 653,654
Reticulated Rivulus 271,272
reticulatus, Corydoras 246,247
reticulatus, Mastacembalus 548
reticulatus, Potamotrygon 105
Retropinna semoni 685,686
retropinnis, Polypterus 390
retzi, Doryichthys 651,652
rex, Percina 42
Rhabdolichops troscheli 201
rhabdophora, Brachyraphis 317,318
rhabdotus, Geophagus 354
Rhadinocentrus ornatus 687,688,689,690
Rhamphochromis macrophthalmus 485
Rhamphochromis species 485
Rhampichthys rostratus 200
Rhaphiodon vulpinus 147,148
Rhinichthys atratulus 24,25
rhoadesii, Chilotilapia 484
Rhodesian Tetra 401,402
rhodesiensis, Hemigrammopetersius 401,402
Rhodeus ocellatus 100,101
Rhodeus sericeus 90,91,101
Rhodeus suigensis 100
rhodostomus, Hemigrammus 187,188
rhombea, Acheilognathus 99
rhombeus, Serrasalmus 145,146
rhomboides, Curimata 134,135
rhombosomoides, Cairnsichthys 689,690
rhynchophorus, Campylomormyrus 395,396
riggenbachi, Aphyosemion 436
riisei, Pseudocorynopoma 157,158
Rineloricaria 248,251,262,263
Rineloricaria castroi 262,263
Rineloricaria fallax 262
Rineloricaria filamentosa 251
Rineloricaria hasemani 262
Rineloricaria lanceolata 263
Rineloricaria species 262,263
Rio Ipixuna Discus 372
Rio Meta Black Tetra 171,172
Rio Napo Rivulus 271,272
Rio Negro,Brazil 331
Rio Trombetas Discus 372
riponianus, Haplochromis 520
rivulatus, Aequidens 342
Rivulichthys 273,274
Rivulus 271,272,277,278,279,280,435
Rivulus agilae 271,272
Rivulus amphoreus 271,272
Rivulus atratus 271,272
Rivulus beniensis 271,272
Rivulus cylindraceus 277,278,280

Rivulus holmiae 277,278
Rivulus limoncochae 271,272
Rivulus magdalenae 279,280
Rivulus ornatus 271,272
Rivulus peruanus 279,280
Rivulus punctatus 277,278,280
Rivulus strigatus 279,280
Rivulus urophthalmus 279,280
Rivulus xiphidius 279,280
roanoka, Percina 37
robbianus, Synodontis 413,414,417
roberts, Hyphessobrycon 179,180
robertsi, Barbodes 428
robertsi, Moenkhausia 169,170
robertsi, Synodontis 416
Robertsi Tetra 179,180
robertsi, Zenarchopterus 639,640
Roberts's Garfish 639,640
robineae, Corydoras 244
robusta, Gila 20,21
robusta, Notesthes 729,730
robustus, Corydoras 237
robustus, Serranochromis 521,522
rodwayi, Hemigrammus 181,182,183,184
Roeboides caucae 149,150
Roeboides descalvadensis 149,150
Rohtee alfrediana 586
roloffi, Aphyosemion 438
roloffi, Epiplatys 450
roloffi, Ladigesia 401,402
roloffi, Pelvicachromis 531,532
Roloff's Kribensis 531,532
rondoni, Gymnorhamphichthys 203,204
Rope Fish 387,388
Rose, Bryconops 195,196
rostratus, Galaxias 673,674
rostratus, Haplochromis 465
rostratus, Rhamphichthys 200
Rosy Bryconops 195,196
Rosy Tetra 179,180
rotundatus, Triportheus 153,154
Rough skinned Banjo 206
Round spotted Puffer 629,630
Roundtail Chub 20,21
Royal Mudskipper 733,734
rubra, Megalamphodus 191,192
rubrifascium, Aphyosemion 441
rubripinnis, Myleus 140,141
rubroocellata, Cychla 358
rubropunctatus, Labeo 433
rubrum, Etheostoma 57
Rudd 90,91
rufilineatum, Etheostoma 56
Rummy nose Tetra 187,188
rupestre, Etheostoma 48
rupestris, Kuhlia 655,656,731,732
russelli, Lutjanus 729,730
Russian Bitterling 90,91
Russian Sleeper 96,97
ruthenus, Acipenser 78,79

sabanus, Ompok 595,596
Saberfin 269,270
sachsi, Puntius 579
Sacramento Perch 30,31
sadanundio, Stigmatogobius 609,610
Saddled Galaxias 673,674,675,676
sagitta, Etheostoma 44
Sailfin Molly 313,314
Sailfin Perchlet 683,684
Sailfin Prochilodus 132,133
Sailfin Shiner 22,23
Saiz Tetra 175,176
saizi, Hyphessobrycon 175,176
sajica, Cichlasoma 332
salamandroides, Lepidogalaxias 675,676,677
salinarum, Brachirus 731,732
Salmo trutta 18,19
salmoides, Micropterus 30,31
Salmon Catfish 425,426,681,682
Salt pan Sole 731,732
saludae, Etheostoma 70
Salvelinus fontinalis 18,19
Salvelinus namaycush 18,19
salvinii, Cichlasoma 329
sanchesi, Corydoras 241
sanchezi, Serrasalmus 142,143
Sanchez Piranha 142,143
sanctaefilomenae, Moenkhausia 169,170
sandei, Glossamia 657,658
Sarawak Betta 615,616
Sarotherodon 523,524,526
Sarotherodon grahami 524
Sarotherodon mossambicus 523,526
sauvagei, Haplochromis 520
savoryi, Lamprologus 517
saxatilis, Crenicichla 345
sayanus, Aphredoderus 17
scalare, Pterophyllum 360,363
Scaphirhynchus platorhynchus 17
Scardineus erythrophthalmus 90,91
Scatophagus argus 605,606,735,736
schalleri, Trichopsis 613,614
Scheel, Jorgen 434
scheeli, Aphyosemion 443
Schilbe marmoratus 409,410
Schilbe uranoscopus 409,410
schmardae, Hemigrammus 187,188
Schmarda's Tetra 187,188
Schmidt-Focke, Dr. Eduard 383
scholzei, Hyphessobrycon 175,176
schomburgki, Myleus 140,141
schomburgki, Polycentrus 203,204
Schomburgk's Leaf Fish 203,204
schoutedeni, Aphyosemion 440
schoutedeni, Cardiopharynx 507,508,509
schoutedeni, Synodontis 420
schoutedeni, Tetraodon 549,550
Schultz, Astyanax 165
Schultz, Dr. Leonard P. 6
Schultz Spotfinned Killie 275,276

773

SPECIAL ACKNOWLEDGMENT

This index was prepared on a Texas Instrument Professional Computer with a 10-megabyte hard disk drive (Winchester). It was printed out on a Hewlett-Packard Laser Printer and photographed for photo-offset without going through the usual typesetting procedure. This is the first time this has ever been done for a book of this size and a data base of more than 8,000,000 characters. The program for this "first" was developed by Mr. Art Ackerson, Professional Computer Services, Key West, Florida. Mr. Ackerson owns the copyright (patent) on this process and he sells this service to other authors and publishers.

Had this procedure been done in the usual way, it would have consumed about 1,600 man hours of work; the Ackerson process takes about 24 man hours.

The authors are deeply indebted to Mr. Ackerson for the great savings in time that this complex task would have taken.